Dual
Citizen

a history of Tracy Staples-Wilson
recorded by Bob Zuber

The authors thank the following for their invaluable input:

Kate Jakobsen, Kelley Page Jibrell,
Anne Donovan Moran, Lisa Raymond,
and the Tall Shiny Silver Figure:

Hebrews 1:

[3] *Who being the brightness of His glory,*
and the express image of His person,
and upholding all things by the word of His power,
when He had by Himself purged our sins,
sat down on the right hand of the Majesty on high:
[4] *Being made so much better than the angels,*
as He hath by inheritance obtained
a more excellent name than they.

Characters of Importance
In Order of Appearance

Tracy's Family:

Moody: First Name: Kindel,
                  Son of Richard and Emma,
                  Married to Granny
                  Raised Vera and Jinny,
                  Grandfather to Tracy, Freddie, Mia, Demi and Marie

Granny: First Name: Jackie,
                  Daughter of Granny Berger,
                  Married to Moody, Mother of Vera and Jinny,
                  Grandmother to Tracy, Freddie, Mia, Demi and Marie

Granny Berger: Granny's Mother.

Vera: Oldest Daughter of Granny,
                  Mother of Tracy and Freddie,
                  Married to Big Freddie, then Bobby,
                  Step-mother to David

Jinny: Second Daughter of Granny,
                  Mother of Mia, Demi and Marie,
                  Married to Squeaky, then Alvin

Freddie: Vera's Second Child, Tracy's younger Brother,
                  Raised with Mia, Demi and Marie

Bobby:	Vera's Second Husband, Father of David
Momma Ro:	First Name: Rosetta, Married to Charlie, Mother of Tori and Bunky, Vera's Best Friend
Mr. & Mrs. Moody:	First Names: Richard and Emma, Parents of Moody and Dris,
Granny Betty:	Mother of Squeaky, Granny's Best Friend
Uncle Alvin:	Jinny's Third Husband, Raised Tracy's 'Runnin' Cousins' Mia, Demi and Marie
Harry:	Tracy's Father, Married to Lynn, Father of Bryan
Lucille:	Harry's Mother, Tracy's Paternal Grandmother
Lynn Marigold:	Harry's Wife
Bryan:	Son of Harry and Lynn, Tracy's youngest Brother

Tracy's Friends

Tori:	First Child of Momma Ro, Sister of Bunky
Kung Fu:	Geoff, Ron, Jean, Jim Charlie
Justin:	Met during a High School Seminar
Todd:	College Roomate at N.C. State
Sabrina:	Todd's Best Friend since Kindergarten
Pete:	Son of Betty and John
Mo:	Became Tracy's Sifu and Close Friend
Ed Michaels:	Tracy's Best Friend in Chattanooga, Friends of Jack and Kathy

Work Acquaintances

Steakhouse:	Beth, Donnie and Mark
Akron:	Carl, Nate, Dale and Amy
Atlanta:	Lady T, Christopher and Vic, Greg and Lisa, Teddy

Spiritual Acquaintances

Aunt Z:	Took Tracy to Pentecostal Church
Darryl:	Led Tracy to Easter Services
Uncle Myles:	Head of Bahamas Faith Ministries
Pastor Sam:	Head of Christian Assembly Church
Peter and Melody:	Faith Friends of Harry and Lynn

Ephesians 2:

Chapter 1

- Vera, 1965

"Jackie," Moody growled. "If the boy's condition doesn't improve before lunchtime, you best better believe I don't beat ya to the hospital," and Moody looked squarely at his wife. "An' by improve, I mean his fever has been under a hundred, and'a stayed that way."

There was no response.

"I'm leaving the truck so you can drive him," Moody stated, because he knew she wouldn't take him if she had to drive the stick shift car. "Now I gotta go to the garage," Moody said, and left so hard he let the storm door slam.

It was five-o'clock in the morning, and the boy's fever had been over one hundred degrees for three days. The toddler woke up when the door slammed, but was too woozy to cry or talk. The child had just turned three, and dozed off again lost in fever. Jackie, the boy's Granny, just sucked on her cigarette, 'considerin'.

The child's Pawpaw's full name was Kindel Winifred Moody, but everyone called him Moody, mostly because he was. He was average height and a middle of the road color - somewhere between mocha and chocolate. His eyes had a glint of steel blue, shone bright and were easy going. He kept an Errol Flynn moustache he thought made him look dashing. His voice was calm, and he loved to talk with people. Moody would talk with anybody, and everyone genuinely liked talking to him. But it went gruff with his wife, because she didn't want to hear it.

Granny, or Jackie back in the day, probably wanted to hear it when they met. She was a force with her confident poise, elegant style and good looks. She was taller and thinner than Moody. She had a lovely smile that hid a sharp tongue and nasal voice, which when employed, made her big eyes dance. But Jackie was understated most of the time, and preferred to assess the situation before she struck. She wore lanky skirts over long legs like the other Jackie - the white one that had been in the White House - until the hardness hit you. When called for, her sharp cuts were followed by a self-gratifying cackle, which were low and to herself. But if it was really good, and if she 'had her drink on', Granny's cackle went full throttle with a head back condemnation heard throughout the store, bowling alley or neighborhood.

What may have been romance between Moody and Jackie was long gone, or was hard to decipher at best. Moody had made it back from World War II in one piece. He served in the only black regiment sent to the Pacific, so he figured there must have been a reason he lived. When they met, Granny was raising two teenage girls on her own. Moody knew it was the right thing to do, if not for Granny's sake, for the girls'. That was what was done back then, at least in Moody's mind. West Virginia in the 1960's was no place for a single black woman with two young girls. Both of their first marriages had fully disintegrated by 1963, so they tied the knot.

But their relationship wasn't easy, because Granny and Moody had hard constitutions. Moody's came from Virginia. He was the son of a minister who lived to one-hundred-and-seven, both of his parents were well educated with college degrees, and both taught school. Moody also grew up in a large house surrounded by hundreds of acres of farmland. Granny, on the other hand, was from West By God Virginia and felt uneducated. Her hard headedness was inherited from the Jim Crow South, and oddly, the fact she didn't grow up there was the important part. Granny Berger, her mother, got out of Alabama, but that was never spoken about under any circumstances, so no one knew how.

And what happened to Granny and Moody wasn't uncommon. Being right gradually became more important than kindness. Argument and bitterness seemed more logical than forgiveness and understanding, so annoying each other became paramount no matter the consequences. But the competition of will and wile made for great stories, and the intrigue of recounting the tales caused by their feuding made the pair infamous. At the center the girls were raised well, despite the grinding of Moody and Granny's relationship. They had their mother's sarcastic wit, and collected quite a bit of Moody's big heart. As the girls got older there were complications. Right now, there was a big one for the oldest, and Vera's three-year-old boy was in serious trouble.

Granny looked down at her grandson, who was red and rashy with heat. To her the hospital was always last resort - you didn't just go to the hospital. Granny called her mother again, and Granny Berger conferred: 'Never go to the hospital unless you're dead.' After all, Granny thought, the boy's fever had to come down soon - it had been three days.

Moody called a little before lunchtime. "Well?"

"His temperature is up to a hundred an' three…" Granny answered, but Moody didn't wait for the rest.

"Jackie, if you're not to the hospital before I am, I swear I'm gonna beat your stubborn ass all the way back from it!"

But Granny was ready and hung up the phone. An hour before she had called down to Vera's house. She had an easy-going soul and was a lot like Moody, even though she wasn't his. Vera was a good height, and her hair was light tan and naturally straight, although she dyed it black to whip it into a bouffant exactly like Miss Funicello. Vera's velvet skin had a soft cushion underneath, which made you want to caress her. That, and the sexiness of her voice made her intoxicating without doing anything. She was statuesque like her mother, was bubbly, and her high cheekbones were always ready to laugh.

Other than her voice, Vera's most striking feature was the complexity of her hazel-brown Creole eyes, which were very tired. Granny had let Vera sleep, because she had been up with her boy so many days already. She held down two cleaning jobs at night, and with her younger boy just turning two, Vera was exhausted. Besides, Granny had things situated. Jinny, Vera's sister, was to stay with little Freddie, and Vera was to come to Granny's to wait for the phone call.

Now was the time, and Vera took her beautiful boy in her arms. They put the child's things in the truck and went straight to the hospital. He was waning fast, and it seemed to Vera his fever made her boy smaller, as if he were evaporating. Hurt, anger and worry gained ground as they went, but what was about to happen wasn't up to this world.

Moody arrived at the hospital just after they had gotten Vera's boy into a room. The mechanic didn't take time to change out of his green jumpsuit. Moody was spattered with oil, radiator fluid and car grease, but he couldn't fix anything there. As the nurses took the toddler's temperature and prepped him, the smells and sights reminded Moody - it had just been three years since the child came into the world. The tiny boy's name was Tracy.

His real name was Tramele, a Creole name Vera liked. When Vera was about to bring Tracy into this world, Jinny called her sister. Vera welcomed the distraction from the noise, sweat, and total discomfort of labor. As Vera dilated, Jinny asked what she was going to name her baby.

"I liked Dell," Vera said, "but Moody said that was too common."

"So what's it gonna be then?" Jinny asked.

"Tramele," Vera answered, and she was sure of it.

"Tramele?" Jinny was skeptical. She had never heard that name, and wasn't sure if it was a boy's or a girl's, but maybe that was the point. "Are ya sure ya don't mean Timothy?"

"Trahm-melle," Vera replied carefully through the cocktail of soothers, hormones and urgers that ran through her veins.

"What does that mean?" Jinny demanded.

"I'm not sure," Vera answered. "I just know that's his name."

"How you so sure?" There was no answer, so Jinny continued on her mission. "But what's gonna be his middle name?"

Vera didn't have an answer for that either. She was just nineteen, and having her first baby was a lot to handle. Back in the kitchen, Jinny picked up the can of peaches she was using to make a pound cake. It was before dawn, and she was baking it as a surprise for Vera because peaches were her favorite. Jinny studied the can and smiled.

"Seein' as you liked Dell, why not Del Monte?" Jinny asked.

"Oooh that sounds nice," Vera cooed. "Delmontei it is!" which became the child's middle name.

Now, three years later, Moody and Granny stood helpless as they looked at their grandson, who had such a fever he was not likely to live. There was definitely something about 'the boy', as Moody called him. Most obviously he was a boy, which automatically made him a different caliber from their girls, whether Moody admitted it or not. But it was more than that. As little as he was, both Granny and Moody saw something in him that could change them.

At the moment that was threatened, and the child was under serious attack. The nurses ran to get ice for the water bath, and Vera stripped the toddler. Then the doctor took him, and he waved him around to get his temperature less than a hundred and five. It was strange to see a baby waved like that, because it looked ceremonial and dangerous. The tiny boy's flesh was limp and wet as he sailed through the air, naked as he came into this world, and it made everyone stop - everyone in both worlds.

In the Highest, the great audience simultaneously stopped cheering. The entire cloud of witnesses held their glasses of joy still as they turned to watch. Their special attire fell silent, and only the gold and jewels of their apparel shone as they stared. Then, He looked down at Tracy with great mercy in His heart. From their unseen balconies, the whole company watched the nurses pour in the ice. They stood in amazement as the doctor held the boy above the water.

In this world, the white enameled basin glistened with iciness. The child realized it was for him, and he rallied to squirm violently. The boy yelled for Moody, but his grandfather didn't come. The tiny child reached harder for his Pawpaw, and screamed so hard he lost his breath. Moody couldn't help but step forward to do something, anything, and Tracy saw his Pawpaw's tears welled up.

Next, there was an audible gasp from the great cloud of witnesses as the Tall Shiny Silver Figure opened the door. A brilliant sliver of light in the shape of a doorframe opened and closed behind Moody. Then, to the cloud of witnesses' amazement, the Tall Shiny Silver Figure stepped through! Unknown to anyone in the hospital room, He stood behind Moody, and held His hand out without saying a word. In the Highest, everyone in the magnificent audience held their breath. Here, in this world, the child saw them: Tracy's comfortable, wonderful grandfather who was scared for him; and the stately, magnificent tall man made of light.

Then, Moody bent toward his boy as tears rolled down his cheeks. The Tall Shiny Silver Figure stood alongside Moody as if a brilliant shadow. His loving hand of light was held out next to Pawpaw's big, familiar leathered hand, and the child reached up for them.

'Pawpaw. You. Pawpaw. You.' That was the choice, little Tracy thought.

The child knew his Pawpaw well, but somehow, he knew the Tall Shiny Silver Figure better. The boy also knew this was the time to choose. As the doctor lowered the toddler into the water, Tracy reached his hand out to Him, and He took the child's hand! The cloud of witnesses went wild with cheers and tossed their hats. Music played along with a terrible noise of fireworks, and the crowd's joy was refilled from the bottom of their goblets as they praised Him.

Back here, the boy cried dreadfully. He struggled in complete misery as his mother, Granny and Pawpaw looked on in horror. Their minds clotted with guilt and regret, and they wondered if they might loose their tiny boy to the cold forever.

But Tracy never felt the ice water. Instead, he was snatched out of his three-year-old body. He was instantly warm and well, and Tracy really did know the Tall Shiny Silver Figure better than he knew his Pawpaw. Besides, He looked like what Tracy's imaginary friend sounded like. Tracy thought it was wonderful to be there sitting on His lap, just the two of them. Tracy also knew he was in his room, the room made just for him, and that it was safe, safer than anywhere he had ever been.

"I want to show you some things," the Tall Shiny Silver Figure said, and He spoke very fast.

The toddler looked at Him, and wanted to take in all of Him. He was so comfortable, even though He was overwhelming with colors and light. Still, little Tracy felt he was the only one in the world, although everyone and everything was there in the room with them. In fact, the Tall Shiny Silver Figure *was* everything. But right now, He was with Tracy.

He was tall, the little boy thought, even when sitting down, and the Tall Shiny Silver Figure smiled when He heard that. He had a large book in His hand, which was so large the book spread across both His legs when He opened it. He held Tracy in one arm, and flipped through the pages with the other. The pages made music that changed with the vibrant scenes, and they were pictures of Tracy's world - the one he was about to live.

The child's eyes grew big as the pages went by, and he got taller. When Tracy saw himself twice as big, and his arms were too long for his body, the Tall Shiny Silver Figure stopped on a page.

"Remember this!" He said with speed and excitement.

Tracy saw woods, and there was fear in them related to a pile of damp sheets. While he sat in the Tall Shiny Silver Figure's lap Tracy didn't feel shame, but wondered if he should. Then Tracy looked up from the scene into the face of his host. His face was so easy, Tracy thought, and it seemed He could only smile. Then the toddler realized his own face looked worried.

"You have nothing to fear," the Tall Shiny Silver Figure said. *"I will help. Just ask,"* and little Tracy snuggled back into his arms.

It would always be all right, Tracy thought, no matter how bad it seemed. Then the Tall Shiny Silver Figure flipped through the book and stopped a few more times. He would say,

"Remember this!" and He picked up the book to show Tracy the whole scene.

As He flipped through more pages, He got more animated.

"Remember this!" He said, and the pages got harder and more complicated.

Then He flipped faster, as if He didn't want to see them. He flipped faster so the times of pain might be shorter than they had to be when suddenly, the Tall Shiny Silver Figure stopped and held the book wide open. He glowed more silver, and almost yelled at Tracy with pure joy.

"Remember this!" He exclaimed emphatically, and bounced Tracy on His knee, and the music from the page was exquisite. He held the book up with amazement, and said it again with ultimate exuberance:

"Remember this Tracy. Just get here!" and He was practically dancing. *"Whatever you do, just get here,"* and caught His breath with relief. *"Just get here, and I will come and see you again! And when you see this again in real life, I will come back and visit you. If you say yes, I will take over your life, and we will have a really good time. Just make it to this Tracy."*

Then the Tall Shiny Silver Figure smiled down at the toddler. He had great love in His flickering eyes as if to remember Tracy the way he was - so new and wondrous.

"Remember this," He repeated on that all-important page. Then His voice faded, and the rest of the pages fluttered away, and the next thing Tracy remembered was waking up in the hospital.

Little Tracy's bed was huge and squishy. But as white and as clean as it was, it seemed dirty from where he had just been. The hospital room was also noisy and smelly. Tracy wanted to go back to his room with the Tall Shiny Silver Figure. It was so nice there, Tracy thought, and when he looked around he saw his mother, which surprised him. Vera sat in a chair next to his bed and was asleep. When the toddler tried to get up, Vera heard him.

"Hi baby," she said, and Vera cleared her throat and smiled broadly. "How are you?"

Vera's voice was soothing, even when talking about the weather. Tracy laughed when he heard it, because he loved his Mom so easily.

"I'm fine," Tracy said in a three-year-old way. Vera put the back of her hand to his head the way mothers do, and sighed in a deep, well-earned way. The ordeal was over, but Tracy tried to get up again.

"Where you goin' honey?" Vera asked.

"I want to get my picture book," Tracy said, and the boy really wanted to get up this time. But Tracy's body was heavy and slow, and it wanted to stay behind. The bed was too big and soft for him to get out, so Tracy laid back in defeat and looked at his Mom.

"Can you get my picture book?" Tracy asked.

Vera looked around, thinking. "You mean the one your Pawpaw got you? I think we left that at home sweetie."

"No Momma, not that one," little Tracy said, and he didn't understand why his Momma didn't know about his picture book - it was so wondrous. "The one with *my* pictures," the boy explained.

Vera yawned. "I can see if they have one here so you can color."

Tracy got upset. "No, I want *my* picture book," he said firmly.

"Calm down honey, we'll find you somethin' to color," Vera said decisively. The boy didn't want to make his Momma upset so he stopped, and Tracy knew not to ask about the picture book any more.

Chapter 2

- Tracy as a toddler

"Trace?" Vera asked from the kitchen. "What are you doin'?"

It was Sunday afternoon, and she was making a cake for her boy. His name was Tramele, but Vera decided Tracy was easier than explaining his name to everyone. Besides, Vera loved Dick Tracy - the primary colors, his fedora and understated manner. Everyone in West Virginia also had at least three names depending on who was talking to or about you, and their relationship to you.

Vera, Tracy, and his little brother Freddie lived in Rand, which was just up the river from Charleston. Granny and Moody lived by the end of Starling Drive near the high school, where they had raised their two girls, Vera and Jinny. Now, Jinny lived five houses down from Granny. Vera lived at the other end of Starling Drive nine blocks away, which just far enough to keep her mother slightly out of her hair. By this time, Vera was married to Big Freddie, Tracy's little brother's father, and they lived across the street from little Freddie's grandparents.

Little Tracy stood with his nose to the glass storm door and pouted. It was a beautiful spring day, and little Freddie was playing in front of his grandparent's house with his 'runnin' cousins'. Tracy was just home from the hospital and felt fine. In fact, he was better than fine, because the Tall Shiny Silver Figure had changed everything.

As if to prove it, "Oh Happy Day" came out. Tracy turned three in the April of 1969, and "Oh Happy Day" was the new gospel hit. It played on the radio on their way home from the hospital, and little Tracy began to glow, because it wasn't the first time he heard it.

"You have the same music here!" Tracy screamed, and he sang at the top of his lungs without missing a beat.

"How in the world do you know all the words?" Vera asked.

"I heard it while we were reading...the book," Tracy said carefully.

"What book?" Moody asked.

"Just turn it up Pawpaw!" Tracy yelled.

But the music wasn't as loud as when Tracy heard it in the Highest. There it resounded and went through everything. The music was sent while Tracy was with the Tall Shiny Silver Figure. Now that it was made manifest, the song was confirmation for Tracy his experience was real. He was real! Vera was astounded as her healed boy sang and practically danced out of her lap.

Moody got the 45rpm the next day, and Tracy couldn't get enough. When Moody came home from work, Tracy begged his Pawpaw to play it. Tracy made him turn the stereo console as loud as it would go, and stood right in front at ear level. Then little Tracy got happy as he danced and hugged the gold-weave fabric of the speakers. It wasn't the same as in the Highest, but Tracy knew the Tall Shiny Silver Figure had given him the best birthday present ever.

But right now, Tracy stood at the glass storm door, and his Pawpaw wouldn't be home for hours.

"I asked you a question little man," Vera continued.

"Nothing," the boy muttered. Tracy looked outside and settled farther into his pout. It was mid-day, he couldn't go out and play, and he was definitely not happy.

"What are you here for?" He asked, and only Tracy heard Him.

Tracy was sure he heard Him, but he didn't see Him. Tracy knew it was the Tall Shiny Silver Figure, but there was no light. Tracy looked around carefully, and turned his little self all the way around to be sure. Then he looked back out the window because now, he wasn't sure.

"What are you here for?" He asked again.

Tracy didn't bother to look this time because it was definitely his friend. His voice was as clear and normal as anyone's, and Tracy felt Him standing right behind him.

Tracy thought His voice was at the right height too. The Tall Shiny Silver Figure smiled when He heard that, and Tracy felt His smile. The Tall Shiny Silver Figure asked a third time.

"What are you here for?"

Tracy didn't understand the question, but knew He wanted an answer. Then Tracy remembered the picture book.

"I don't know," Tracy said out loud. "What *am* I here for?"

Vera heard her little man. "You ok Trace?"

There was no answer. Then Vera heard Tracy talking again and getting excited, so she stuck her head out of the kitchen.

"Who are you talkin' to Tracy?" Vera asked.

"I'm just talking with my imaginary friend," Tracy answered.

Vera smiled and thought, 'What three-year-old child doesn't have an imaginary friend?'

"What does that mean?" Tracy asked aloud, and Vera listened.

She had never actually heard her boy talk with his imaginary friend, and Tracy's side of the conversation seemed perfectly normal. Some people thought it was healthy, Vera reasoned, and Tracy had mentioned his imaginary friend before. Ever since he could talk, Tracy knew when the phone was going to ring. He would tell his Mom or Granny, and the phone always rang.

The previous Thanksgiving, Vera's two-and-a-half-year-old unexpectedly came into the kitchen. He made the pronouncement the phone would ring, but this time he had more details.

"Momma," Tracy said.

"Yes baby?" and Vera turned from her dishes.

"My friend told me to tell you the phone is going to ring, and that it will be Granny. She will ask to borrow a cup of salt."

Vera was taken aback, and then she was bewildered. "You mean a cup of sugar, don't you sweetie?"

"No," Tracy corrected. "He said salt," and he went back to his playroom. Before Vera could turn back to the sink the phone rang.

"Hey baby girl," Granny said. "You got a cup of salt I could borrow? I'm brinin' a turkey, an' I'm a little short."

Now, since Tracy returned home from the hospital, things were more different. As Tracy stood and looked out the glass door, Vera heard her toddler get more animated until he almost shouted.

"I don't understand," little Tracy said. "You want me to demonstrate the love walk? What's the love walk?"

Vera dropped what she was doing. Tracy heard the mixing bowl spin on the kitchen floor as she ran through the dining room. Vera scooped little Tracy up under her arm and pushed through the front door. She ran directly across the street, yelling at little Freddie and his cousins to get inside. When she burst into the house, Freddie's grandfather woke up ready for a fight. But he was too drunk to roll out of his recliner, let alone hit anything.

Freddie's grandmother was in the kitchen cooking up a storm as usual. She was startled by Vera's speed as she grabbed the phone, still holding little Tracy under her arm.

"Lock the doors!" Vera screamed, and she was shaking.

The kids came in while Freddie's grandmother held the door open, and she looked up and down the street to see what was on fire, or from which direction the tornado was coming.

"Get inside!" Vera instructed, "and get the kids together."

Tracy pulled his Mom's sleeve as the phone kept ringing.

"Mom," Tracy tried. "Its ok. He's really nice."

"Hush young man," she scolded, because that statement made it worse. Vera motioned for little Freddie who came over, and she placed Tracy between her feet next to him. The cousins collected around their grandmother, and no one said anything. Finally someone answered the phone.

"You gotta get down here right away," Vera pleaded.

The boys heard Pawpaw's voice on the other end, and Moody heard the terror in his daughter's voice.

"I don't know where he came from," Vera exclaimed. "All I know was Trace was standin' in the living room, just lookin' out the storm door. I distinctly heard him talkin' to someone, a man I guess, and Tracy got agitated. Then Trace said something about demonstrating the love walk," which was all Moody needed to hear.

The next thing Tracy remembered was his grandfather and neighbors arriving at Freddie's grandparents house carrying shotguns. Moody brought the German shepherd, Collie, and whatever mixed-breed dog they had at the time. Once Moody checked on Vera and the kids, the mob went across the street to search Vera's house with the dogs. When they didn't find anything, they left to hunt the area.

As folks found out, more guns and dogs gathered. Soon, the entire neighborhood was involved. The search was an odd thing, which added to the urgency. The group systematically scoured block after block looking for the pervert who tried to get Vera's innocent boy to 'demonstrate the love walk'. When they thought about it nobody knew exactly what the phrase meant, but no matter, they knew it was disgusting.

Late in the afternoon, the mob escorted the kids to Granny's house. By this time, Granny, Vera and Jinny had made dinner for the posse. By evening, Vera's two boys, Jinny's two girls, and the neighbor's kids were corralled in the living room while the men did a final sweep. The kids were relatively safe under the guard of Uncle Squeaky - Jinny's husband at the time. Because of the severity of the situation, he only knocked out two beers by dinnertime instead of a six-pack. Besides, Granny and her girls knew how to handle their guns.

Tracy, the intended victim, realized everything happened because of Him. From then on, Tracy decided to keep the Tall Shiny Silver Figure a secret. Tracy wasn't about to let his new friend get him in trouble again, so the toddler tried to get rid of Him. Tracy's babysitter noticed the change when he began hitting his head against the wall.

"Why you doin' that?" she asked.

Tracy knew better than to answer, but he was trying to get His voice out of his head. It was most severe when adults told Tracy to do something that wasn't correct. Tracy got mad because the voice told him the truth, but the adults wouldn't hear of it. They couldn't understand, so Tracy hit his head against the wall. Little Tracy's nickname became 'Boomer', which morphed into 'Boomey-doo'.

When Tracy didn't stop, Vera secretly phoned Tracy's father in Ohio.

"Is there anything along your family lines I should know about?" Vera asked, and she explained how Tracy's behavior had changed since he had come back from the hospital.

"Ask Tracy what his friend's name is," his father said.

"Trace?" Vera shouted. Tracy appeared. "What is your imaginary friend's name?"

"He didn't tell me what His name is," Tracy said.

'I am your friend,' the Tall Shiny Silver Figure said to Tracy.

"He just said, He was my friend," Tracy told his Mom.

Then, not long after the 'love walk' incident, things changed for Vera. She decided that she had had enough of big Freddie's father and his drinking. Vera also couldn't shake her thoughts of little Freddie's grandmother, who was always in the kitchen cooking and eating, and Vera didn't want to end up like that. So this was the second time, and second child Vera had with someone that didn't work out. There were a lot of complications with Tracy's father. A lot had to do with Granny, and a lot that had to do with how young they were at the time.

Vera married little Freddie's father because she had two boys and nowhere to keep them - much like why Moody married Granny. It worked for a while, but the more Vera saw of Freddie's family, Vera decided she would rather be by herself. Two boys were better than three she reasoned, so Vera divorced the biggest one, and it didn't take long.

Vera was still a young, beautiful woman in her twenties, even with her kids. The next summer she took her boys to a family reunion to see their cousins on little Freddie's side. In no time, Big Freddie's cousin Bobby approached Vera at the barbeque. Vera was charmed, and Vera and Bobby were together for the next eighteen years.

But little Tracy watched the new couple carefully. He felt murky forces trying to squirm themselves into his life. Demons desperately wanted to edit the picture book, and Tracy knew it. Tracy also recognized the darkness because he had been with the light. Since he had met the Tall Shiny Silver Figure, Tracy felt light and dark immediately, and Bobby had deep shadows.

Nevertheless, Vera and Bobby married within the year. The newlyweds moved to Washington, D.C., which was exciting for Vera. To her, the city was a chance for fashion and marvelous parties. It was also a fresh start and far away from the confines of West Virginia. Like Moody, Bobby was a mechanic, but that's where the similarity ended. Bobby worked for the city and drove a cab on the weekends for extra money. Vera found secretarial work because the family immediately grew by one. Bobby had a son from a previous marriage. He was a few years older than Tracy, and came over every other weekend.

The new family lived in a high-rise in Southeast D.C. It wasn't the best neighborhood, but it wasn't the worst. Tracy had never seen so many annoying kids, but little Freddie thrived. There were enormous stairways to race up and down, and Freddie could visit his buds down the hall whether it rained or not. But Tracy couldn't get over so much busyness, noise and concrete. To him, even the trees seemed sad. The trees in West Virginia were glorious and his Pawpaw was far away. Worst of all, Tracy now lived with Bobby and his darkness.

But once they got settled, the next thing Vera knew it was the first day of school. She got to the schoolyard early to pick Tracy up, and with so many kids and such a steep grade, the grass didn't have a chance. A very tall, caramel-colored woman stood next to Vera with her arms crossed. Her demeanor was steady, and she stood in running pants, a gym jacket and immaculate sneakers. Most remarkably, the woman hummed a bright tune totally unconcerned if anyone could hear.

"Is this your first one?" the woman asked with a warm Carolina accent.

Vera turned and let out a little laugh.

"Yes," she answered. "Why, yes it is."

The two immediately relaxed because they both spoke country, which was so much easier than the guarded speech of their citified counterparts. It also meant they probably had a lot in common.

"I'll get used to it," the woman said. "I suppose I will anyway, sendin' them out into the world," and she looked at Vera. "This is my first as well," and she picked up her humming tune. The bell rang, and the children burst into the yard yelling as they fell down the hill.

"My name is Rosetta," and the woman reached out.

"I'm Vera," and they shook hands. Vera almost stepped back from the force of Rosetta's shake, and then she laughed. "It's strange to think I'm here already."

"I know sugar," Rosetta crooned in her sing-songy way. "Don't I know," and she shook her head and patted Vera on the back. The mothers looked for their kids some more. Vera sighed before she looked at Rosetta carefully. She really needed that pat on the back, and she was grateful.

"You know," Vera said. "I don't know why, but I feel I know you."

Rosetta just smiled and looked at Vera as she hummed, which returned the sentiment.

"But it's more than that," Vera continued. "I think we're going to be good friends."

"I was just thinking the same thing shug!" and Rosetta really meant her excitement. "I've been askin' for someone when I've been in my prayer closet, and I think it's you," and Vera laughed.

15

"It's been a while since I've had anyone to really talk to, you know, besides my husband," Vera admitted.

"An' he don't talk at all, does he," Rosetta said, and Vera laughed more. "You know I'm right. I got one home the same way. In fact, he's so tight-lipped, I can't even say what he does for a livin'," and Rosetta laughed too. "They actually hired him for it!" and Vera was in hysterics. "It's just no way to live Vera," Rosetta concluded. "But Jesus listens."

Vera turned and stopped her laugh. "He really does, doesn't he," and Vera marveled at Rosetta.

"Let me give you a hug sugar," Rosetta said, and put her tall self all around Vera for a hug that meant everything. "An' you should call me Ro."

Vera felt like crying because she was so relieved. She knew she had a friend – no, a sister, and Rosetta knew it too. Then, it was Ro who laughed as they separated.

"Do you know what I see over yonder?" Ro asked.

Vera looked across the schoolyard. Her boy was giggling with a tall girl from his class. It was the first time since they had moved to D.C. that Vera saw Tracy laugh with anyone but his brother. Then Vera noticed the way Ro looked at her boy and the little girl.

"Is that your daughter?" Vera asked.

"I know you know it is," Ro said with a lilt.

Vera laughed again, but it hurt a little this time. Then Vera realized she hadn't really laughed in a long time, and a lot of the past few years fell off her.

"That's him isn't it?" Ro said. "That's your little one carryin' on with mine."

"I know you know it is," Vera said, and slapped Ro on the back this time. "That's my little man, Tracy, and he's finally looking happy."

Ro stopped laughing and looked at Vera. It was a sudden change, but Vera knew it too. Rosetta took Vera's hand as mothers - as comrades - and they faced each other.

"Now shug," Ro said. "You know we're gonna take care of them together. Just you and me, even if there's nobody else in the room but Jesus."

Vera was truly going to cry.

"I'm serious sugar," Ro stated. "Your boy is my boy, an' my girl is your girl, an' we're gonna get through this, all of this," and Ro passed her hand at the fenced-in dirt, and the bleaker school behind.

All Vera could do was open her arms for another one of Ro's fabulously tall hugs, which she got.

"I'm serious girl," Ro repeated. "We're gonna be all right, an' we're gonna laugh an' cry all the way through, whenever we need to," and Ro stepped back from their hug. "An' speakin' of our little angels, here they come."

The children came at their mothers in a dead heat, and had to catch their breath when they arrived.

"Mommy! Mommy!" the little girl yelled. "This is my new friend," she panted. "His name is Tracy."

"I know shug," Ro said, and bent down and kissed her girl on the cheek.

Vera scooped up her little boy, gave him a big hug, and held him back to ask.

"And who is your new friend little man?" Vera asked, but Tracy just giggled. The little girl jumped up and down.

"My name is Tori," she yelled, "and Tracy and I are really good friends."

"I see that," Vera said, and kissed Tracy on his forehead before she set him down next to Tori. "Now Tori, you can call me Aunt Vera," she said, and Vera put out her hand and Tori shook it.

Then Ro scooped Tracy up, which took him by surprise because she was so tall. His new mother also had music in her, and she practically glowed with a pure silver light.

"An' I'm your Momma Ro," Ro said, "an' me an' your Mom are really good friends too."

Chapter 3

- Momma Ro

"I don't know what I'm gonna do shug," Ro said. "I think she's tryin' to kill him."

Vera shook her head and picked another card. They were playing Snap with the kids, but they had gotten bored and went outside.

"Oh come on Ro-Ro," Vera scoffed. "It can't be as bad as all that."

"Wait till ya see," Ro said, except for her quiet, "Mmm-hmm" that followed for emphasis.

A year had passed, and Ro was home on maternity leave. She took care of Vera's kids for spring break while Vera worked. But it was a Saturday, and Vera found any excuse to get out of the high-rise. Bobby was out 'hackin' as he called it, which meant picking up fares in his taxi between visiting women on the side. If Vera was at Ro's, it was easier for her not to think about what Bobby was really doing, and Ro's house was comfortable. The rancher had a finished basement, and a large backyard fenced in for the dog and kids. There was more space across the street. A thick tangle of trees stood where no one had thought to build yet. The birds were back for spring, and Ro's house was truly a breath of fresh air.

Ro snapped another card, and Tori came out of her room in a sulk. Vera had to muffle a laugh. Tori was taller than anyone her age, but had become meaner and more dramatic. When Ro was about to deliver, Tori already had a few seizures. At first it seemed serious, but the doctor proved it out: Tori wanted to be an only child. More dramatic collapses followed.

18

By the time Ro brought the newborn home, his jealous sister realized seizures were not enough, so Tori decided to go blind. Since her blindness continued, the doctor thought he missed something. He outfitted Tori with special glasses to focus her vision. As with all children's medical appliances, they were huge and strapped down with medieval strength. The glasses had large black cones wrapped in a wider brown cloth, which made them look like beehives. If anyone peered into the lenses to see Tori's eyes, they were literally as big as her head.

"Come here baby," Ro said, and muttered to Vera, "didn't I tell ya?"

Vera tried not to laugh as Tori staggered closer, and the girl eventually managed to find her mother.

"Your Auntie Vera is here," Ro said.

"Hi sweetie," Vera said. Tori suddenly turned in the direction of Vera's sexy voice. The little girl looked for Vera through her magnified lenses. All Vera could see were huge brown saucers of eyes searching everywhere, which caused Vera to laugh in little Tori's face.

"You see Momma, I'm hideous!" Tori screamed.

"Now Tori, this is just silly," Momma Ro said. "You're just fine."

"No I'm not," and she began to cry, but Vera couldn't stop smiling.

'How could the girl possibly cry with all that strapped to her eyes?' Vera thought. Then she wondered if it was possible little Tori could drown, which made Vera laugh out loud again. Luckily, Tori stopped her fit almost as immediately as it started.

"Momma, can I go outside an' play?" Tori said in a small voice. "I want to see Tracy."

"Tori," Ro said sternly. "How you gonna go outside when you can't even get down the hall? You got a death-wish girl? Look, if ya can't see, ya can't see, an' that means ya cain't see nobody."

Tori stomped her feet.

"Now get back to your room until you get yourself straightened out," Ro decided, "an' that means decidin' you don't need those ridiculous glasses!"

Tori huffed, stormed off toward the couch and stopped. When she realized she was in the living room, Tori cocked her head, looked through her goggles again, and found the hall back to her bedroom. When she finally got there, she promptly slammed the door.

"She best not have woken up that baby," Ro warned.

Vera fell to pieces. "I'm sorry Ro, but that was just too much!"

"Oh I know. It's too much for all of us," Ro determined, and she looked down the hall before she whispered. "But I think Tori might be tryin' to kill the baby."

"Well," Vera managed, stifling a laugh. "The good thing is if she tries, she won't be able to find him!" and they collapsed with laughter. "But if you think that's somethin', let me tell you about what my babies did last week."

Suddenly, Rosetta had to hold herself. "Ooooh I gotta be careful, or I might break somethin' I just got fixed. But if you don't think I'll rupture, tell me."

"Well," Vera said. "I was makin' Freddie's birthday cake, and the boys were watching cartoons. I had to go to the bathroom, so I took out the beaters and left the batter in the bowl. Mom called before I had a chance to go, but when I heard my angels in the kitchen, I told Mom I'd call her back."

"An' what did your babies do?" Ro asked, as if she didn't know.

"Just as soon as I left out, the boys went in the kitchen and got the beaters. Tracy teased his brother, going on about how good it was while they licked the beaters clean. Then Tracy said maybe they should have some more. After all, he reasoned, it was going to be Freddie's cake."

Ro hummed and picked another card.

"Freddie said he didn't want to get in trouble, because he was always the one who got in trouble. But Tracy kept going on about how good the batter smelled. He put his face right down in that bowl and took a big whiff."

Ro sang an "Oooh child," for emphasis.

"When Tracy took his face out of the bowl," Vera said, "he kept on about how wonderful the cake batter smelled. 'You wanna try?' was all Freddie needed. He followed Tracy's lead, and put his face down into that bowl. When Trace saw that, it was just too much for him. Tracy put his hand behind Freddie's head and bloop! He pushed Freddie's little face right into that batter. Freddie came out screamin' with batter drippin' all down his face. But when I came around the corner to scold them, and I saw Freddie's batter-face, I laughed so hard I fell on the floor."

Ro couldn't control her laughter, but Vera got out a full confession.

"Oh Ro it was terrible. My baby was screamin' for vengeance with batter drippin' all over his face, and all I could do was writhe on the floor for laughin'."

Vera lost her breath, and Ro's laugh went deep.

"And Ro, I laughed so hard I wet myself! There I was, literally peeing on the floor, helpless while my little baby got madder and madder. All Trace could do was laugh. But bless his heart, he went to get a dishtowel for Freddie to clean up. Then Trace thought better of it, and got a spoon to eat the batter directly off Freddie's face! Then Tracy got a spoon for Freddie!"

Ro's baritone rang throughout the house and woke her newborn. She couldn't stop, but got up to see to him. As she passed down the hall, Tori suddenly opened her door.

"Serve's you right Momma, laughin' at my expense like that," the goggles said, and Tori slammed her bedroom door again.

Ro laughed harder and collected Bunky. She brought him out to the card table, and got him to stop fussing. When Vera returned the women sat, and thought about all they had been through the past year.

"Yes," Ro said. "It seems no matter what he does, it seems your little Tramele can do no wrong, even when you saw him do it."

"I suppose that's true," Vera said. "He has my heart in a different way. Freddie is mischievous like his father, where Trace is more like me. We take things in rather than instigate."

"Even with that batter drippin' down your little one's face?"

"That's why it was so funny Ro, Trace isn't usually like that!"

"Well, we all got our thing we do," and Rosetta hummed and looked at Bunky. "I don't know what this one does yet, but I think he's more like me than Charlie."

"Tracy is my little man," Vera admitted, "but he surely doesn't like my husband," and Ro looked at her. "Trace has always disliked him, right from the start, and I know why."

Ro waited because she wanted Vera to say it, but she didn't.

"Bobby's a hard man," Vera admitted, "but he's no harder than Moody."

"Moody's not as hard as Bobby girl," Ro argued, "an' you know it. I mean, Moody might say things, but he wouldn't…" and Ro stopped. Vera wasn't embarrassed, but she didn't want to talk about the abuse. Instead, she picked up where she left off.

"No," Vera assured. "I think it's because when we moved here Trace was old enough to miss West Virginia. But they truly don't get along, and it's getting worse."

"Whataya mean shug?" Ro asked, but Vera didn't answer. "Are ya sure you don't need to get out?"

"No," Vera said. "It's not that. I can handle myself with Bobby," and Ro shook her head, and her hum went rigid. "It's just how hard it is on Tracy," Vera continued, "and he's been wetting his bed."

"Well honey, that's not unusual. It happens from time to time."

"No Ro, I mean he wets his bed every night. I thought he would grow out of it."

"What does Bobby do?"

"He doesn't know," Vera said.

Ro looked doubtful.

"So far I've managed to keep it from him. I get up early and change the sheets before anyone knows," and Ro's eyebrows furrowed deeper. "But I don't want you to do anything," Vera decided.

"Are you sure?" and Ro had to let her anger out. "Because I would love to give that man a piece of my mind. An' ya don't need to put up with it Vera, any of it. You could come here in a minute."

"I know that Ro," Vera said, and a small tear escaped down her cheek, "but I don't want to come here. You're busy enough. You have your new one, and we would be too many."

"I can handle Charlie too," Ro determined. "Think of your boys."

"No, I can't come here," and Vera's voice got hard. "An' I certainly don't want to go back home to Mom, not after all this time."

Ro rocked Bunky, and Vera stared into nothing.

"Well sugar, we'll get through this," Ro decided. "Just like we said we would. Remember? The first day we met?"

Vera couldn't talk anymore.

"But we will," Ro decided, "an' Jesus will help us."

Chapter 4

- The Wanderer's Inc.

And Jesus did help Vera and Rosetta fight the darkness. By the end of the school year there was a miracle: the scales fell from Tori's eyes, and the blind could see. In fact, Tori liked having a little brother to play with because she was growing up. Then the boys were to spend the summer with Granny and Moody, so Vera got Tracy and Freddie packed to go. It gave Vera a break, and Moody loved having the boys there. Granny did too, but Moody actually took time off work to take them in the camper, and Granny and Moody's camper had history.

As ornery as the pair was to each other, they did some extraordinary things. Back in the day, Granny started her own girl scouts for Vera, Jinny, and the neighborhood. It was West Virginia in the fifties, and while the great middle class expansion after the Great War was one of America's greatest achievements, the advances reverted back to white. Moody still left the house at 5 a.m. and came home around midnight, working as a mechanic by day and janitor by night. Granny cleaned houses and took care of old ladies during the day.

However, when Granny ate lunch in the kitchen, and read ads in the circular full of blenders, toasters and Tupperware, the models that displayed them were still white. Turntables of Detroit cars had lovely girls with higher hair, shorter skirts, and ever more revealing bust lines, but as yet, there was no variety in skin tone smiling back at her. So it was no surprise Vera and Jinny weren't allowed to join the official troup of Charleston.

At first this wasn't a problem. The troop leaders didn't notice who dropped the new girls off. Granny also took care to shoo them out of her car for a quick get-away. Most importantly, Vera and Jinny were definitely passé blanc - especially Jinny with her good looks, whiteness, and naturally auburn hair. The two girls were also extremely polite and comfortable with anyone, which made their heritage less obvious to the establishment's assumptions. But when Granny arrived after the troop meeting, things got ugly.

Unknowingly, the troop leaders looked forward to meeting the mother of the two lovely girls, and had even decided to invite her to a luncheon. Late in the afternoon, Granny pulled up in her white V-8 Impala. She honked the horn, and her girls ran from the park lodge. Granny got out and closed her door, and left the motor running as the troop leaders' faces fell. After she gave Vera and Jinny their hugs, Granny gave a bigger wave to the two women who stared at her. For a moment they didn't know what to do, but in the end, Granny couldn't pass for any kind of white, cream, caramel, or even coffee. Truly - the only white thing about Granny was her car.

"Get in the car girls," Granny said to her incognitos. They did, and the troop leaders came over. Granny raced towards them with a huge smile and outstretched hand.

"Melinda," Granny exclaimed. "Why, I haven't seen you in years!"

"Jackie," Melinda answered. She ignored Granny's hand, but managed a polite ladies' hug because they did know each other.

"And who are you?" Granny asked troop leader number two, but for some reason she couldn't move or speak, which made Granny wonder if she was a mannequin.

"This is LuAnn Jackie," Melinda said. "LuAnn, this is Jackie, Vera and Jinny's mother." LuAnn stayed dumb, and Granny smiled more. The silence held for a moment.

"Now Jackie, you know this isn't going to work," Melinda said.

"Well I don't see why the hell not," Granny retorted, her smile erased, and LuAnn actually gasped. "I paid my money for the girl's dues, an' my girls got as much right to be here as anyone," and LuAnn was truly agog now, but in silence.

"Jackie, I have to say that I agree with you," Melinda began...

"Good," Granny said.

But Melinda was tested. "There are rules Jackie."

"Who's?" was all Granny said.

"Well, in the bylaws," Melinda stammered.

"Yes," LuAnn confirmed immediately. "There are definitely rules that we do not have the authority to change without the due course of a petition."

Granny stood back in amazement, looked her up and down and said, "It *can* speak."

"Now Jackie, you know we go back a long time," Melinda said, "and I will always be grateful how you took care of my mother all those years, especially toward the end."

Granny had a whole paragraph ready, but she didn't want to bother.

"But this is not up to me," Melinda finished, and they all knew that was the line that could not be uncrossed. That statement completely 'hid' the ugliness and injustice of racism, and for some ridiculous reason made the blatant injustice 'right' and 'unchangeable'. The silence that followed proved it.

"Well, you can both go to hell," Granny said, and left for her car.

LuAnn was vindicated, but Melinda did care. "What about your dues?"

"You can keep your damn money," Granny shouted, and opened her massively white door. "Maybe it will do the other girls some good, even if it's too late for your sorry asses," and Granny slammed the door, revved her V-8, and peeled out of the dirt lot with an amazingly satisfying amount of dust trailing behind her.

That night, Granny waited up for Moody, and they talked into the early morning hours. The next day they had a scratch pad of activities, destinations and curriculum planned, and "The Wanderers Club" was born. The whole neighborhood got involved, particularly Mr. Wilson. He was close enough to white to get through vocational school without anyone noticing.

Mr. Wilson passed so well he got more degrees. He ended up teaching at the local college where he met Moody, who used his GI Bill to get his degree in agriculture. Moody always wanted to go back to the farm in Virginia, even though Granny wouldn't hear of it. Somehow Mr. Wilson got wind of this, and figured Moody needed a backup plan. At night, Mr. Wilson took it upon himself to teach Moody to be a mechanic, and that was what made the little town of Rand tick.

Networking groups wove the community together. During summers they took their schooling on the road, and the Wanderers wandered. Children and their parents went on trips, and the kids not only had fun, they learned things black kids weren't taught in school. The elders wanted their kids to know they could do more than clean houses or mop hallways. In a few years, the group had more members with money to buy more campers. They turned them into mobile classrooms complete with libraries, chemistry sets and microscopes. Then "Wanderers Inc." really took off, and expanded past the confines of Rand, Charleston, and the limitations the 1950's had put on the black community.

A generation later, Tracy's first memory of the camper was at five. He sat in his 'car seat' that had a steering wheel and horn. It came with rainbow-colored keys, which made a revving sound when Tracy turned them in the steering wheel's ignition. When Moody started his truck, Tracy started his steering wheel, and the piggyback camper took off. Then Moody slipped in his worn eight-track and played "Mustang Sally" so many times, Granny called it Moody's Blues. But Tracy loved honking his horn with the horn section, and revving his keys between verses. They went to the Summerville KOA just upstream from Rand, and past Mount Nebo.

By this time, the Wanderers included doctors and professors from West Virginia University and the technical college. They played educational games, and studied astronomy with telescopes bigger than their kids. Doc Henderson's extensive entomological displays were most popular. He collapsed beer cases and pinned up insects the kids caught and identified. Andy helped, and it was probably coincidence the diner owner had a love for bugs. But Doc had the most famous story. He lived in a grand house up the hill from the colleges.

Like Moody, Doc had one fear, and they were fishing at the lake when Moody warned him.

"Be careful of them snakes," Moody guffed.

But Doc had to go, so he went up the bank into the woods. As soon as he commenced, the pile of leaves he peed on moved. Doc didn't have time to zip up before he hopped back in Moody's boat, which became one of Moody's favorite stories.

As for Tracy, his first camping trip included a plane ride because the WW II vet couldn't resist.

"How much to take my grandson up?" Moody asked.

The pilot rattled off figures, and explained why the ride was so expensive. But Moody knew how to 'cut off the game' before it started. He also knew exactly 'what was what' from fixing planes in the war, so a 'lot of cussin' went on' after that. Eventually money changed hands, and Moody strapped himself in with the five-year-old on his lap. They circled over the town twice and went over the lake. Then little Tracy wondered if he wanted to become a pilot, which was the point. Moody wanted him to know anything was possible, which was the Wanderers' mission: to encourage kids to come up higher from what they could see from the ground.

By the late 1970's however, trips in the camper were more travel and fewer curricula. During their elementary school years, Tracy and Freddie's excursions didn't involve a chemistry set unless you counted the bar set up for Granny's gin and tonics. Moody still played "Mustang Sally", although now, "Telephone Man" ran a close second. The trips also didn't include historic sites so much as campsites next to fishing holes. Granny loved to fish, although she got caught.

On one of their later trips to the farm in Virginia, Moody wanted to go to the lake one last time. The family had broken the land into lakefront lots to sell. Moody was 'dead-set against it', but was overruled. Besides, one of the reasons the farm was failing was because Moody stayed in Rand with Granny. He took his lumps, but Moody wanted to teach the boys to fish where he had learned.

It was a beautiful summer day. Tracy, Freddie, Granny, and Moody stood on a skinny bank of soft cobbled rocks that backed up to the woods. The boys were doing well, but Granny wanted to get her techniques across too. She stood behind Tracy while he tried another cast. Freddie stood next to Tracy, and both were careful to cast on either side.

"Jackie," Moody warned. "Don't stand so close behind the boys."

"I'll stand wherever the hell I want to stand," Granny snarled.

Almost immediately, Tracy drew his rod back and the hook caught Granny's eyelid. Freddie turned and his eyes got big. Tracy thought he caught his hook on a tree branch, so he yanked. The only thing Granny said was, 'Ow,' which made Freddie's eyes bigger. Tracy pulled again, and Granny said 'Ow' again. Finally, Moody realized what happened.

"Aw hell Jackie," Moody yelled. "I told ya not to stand so close behind the boys!" and Tracy looked.

There was Granny, with his fishhook hanging off her eyelid plain as day. But all was quiet, and Granny wasn't screaming in pain. Even

Moody was surprised. All he could figure was her gin and tonics had kicked in to prevent panic, and it was true, that amount of anesthesia would have done the trick. But Moody got Granny to the hospital without incident, except for the arguing.

"I told ya not to stand so close behind the boy," Moody kept saying.

"An' I told you, I'm gonna do what I'm gonna do," Granny stated, and chugged another gin and tonic. Granny was a sight as she stood mixing her drinks on the way. Despite the bumps of back-ass Virginia roads, and the over-pumped shocks of the camper, she mixed just fine. Even with a lit menthol 100 tucked in her lip, and a fishhook sticking out of her eye, Granny didn't spill a drop.

In the end, Granny's eye wasn't seriously injured, but she had stitches. The doctor gave her an eye patch just like a pirate. The only problem was when she got home. For the next week, Granny couldn't bowl on bowling night. This compounded Moody's misery for the next two Wednesdays, which created billows of cigar smoke. Whenever the pair fought Granny lit up, and Moody would try to smoke her out. Clouds of menthol came from the kitchen, while Moody's cigars filled the living room, and the boys were forced to crawl outside in search of oxygen.

But the earlier trips to the farm in the piggyback camper - they were the stuff of boyhood legend.

"So, what's it gonna be this summer?" Vera asked.

She sat at the kitchen table with her boys. It was the same wood-toned oval Formica table Vera sat at in her teens, surrounded by the same meridian blue walls. The familiar hand-made maple cabinets surrounded her with varnished warmth. Although now, a single vertical row of mirrored squares in a diamond pattern signified the 1970's. For the kids, the tiny TV set at the end of the table was the marvel, because they were able to eat breakfast and watch TV at the same time. Moody put his newspaper down and smiled, because he 'loved him some Vera'.

"I thought we'd take the boys back to the farm," Moody said proudly.

Granny sighed loudly.

"You don't need to go if you don't want to," Moody snapped back. Everyone knew Granny's practiced hatred of the farm, but Tracy and Freddie got excited.

"Did you forget what happened last year?" Granny chided. Then she made her arms into chicken wings, and flapped a few times toward Freddie.

Freddie dropped his spoon in his cereal bowl, and ran out of the kitchen screaming. The first time they went the farm was a revelation for the boys, who were six and seven. They had never seen pigs or horses close enough to smell them. Chickens though, they were most fascinating, probably because of their size and how freely they ran around the yard. Freddie was captivated, and it cut both ways. The chickens usually minded their business except when he was around. But Freddie was convinced the rooster had it out for him, which may have been true. The shiny-feathered cock would strut around and follow Freddie everywhere. Then again, Freddie didn't do much to soothe the relationship.

One morning, Granny Berger went into the henhouse. She came out with eggs for breakfast, which was wondrous. Most of the family was there for a gathering, and cousins on both Granny and Moody's side attended. Granny Berger went because she loved the farm. She loved the rocking chair on the front porch and free tobacco. She never stopped trying to convince her daughter to give up Rand and move to Virginia, because the senior Mr. and Mrs. Moody had a magnificent home.

There was a grand piano in the parlor, where couches and settees matched red velvet draperies. Converted brass gas lamps hung from the middle of each room, and the dining room table sat twenty-four on low seats. But the entire Moody house, including the kitchen and attached L for bedrooms, was clearly from the nineteenth century. The exception was the large RCA black-and-white television console in the living room. It worked but didn't get any channels, which confounded and annoyed the children, much to the delight of the eldest Moody.

In fact, by the mid 1970's the farm, house, and great grandparents were a vastly foreign world to the boys. But Pawpaw Moody Senior was born in 1875. He smoked his own tobacco and raised his own food. His dining room furniture was made from black walnut trees cut on his farm, and the boys certainly couldn't appreciate the accomplishments of the dark black Virginian man, who was born soon after the Civil War.

The Moody family started out working in the brick factory. Then Emma taught school along with Richard, and he built the church he ministered. The couple helped everyone live through all the wars, and enjoyed the community's respect. Even so, Richard, or Great Pawpaw

Moody, was a tall, modest, and extremely quiet man - perhaps because his church, house, farm, and way of life spoke for him.

On the other hand, little Freddie was loud, rambunctious and seven. To him, eggs came out of a carton from the refrigerator. So when Freddie saw Granny Berger go into the henhouse and come out with eggs, he was determined to investigate. Once the boys' 'runnin' cousins' were posted and kept watch, Freddie went into the henhouse. It was mid-morning, so most of the hens were out and about. However, when they saw Freddie, the few hens left inside ran out the opposite end by Tracy. Freddie didn't see any eggs, so he searched the boxes. Sure enough, Granny Berger missed one. When Freddie picked it up, he heard Tracy speak in a hush.

"He's comin' to see what you're doin'!" Tracy warned, because the rooster wanted to know what had riled his girls. He was definitely not pleased to see Freddie in his house.

"I ain't scared of him," Freddie countered.

Freddie picked up the egg and shook it a little. Then he thought a chick might be inside, so he cracked it open. When the egg yolk fell onto the floor, all hell broke loose. The rooster went after Freddie full bore, and Freddie ran out the opposite door at Tracy's heels. The rooster ran much faster, so he cut Freddie off toward the cornfield. Tracy saw his chance, and he and his cousins ran straightway to the house. But when Freddie made it to the kitchen, his cousins held the door shut for fear the rooster would come in after them. Freddie took off with a scream and headed for the front door, but the rooster passed him and sent him back. Eventually Freddie got inside, but it wasn't over.

The next day, the rooster waited for Freddie to come out of the house. He let the other kids out and didn't bother them a bit. But when Freddie cracked the kitchen door the rooster charged, and Freddie retreated. Then Freddie crept through the house on hands and knees, so his head couldn't be seen through the windows. When he cracked the front door open, the rooster clucked in Freddie's face and tried to peck him. Little Freddie slammed the door, whimpered, and slunk down in utter defeat. Then there was the low rumble of laughter, which came from the big comfortable chair in the living room. There wasn't a light on, but Freddie heard the understated bass clearly.

"I told you not to mess with that rooster boy," Great Pawpaw Moody said, and his chuckle rolled some more before he went back to studying his Bible.

Chapter 5

- Tracy and Freddie

"Come here boys," Granny said.

Tracy and Freddie were done with lunch and watched TV. Once Moody got home from work, they would be on their way to the farm.

"Since we're goin'," Granny said, "we might as well have some fun." The boys followed Granny into the living room. She came out of her bedroom with wrapped packages that were long and skinny, and handed the slightly heavier and shorter one to Freddie.

"Well go on," Granny said.

The boys tore into the paper, which revealed a popgun and bow and arrow set. Freddie's gun was easily pumped up, and had a heavy string attached to the red stopper. Tracy was growing so fast, his bow was already shorter than he was. The arrows had rubber suction cups that wouldn't stick to anything, but he loved it anyway. Once Moody got home they were off, and there was a reason they took the camper. Granny had laid down the law with Moody. Even though the farm in Virginia was a marvel in many ways, particularly for the boys, there were realities. The house and furnishings were authentic nineteenth century - complete with turn of the century heat and humidity, rat holes and bedbugs.

Years later, during one of their chats, Moody and Tracy had a good laugh about it.

"She never did figure it out," Moody said, and then he mimicked Granny's gravel. "Why are there only rats in Dris's room? In the mornin', he brings 'em out two an' three at a time!" and Moody winked. "I couldn't let her know we had just as many in our room. The only way was to take up the traps, so they wouldn't be snappin' all night."

But Granny figured out the bedbugs, and when the boys were little she didn't take any chances. When Tracy was in the bathroom in the morning, he heard the aerosol spraying in their bedroom as Granny disinfected their bed. At night, once Granny got the boys settled, she pulled back the sheet. She instructed the boys to shield their eyes and hold their breath, and she sprayed another coat of bug spray over them for safekeeping.

So enough was enough, and they took the camper to the farm. This also gave Granny refuge from Pawpaw Moody Senior, because it was safe to keep her cocktail bar set up without judgment. Mr. Moody was just as happy with the arrangement. Of all the things his son could have done to continue service to his country, marrying Granny was not one of them.

Moody tried to help keep the farm running, which was why he had studied agriculture. But he was too far removed, and when Moody came back from the war there was an incident. The white man that ran the gas station had a younger boy pumping gas. The young man was familiar with the Moodys, but had never met Kindel. Warrant Officer Moody was fresh from the Pacific where things had been different. Moody certainly wasn't expecting the reception he got at the pump.

"We don't serve niggers here," the snotty white boy said.

Moody asked for the manager, but he wasn't there. Moody told the boy not to move, and went up to the farm to get the deed. By the time Moody got back, the manager heard what happened and waited for Moody. He made his son apologize to Moody, which he did, and the father made excuses that his son didn't know who Moody was.

"Your boy didn't need to know *who* I was," Moody decided. "You got twenty-four hours to get out of my station Earl. I'll see you day after tomorrow for the keys."

Years and years later, the gas station at the intersection sat empty. Everyone knew what happened, and what wouldn't happen again. It might have opened back up if Moody had stayed. He would have healed the situation, which was what he excelled at with everybody except one. There was no way Granny was going to pack up her girls, and move to Moody's tiny little town in southern Virginia. There was talk of Moody running the farm during summers, but Granny and Moody couldn't agree on that either. Consequently, the rift between Mr. Moody and Granny ran deep, even during prayer.

Now, at the family dinner, Granny Berger, Granny, and Mrs. Moody senior had been cooking for days. German chocolate cake, fresh peach, and sweet potato pies lined the sideboard. Collards had boiled on the back burner for two days, and mounds of muscadine grapes intertwined at even intervals between the sherry glasses. Mrs. Moody was kept busier by small hands that came from nowhere. They stole the grapes and slipped around the corner, because Tracy and Freddie couldn't stop eating them. Slightly smaller than a ping-pong ball, the boys could only hold three at a time. But the grapes' pink dappled sheen screamed deliciousness.

Usually, the boys got their bounty directly off the vines that grew on the fence around the bullpen. However, that summer the bull was particularly aggressive, and Moody warned them. True enough, as soon as the boys crept close, the bull jousted his horns against the fence. This gave Freddie a rooster flash back, and sent him screeching through the yard. Yet evening finally came, and ham from the smokehouse sat next to buttermilk biscuits. Fresh vegetables from the garden and three types of gravies, one from each matron, vied for room. Then, the large family stood in front of their chairs ready for prayer.

Back home in Rand, when Granny cooked she cooked, and when she ate, she ate. Moody told Tracy, 'Your Granny's stove has two settings: Off and High,' which Tracy witnessed first hand. Granny had to have her food 'piping hot'. When whatever she had torched was done, Granny called everyone to dinner as she brought the food to the table. If no one was there by the time her slender butt hit the chair, Granny bowed her head and said her prayer in fast forward:

"Fatherwethankyouforthisfoodwhichweareaboutotreceivefornouris hmentuntoourbodiesinJesusnameAmen."

Back at the farm, the great Mr. Moody stood at the end of the table in front of the black walnut china cabinet. After a pause, he commenced his prayer in his low, slow voice. The seasoned minister was careful not to forget one blessing, no matter how small. About the time the last curl of steam was about to rise off the mashed potatoes, he was interrupted.

"Aw shit," Granny shouted. "If you really wanted to bless the hands who made this, we'd eat it while it was hot!"

"You selfish ole woman," came immediately from the curled lip of the preacher.

"Selfish!" Granny cried. "You're the one grandisin' with all your flowery words!"

"You have no more respect," Mr. Moody stammered...

"Respect?" and Granny was truly hot now. "I'll show you respect!" and she started dishing mounds of potatoes onto nearby plates. "We'd all be dead by the time ya got done listenin' to yourself," and she grabbed the greens spoon to 'start slingin'. "Did Jesus make the five thousand wait, as hungry as they were?" and Granny pointed her spoon at the preacher. "You jes keep talkin' to the Lord over there, but as for me an' my Jesus, we're gonna eat!"

After a time, Mr. Moody tacked on an Amen and sat down along with the family. Then Mrs. Moody politely began spooning. But the steel blue glint of the retired schoolteacher's eyes was bright, so she turned in her chair to keep her husband from catching her smile.

On this visit, Granny had the camper and gin and tonics to get her through. Granny also had an ally. Miss Odell lived across and down the road from the main house. In fact, most of the Moody's lived somewhere on the four hundred acre property, even if part-time. Moody's older brother Garrison lived on a hill northeast of the main house. He ran the farm when he got back from 'Nam', and stayed to himself. Moody's younger brother Dris had moved to Richmond. He had a plumbing business there, but came home on weekends.

Miss Odell was a cousin of Moody's, who lived back in the woods. She had outbuildings scattered around with mismatched stuff spilling out. One had a still hidden under the floor, which was where Moody got his 'shine'. There was a swamp on the way to her place and it was quiet there, except for Odell and Granny. Their kindred voices rang through the white oaks that surrounded her corner of the property. Once they arrived at the farm, Moody knew Granny would be 'fixin' to go'. He parked the camper by the main house and got Tracy to help him.

"Be careful," Moody would say. "Go slow, your Granny's in there."

They cranked the heavy steel legs down on either side of the truck. When they got it level, Moody drove his green pickup from underneath. After supper, Granny went to Odell's, but on one particular evening it got later than usual.

"Come on boys," Granny instructed. "Get your guns 'n arrows, an' let's have an adventure down to Miss Odell's."

The three hopped in the truck with their weaponry: Freddie with his popgun, Tracy with his bow and arrow, and Granny with her gin and tonic. About dusk, they pulled down Odell's road and Granny stopped the truck.

"Alright," Granny said. "Let's see what you can do," and the boys looked at her. "There might be some big game out there," Granny explained, "or a possum or somethin'. You got the equipment. Let's see what ya can scare up," and Granny really didn't know what was about to happen, and the boys looked at her more. "Aw hell, just get out of the truck, an' go on up the road. I'll follow ya. An' be on your lookout."

So the boys got out of the truck. They stalked down the road with cocked popgun and drawn bow, and it was fun. Granny followed about fifty feet behind, and let the truck coast while she lit a cigarette. There was just enough light to see, and lightning bugs were in the trees. But the other bugs were quiet – no crickets or cicadas, which was a little weird.

The road eased down the hill into the swamp. The boys walked at the ready, scanning the roadside for any sign of movement. About that time, a bull moose noiselessly came from the woods into the road. In reality, the 'moose' was probably a fourteen-point buck. But from their vantage point, and from all the hours watching "The Rocky and Bullwinkle Show", to the boys it was a moose. Tracy silently 'turned heel' and ran for the truck, but Freddie couldn't move.

The brave little seven-year-old stared at antlers wide as the road. They dripped with red velvet and looked angry, although the moose wasn't at all upset. He simply looked at Freddie, who stood knee-high to the colossus. The animal chewed, and Freddie held his gun tight against his chest at the regimented forty-five degree angle of attention. All of a sudden it went 'pop', and the red stopper flew up and out, and then swung limply from the end of the toy.

"Get in the truck! Get in the truck!" Tracy yelled back.

Granny looked up, the end of her cigarette grew bright, and she honked the horn. The moose was not impressed as he watched the boys run, but if a moose could chuckle he probably did. Then the animal continued across the road, and disappeared as fast as he had appeared. The boys hopped into the truck and burst into all kinds of words. Then they went straight to Odell's, and she laughed and laughed.

"Oh yes, that one," Odell chortled. "He's a big one, but he's a pussycat," and Miss Odell arranged herself in her rocking chair.

She needed to sit wide for the heat as she sipped moonshine and took snuff. The boys sat on two short stools in the middle of the porch. Granny took the chair in the other corner. It was dark and a little cooler now. A big moon was on the rise, and the bugs were singing again. Even though they couldn't see the huge trees surrounding the split log cabin, they could hear them. The cicada larvae had crawled out and hardened. Now, they caught up on the business of decades, and made their way to the canopy for the frenzy of alternating vibrations in the next day's heat.

"I'm pretty sure his name is Eddie," Odell said, and she used her hand-fan, but she still looked hot.

"Whose name is Eddie?" Freddie asked.

"The 'moose' you almost popped," Odell answered.

Then Miss Odell got up, and went through the moonlight to a loose shed of thin cedar logs. She came back with a few leaves of tobacco. She pulled her rocker up to the eating table, and laid the leaves out to smooth them. Some were wide, and some were pieces from the last time, but they all looked like leather. She had a rectangular knife at the ready. It was thicker than a razor, and its sharpness gleamed under the yellow bug light. Odell rolled wide shreds into a wad longer than her palm, put them on half a leaf, and cut next to the leaf's vein. Then she cut the top and bottom in a square the length of a cigar. She skillfully picked up the stuffed leaf, and as easy as anything, Miss Odell pulled up her skirt to roll the stogie up and down her inner thigh. With the pressure, heat and moisture, the action sealed the cigar. Then she cut off the tapered tip, and held it up for Granny to see.

"You want one?" Odell asked.

"Now you know I hate those damn things," Granny growled. "It's bad enough Moody's always puffin' 'em 'round the house." Odell looked at her. "But you know you're fine," Granny conceded. "Hell, this is your house Odell, but I'll stick with my ciggies."

Odell lit up, and sat back for a long toke. Then she took snuff, and chased it with moonshine.

"Besides, I'd get confused with all that," Granny said, and waved her hand in a circle. "Yeah," Granny decided. "That would be too much for me. I only have two hands."

Odell didn't answer except to rock, puff, snort and sip, mostly for show this time.

The boys just sat. It was that kind of place and time, and everyone's mind wandered. Freddie thought the moose's name probably was Eddie. If anyone knew, it would be Miss Odell. Maybe he came by every so often for one of her cigars. But would he smoke it, Freddie thought, or eat it?

Tracy was also lost in thought, although his were older. He missed his Mom, but didn't want to go back to D.C. Then, Tracy noticed how soothing the sound of the cicadas was. He was himself here at the farm, especially with Moody. And Granny and Moody, Tracy thought, even with their bickering, they took care of him and Freddie, and they were safe here.

"Did I ever tell you about Moody's rabbit huntin'?" Granny asked.

The boys giggled, and Odell shook her head no, even though she had heard something of it. She sat back for the tale, and blew cigar smoke into the porch roof.

"We were out here years ago," Granny began. "It was shortly after the girls were off and married, so we were by ourselves. Moody was always exhausted as soon as we got here, but there was a rabbit in the garden," and Granny sipped her tonic to oil her voice.

"I think I know where this is goin'," Odell said.

"An' Moody was determined," Granny continued. "But I was pretty sure it was just an excuse to get away from his busybody family. A day went by an' no rabbit. He'd go out past the henhouse, an' set himself up by the big locust tree, sittin' and leanin' against the trunk. The second day he came back empty, I asked him how his nap was. Well, he got all puffed up, talkin' about how he almost got him. An' there was a shot every so often, but I thought I knew why."

"Yep," Odell agreed.

"On the third day," Granny said, "I waited an hour before I went out there. Sure enough, you could hear that snore from the kitchen. So I snuck out. Damn if that rabbit wasn't gettin' his fill chawin' on greens, an' just lookin' at me!" and Granny made her teeth nibble like a rabbit for the boys. "So I decided I'd fix him. I got myself on the opposite side of that locust tree, an' went down on hands an' knees to ear level. Then I snuck up behind him, an' I yelled, 'Moody!' He woke up, an' the gun went off pretty much at the same time, just shootin' everywhere," and Granny laughed, because telling of her exploits with Moody was one of the few things that made her truly happy. The boys laughed themselves off their stools, and rolled around on the porch floor.

"He had to change the tractor tire the next day," Granny finished, "in a totally 'unrelated incident', but I think we all knew what happened."

"Jackie, you are jes not right," Odell stated, and puffed her cigar.

The boys recovered. They got back on their stools to look out into the night, and Freddie was ever so proud. Now, he knew he had more in common with his Pawpaw, and didn't feel so bad about being such a bad shot.

- Tracy and Granny in 2007, Granny wearing Moody's Wanderer's Inc. jacket

Chapter 6

- Granny and Moody's Kitchen

At summer's end, the boys couldn't wait to tell their Mom everything. Vera was just as excited to hear it first hand, as she sipped her coffee at the Formica table. The boys also turned off the tiny TV set, because Miss Odell was that important.

"Ma," Freddie shouted. "You wouldn't believe how big he was! He just came outa nowhere, but I didn't move," and Freddie straightened and screwed up his face.

Tracy rolled his eyes. "Yeah Mom, you shoulda seen his 'pop'."

Granny was in the backyard hanging clothes on the line. The river was down because it was August, but Vera could still see the Kanawha's ribbon over the kitchen sink. Coal cars lumbered along the other side next to the highway. Vera heard the familiar rumble and distant whistle as she rinsed her cup.

"An' Pawpaw shot out the tractor tire!" Freddie squealed.

"Again?" Vera asked absentmindedly.

The boys looked at each other as if they were in the presence of a rock star. "You were there when it happened?" they asked in unison.

"No," Vera said, "but your Granny told me about Moody's rabbit huntin' many, many times."

The boys snickered and dove back into their cereal. Moody was at work as usual. Vera looked over the yard to see how far Granny was with hanging laundry on the line, and decided there was enough time. She looked at the backhouse, the pole at the end of the clothesline, and the cherry tree. Readied, Vera turned to her boys with mischief.

"Did you know your Pawpaw is terrified of snakes?" she asked. The boys stopped eating, so Vera knew she had them.

"When your Aunt Jinny and I were a few years older than you," Vera said, "your Granny got upset with Pawpaw spending his weekends in the backhouse."

"How long would he be out there?" Tracy asked.

"All day," Vera said. "Your Granny thought Pawpaw should be fixing a gutter or something. She also wanted him to mow the lawn, which was why Pawpaw went out to the backhouse in the first place."

As she said it, Vera realized Moody was exhausted from his two jobs, and she could relate. What a wonderful thing to go out, sit in a quiet familiar place and nod off.

"But he'd go out there and not come back," Vera explained. "So your Granny decided she'd fix him. The next week, while your Pawpaw was at work, your Granny got to work plottin' her scheme."

Vera looked out the kitchen window again. Granny was inspecting her tomatoes and looked at the garden hose, so Vera knew she would be a while.

"Well," Vera continued, "your Granny got the drill from the basement, and spent a whole day drilling holes underneath the sink. Then she threaded fishing line through the cement wall. The next day, she went out to the clothes-line pole, and put a tiny pulley just below the grass line," and Tracy started drawing it out in his mind. "She did the same with the cherry tree on the other side of the yard."

"But," Freddie began to ask, and Tracy patted Freddie's knee.

"Just wait Freddie," Tracy determined. "We'll understand in a minute, at least I think we will."

"You will," Vera said, proud of her boys. "You see, your Pawpaw really is terrified of snakes."

The boys crinkled their eyebrows, because they didn't think Pawpaw could be afraid of anything.

"It's true," Vera confirmed. "A snake of any kind, no matter how big or small," and the boys relented. "So your Granny went out and got a big rubber one, the biggest one she could find," and Freddie giggled. "That Friday, she spent the day laying out her line between the pulleys. Your Granny had a whole system. Because the grass was so tall, Pawpaw wouldn't see the fishing line," and Vera laughed, realizing her mother's point about mowing the lawn.

"By Saturday morning everything was set," Vera said. "After breakfast, Pawpaw went to the backhouse, and your Granny opened the cabinet under the sink," and Vera opened the sink cabinet, and the boys were amazed. "She waited for your Pawpaw to come out with the lawn mower, but he came out with trays filled with soil instead."

Vera mimicked Moody coming across the yard carefree and whistling, carrying seedling trays. Then she crouched to mimic Granny, watching her prey just above the sink. Then Vera saw the reaction of her boys, who wondered how she knew all this.

"About that time," Vera said, "I walked into the kitchen with your Aunt Jinny, and Momma was all bent down. 'What in the world?' we asked, but your Granny didn't miss a beat. 'Get down!' she hushed, so we did. Then your Granny turned to us with a grin and said, 'Watch this girls.'"

Vera got lost in the memory, and acted out what she described like it was yesterday. She hunkered down to the level of the counter. Then she rose to see out the kitchen window. Vera imagined the three pair of eyes - hers, Jinny's, and her mother's peering at Moody as he started across the backyard.

"So here comes your Pawpaw out of the backhouse," Vera said, "his arms stacked with trays full of soil to plant. And here was your Granny, waiting for him to get close enough." Vera crouched lower. Then she put her hands out to mimic Granny holding the fishing line.

"'Now!' your Granny said to herself, and she pulled on that line fast as she could," and Vera pulled furiously on her pretend line. "Sure enough, that rubber snake slithered right through the grass at Pawpaw's feet!" and Vera drew a slither through the air mimicking the snake. Then she stood to pantomime Moody's part: "And your Pawpaw threw up his trays, pots and soil going everywhere, and he hightailed it to the backhouse!"

The boys erupted with laughter, but Vera wasn't done. Neither was Granny.

41

"While she waited, Granny got her snake all the way over to the cherry tree, and she got her other fishing line ready to go. After a few minutes, Pawpaw came out of the backhouse again, but this time he had the ax," and Vera put a pretend ax in her hands, and imitated Moody starting across the yard.

"Pawpaw came out real quiet," Vera said, "and he looked everywhere for that snake. Then he went toward the clothesline," and Vera paused, and the boys couldn't breathe.

"Suddenly, Granny pulled her line, and her snake came at Moody from the cherry tree," and Vera did it. "And Pawpaw threw his ax in the air, and ran for the backhouse in double time!" The boys were beside themselves as Vera's eyes glistened. "The next time Pawpaw came out with a hoe, and Granny had the snake coiled by the clothesline."

When Vera mocked Moody's tiptoe from the backhouse, Freddie got up to join her. Then Tracy watched his Mom and little brother tiptoe across the yard with their hoes above their heads, ready to kill that snake.

"Once Pawpaw got half-way across," and Vera went over to the sink to crouch with her fishing line, and Freddie kept tiptoeing. "Your Granny pulled the other line just as fast as she could. Sure enough, Granny's snake slithered back across the yard to the cherry tree fine as anything!"

Vera cued Freddie by drawing a snake slither. Freddie threw up his hoe, screamed, ran in a fast circle, and sat back down before they all collapsed with laughter. They were in such an uproar; none of them knew that Granny had come in.

She heard the commotion through the open kitchen window, but passed quietly underneath. Then she made her way up the side of the house to the front yard. After inspecting her hostas, Granny came through the front door. That was about the time Vera mimicked Moody coming out of the backhouse with his hoe, and Granny appeared in the kitchen doorway to watch the grand finale, performed by Vera and Freddie.

"I kept your Pawpaw out there all day with that rubber snake," Granny said, and her laugh was low and satisfactory. The boys were startled into more hysterics, and Granny looked at Vera sweetly. "I'd forgotten about that."

Tracy got up to look into the cabinet under the sink.

"Go ahead," Granny said. "They're still there."

Tracy turned back in amazement, so Freddie went to the cabinet and peered in. Sure enough, to the right of the drain were two tiny little holes of light just big enough for a fishing line. The boys looked back at their grandmother.

"He never knew," Granny gloated. "To this day, Pawpaw thinks that snake just had it out for him."

"That snake did have it out for him," Vera stated. "He just doesn't know the snake was you!" and even the boys laughed at their Mom's slam, because the truth was the truth.

"Well," Granny sighed. "I couldn't help myself," which was also true. Then Vera looked at the clock and came back to motherhood.

"Ok men," Vera said. "Enough about snakes. Go and get yourselves packed up."

The boys went to their room slithering snakes across the yard, and throwing axes and hoes into the air. Granny got more coffee and Vera sat down.

"Speaking of snakes, are things better with Bobby?" Granny asked.

"I was about to ask the same about you and Moody," Vera snapped back. Granny and Vera spoke by phone every Sunday afternoon, but being in person made it more fun.

"Bobby's just a hard man," Vera continued. "It's better when it's just us, and it's different having David home, just him, and the boy that's actually his."

"Freddie seems to be ok with him," Granny said.

"Yeah," Vera said. "He gets along with Bobby, probably because they all come from that clan up the road," and Vera raised a brow. "I see Freddie's father more and more in that little boy, and it worries me."

Vera got up for another cup of coffee, marveling at her life decisions. A lot of them had to do with getting away from the person she was talking with, because it was Granny who pestered Vera to the point of escape. Bobby said the same kinds of things, belittling her as her mother had. But her husband's physical abuse wasn't something Vera ever expected. On the other hand, Vera always thought of herself as a city girl. She liked having nice things, and being expected to dress up. At least Bobby let her have that.

"But Bobby and Tracy truly hate each other," Vera concluded.

"I can see why," Granny said flatly.

"Tracy sees Bobby's pride somehow," Vera agreed, "and he knows when Bobby's in the wrong," and Vera realized it. "Tracy knows immediately. It's uncanny Ma, and it just makes Bobby meaner."

"You certainly have your hands full," Granny said, and flicked her cigarette ash.

"But I'm making it through," Vera said. "The boys are getting older, and who knows, maybe they'll find something they can agree on."

Then Vera took the boys home, but things didn't get better. Tracy and Freddie did help save their mother from evacuating the high-rise. Vera insisted on bringing her cast iron skillets from West Virginia. She made pancakes on Saturday mornings, which could set off the fire alarm.

The boys sat and watched cartoons until they heard the butter hit the pan. When the first billow of smoke eased from the kitchen into the dining room, Freddie got up to get a magazine. Tracy headed for the sliding door to the balcony. As the pancake smoke wafted through the living room, Tracy opened the door and Freddie fanned the smoke detector. They didn't want the alarm to go off again, or worse, have the neighbor's kids smell pancakes. If they did, they lined up by the door and shouted to be let in. If it was warm out, Tracy was careful to open the sliding door quietly. That way the boys weren't seen on the playground either, and the boys could eat their pancakes in peace.

But soon, Thanksgiving and Christmas trips back to Granny and Moody's brightened the gloom. Then, the next year began, along with the grind through the noise of the high-rise, the dirt of the school, and the grayness of the D.C. trees. In April, the great Mrs. Emma Moody died. She had lost knowledge of who and where she was. She stayed in Dris's old room because it calmed her. But in the middle of the night, she went to the bathroom and didn't make the turn. She went over the low railing, and fell head first into the first floor hall. She probably never realized she was gone. Great Pawpaw Moody heard her fall from his bedroom, and he told Buddy, who ran the local bait store.

"I knew she was gone as soon as I heard her fall," the great Mr. Moody said. "There was no point in calling anyone until morning," and he paused missing her, before he looked at Buddy. "But it was truly a blessing," Mr. Moody concluded. "She is so much better off."

So the steel blue twinkle of Mrs. Moody's eyes went out at eighty-nine. It was dark the morning of her funeral, and it didn't seem fair a day so dismal was to celebrate a woman of such good humor. Yet the tiny town packed the Moody family's church, despite the rain. Overflow guests stood through the vestibule, down the steps and wrapped themselves around the church, where they listened through the open stained glass windows under umbrellas.

During the service, the heavens opened up and dowsed everything. Then, after the last hymn rang out loud enough for Jesus to hear, every last person went to the farm. Outside, Tracy tried to dry Moody's face from the rain. But he ducked away, and Granny explained the rain was a cover for his tears. Then the rain let up, cars filled the hayfield above the pigpen, and hundreds walked silently across the road.

The casket led the crowd to the backside of the house where the family stones were flush to the ground. Unless you knew, the family cemetery was just a well-kept lawn opposite the bullpen. Once Emma was laid to rest, the sun broke forth over a freshly washed world. In no time, bees were back on the peach blossoms, the birds sang, and the congregation was ready to eat. Food tables followed the semi-circular driveway around the house. Eating tables were laid out five deep, and eight long toward the meadow. Because everyone knew what everyone made, the meal was complete. Tracy's Pawpaw also put out eight hams from the smokehouse, which was none too many.

However, Moody stayed scarce to Tracy, and asked Vera to keep 'his boy' at a distance. It would be too much for Moody while he said goodbye to his mother. He never spoke of it, but Moody's love for her and his family was unshakeable, even though Granny had trumped it. But something changed after his mother died, and Moody went to the farm every few weeks. The great Mr. Moody had only turned one hundred that September, and had seven more years to go.

Oddly, the way Emma died gave Richard ammo for still using the outhouse, and he had no use for artificial light. He read during the day, so there was no reason to switch a light on after sundown. As long as Richard lived, he also couldn't bring himself to use indoor plumbing, despite the fact his son was a plumber. The way his wife died proved his point beyond any doubt, because as far as the preacher born in 1875 was concerned, no one ever died using a slop jar in the dark.

Over the next seven years, Moody brought his father canned goods and stocked his refrigerator. After breakfast, the two went outside. Moody set an old white metal chair underneath the locust tree, or under the porch if it rained, and he gave his father a haircut and shave. They didn't speak much, but looked over the farm from the top of the hill and down each side to whatever it contained - the cow pasture over the cornfield back to the woods, or the space of the garden through the orchard down to the meadow. With Mrs. Moody gone, the chicken coop was silent. The pigpen would soon be empty, and both knew it would all fall silent. But they knew the light would be back, eventually. Until then, the darkness gathered to do what it could to interrupt Moody and Tracy's lives.

- a tobacco drying house
on the farm

Chapter 7

- Tracy and Freddie, 1977

The following summer, Granny decided the boys needed something to do. She got Freddie a bb gun to shoot squirrels off the power lines, and he took to that right away. As for Tracy, he knew his gift was unusual even though he knew what it was. The package was longer and sturdier than last year's bow and arrow set. It was carefully wrapped in brown paper that smelled like the attic. Tracy looked to be sure he should open it.

"Go on," Granny said. "That was your Mom's," and Granny smirked. "Maybe it will come in handy some time."

The bow fit Tracy even though he was taller, and the arrows had real feathers with weighted tips. Once they had the target set up, Granny showed Tracy how it was done.

"Now, ya don't take your eye off the target," she instructed. Granny stood with her feet shoulder-width apart and rod-straight. She picked up the bow with her left hand, and the arrow with her right. She fixed her eye on the target, arched the bow above her head and down the axis of her face. She touched the arrow to the bow, and held her breath as she brought the bow down and the arrow back. Without stopping, she pulled the arrow taught, released the arrow and hit the bulls-eye.

Tracy looked at Granny and saw a Japanese warrior, because what she did was textbook Samurai. Tracy half-expected Granny to put her hair in a tight bun, and take him to see her sword collection hidden behind a secret panel in her bedroom. Either that, or reveal her Native American name was 'Shoots Straight With No Bullshit'.

"Where'd you learn to do that!?!" Tracy screamed.

Granny just handed the bow to Tracy and said, "Now you try it," and he did.

The boys were ten and eleven, and Freddie carried on, but more so. As Vera feared, Freddie now hung out with his cousins on his father's side. Granny tried to intervene, but it didn't work. Freddie reached puberty early, and his conversion was startlingly quick. In what seemed days, Freddie became more of his father and less of Vera and Granny. Tracy wondered if a werewolf bit his little brother, but then again, he watched way too many Lon Chaney movies.

After his mother's death, Moody went to the farm often to 'get things settled', and each time he came back darker. That summer, Moody only took the boys on a few camper trips. Everyone was changing except Granny. She relished staying in her little town just 'smokin', bowlin', an' talkin' shit'. For Moody, the farm was slipping away and his world was a much narrower place. He was also worried about Tracy. At the end of the summer, Tracy was about to enter the sixth grade. Moody's 'boy' was the one he never had; and even though they weren't biologically related, Tracy and Moody also shared the light inherited from their fathers.

Consequently, Moody sensed the dark as intensely as Tracy did, and before Tracy headed back to school Moody made a decision. The Sunday before Vera came to take the boys back to D.C., Moody asked Tracy to help him. This was the first of a lifetime of 'meetin's' disguised as 'doin' somethin'.

"Wanna help me crack some walnuts?" Moody asked. They were in the kitchen. Tracy vaguely watched TV as he munched spicy tortilla chips.

"Not really," Tracy said, which puzzled Moody.

The boys had ridden their bikes all day, and Freddie was with his cousins. Granny was down at her mother's, so they were alone. Moody sat down and grabbed a chip, but he wasn't a fan.

"But you always wanna help me," Moody said, which was true. But the summer went by fast, and Moody hadn't been around.

Tracy shrugged his shoulders and picked up another spicy chip. He looked at both sides, decided, crunched it, and Moody saw his 'in'.

"Why do ya look at it before ya eat it?" Moody asked.

Tracy looked at his Pawpaw and saw something unusual. First, Moody really wanted to know. Second, his Pawpaw needed to talk to him, not the other way around, so Tracy softened.

"I look at both sides to see which side is gonna have more flavor," and Tracy picked up another chip to demonstrate. "Then I put that side on my tongue," which he did, followed by another crunch. Moody picked up a chip, studied both sides and ate it, and it was better.

"I see your point," he said. "But it takes too long, that is, if you're gonna eat the whole bag," and Moody nudged Tracy, "which we both know ya are."

"I can see your point," Tracy repeated, and crunched a chip in his grandfather's face. "Come on Pawpaw, let's try some walnuts instead."

Moody went downstairs and grabbed two large pliers, and they set off for the backhouse. They swung the wide plywood doors open. Tracy unfolded the webbed lawn chairs, and they settled themselves in front of the Gravely. The tractor was the standard walk-behind two-wheeled model, which was attached to the rototiller at the moment.

Moody grabbed the bag of black walnuts from the farm, which had spent the year aging in an old onion bag hanging on the wall. The nuts were a little easier to get into now, but not by much. Moody set the bag between them, and the pair looked like two old men from a scene in a movie doing something they always did, even though none of that was true.

"Come on," Moody said. "We both know we didn't come out here for these horrible things," and Moody reached into the bag. "What's eatin' ya son?"

"Whadaya mean?" his boy asked.

"Well," Moody said. "I know I'm not as much myself this year," and Moody's channel locks made a sharp crack, and a piece of shell scattered with enough force to ding a shovel hanging against the wall. Tracy didn't know what to say. He knew they were talking man to man, and that Moody spoke about his mother's death, which wasn't something Tracy ever thought they would talk about. So Tracy just kept working his pliers, and tried to get a crack for himself.

"Wanna try the hammer?" Moody asked.

He picked up the ball peen that leaned against the wall next to a brick. He put the brick in front of his lawn chair. Then Moody leaned over and placed the walnut with the ridge facing up. He whacked it with the hammer, and the walnut lay over on its side unimpressed. Next, Moody turned the nut so the opposite ridge was exposed. The second whack split it evenly across the middle.

"That's cool!" Tracy said.

"The only other way is to run 'em over in the driveway, but that's a lot of dirt to pick out. Not really worth it," and Moody realized he felt that way a lot lately. "Wastes gas an' time, an' it's a lot of dirt."

Moody took the walnut meat out in one piece and handed Tracy half. Then Moody tossed his half in the air and caught it in his mouth. Tracy did the same, although not as high, but caught it just the same. To Tracy's surprise the nut was oily and bitter, and Moody noticed.

"They're much better in muffins," Moody said. He handed Tracy the brick and hammer, and they were in business. After a while, Moody asked again.

"Are you doin' ok with Bobby?"

Tracy's hammer hit his walnut with unexpected force, which was the answer. More silence followed during the shelling.

"Personally," Moody stated, "I think the man's a complete asshole."

"He is!" Tracy cried out, and wondered if he should be embarrassed.

"It's all right son," Moody said. "We all know he is, an' you can talk freely. That's why I haven't been back to D.C. - since we tried doin' the bikes with the fuckin' bastard."

Three years earlier, Vera and Moody decided to get the boys bikes for Christmas. Moody asked Bobby if he wanted to help put them together. When the time came, Bobby was too busy sipping whiskey and watching "The Poseidon Adventure", and Moody wasn't going to ask a third time.

After Christmas, when Bobby saw Tracy and Freddie having so much fun with their new bikes, he made a decision that nailed the lid. When it came time to for the grandparents to leave, Vera, Bobby and the three boys lined up for their hugs. Then Moody and Granny said goodbye, and turned toward the front door.

"Ain't ya gonna take the bikes?" Bobby asked. Moody was astonished.

"Why the hell would we be takin' the bikes?"

"The boys are too little," Bobby stated, but Moody didn't understand. "They can't take 'em up an' down the stairs to use 'em here," Bobby explained.

To Tracy's mind, Bobby didn't want to be tripping over them. David would take his bike over to his grandmother's house, because David only came to stay with them every-other weekend. But Moody still couldn't believe it, and could barely contain his rage.

"Get your little brother," Moody growled at Tracy, and he did.

Vera and Bobby's apartment was only on the second floor. Granted, Tracy was in third grade and Freddie was still pretty small, but Moody assumed any parent would be interested in their child's happiness. But that was it: Tracy and Freddie weren't Bobby's kids. Tracy reappeared with Freddie, and they knew it was serious.

"Get your bikes boys," Moody said.

Bobby stared at them, but the boys' allegiance was clear. Tracy and Freddie got their shiny new prizes and wheeled them over.

"Now Tracy, I want ya to help Freddie with the doors," Moody instructed. "An' if the stairs are too high for him, take his bike down first. Then ya can come back for yours."

'It was nighttime,' the boys thought, and the boys looked at each other and simultaneously wondered, 'why would Pawpaw…' until each boy looked at Moody's face. Moody shot a look back without saying a word. Then, Tracy narrowed his eyes and looked straight at Bobby.

"Come on Freddie," Tracy said. "We got this."

The boys took their bikes outside and back so there would be no question, and Moody was proud.

"Well I don't care," Bobby said flatly. "You need to take the boy's bikes back where they came from," and Bobby turned for his recliner.

"Come on Jackie, let's get in the car," Moody managed to say. Then he picked up Tracy's bike, and went out of that door for the last time. Granny looked at Vera with a laser in her eye.

"We're gonna be talkin' more often," Granny said, as she puffed on her cigarette. Then Granny picked up Freddie's bike. Even though she was wearing high heels and a dress, Granny carried the bike and her purse down the hall with her lit cigarette, all the while keeping a fixed stare on Vera as she descended down the staircase and out of sight.

51

Now, Tracy became angry as he thought about the bikes, and he smashed another walnut. On the upside, Tracy thought, he could call Bobby an asshole with his Pawpaw out loud, so things were getting somewhere. However, Moody was still troubled.

"I know things are hard there Trace," Moody said, and he paused.

Tracy rarely saw his Pawpaw in thought. Moody was always busy, and knew how to do whatever he was doing. Right now, he just cracked another walnut.

"Sometimes I think we could use some help around here," was what Moody came up with.

Tracy wasn't sure what Moody meant, but thought he did. Tracy never felt at home living with Bobby, or how he abused his mother.

"I'd have a hard time not killing the man," Moody finished.

"It's crossed my mind," Tracy said, and he smashed another walnut.

"An' sometimes there's good reason to kill a man. I did it in the war. Sometimes it seems even more fittin' with family," and Moody smiled. "But if that was right, your Granny'd been long gone by now."

"Yep," Tracy said, "an' I woulda taken out Freddie."

"But Bobby truly is an asshole Tracy," and Moody paused for a second. "An' what he does to your Mom isn't right, but it's gotta play itself out."

"It's not right Pawpaw," Tracy said, and he started to cry and get angry at the same time. "I just don't want to be there. I mean, I love Mom, but why does she put up with his ass?"

"I don't know," Moody said. "But hang in there, an' we'll try to get this sorted. I'm almost done with what needed doin' at the farm. Then maybe we can see about gettin' ya outa there."

"I love you Pawpaw," Tracy said quietly, and put his hammer down to wipe his tears.

"Yeah," Moody said, because Tracy's tears confirmed his decision. "We'll get ya outta there."

The next day, Vera took the boys back in D.C. Vera was busier with work, and Bobby found out about the bedwetting.

"Vera, that sissy boy needs to do his own damn laundry," Bobby shouted one night. "Maybe then he'd stop not bein' able to control himself."

Bobby came out of the bedroom and passed the boys trying to watch TV. "Ultraman" was on, and even though the cartoon was dubbed into English from Japanese, it was Tracy's favorite. He wanted Hayata's spaceship and ability to fly. Most of all, Tracy wanted his Beta Capsule that made Hayata big enough to fight off all varieties of monsters and demons. At the moment that adversary was Bobby, and the cartoon didn't allow escape. Instead, Bobby pointed at the back of Tracy's head.

"The boy needs to grow up an' be a man for God's sake."

But Bobby needed to do some growing up of his own. Vera found hairpins when she got back from picking up the boys. They were in the carpet of their bedroom, and were definitely not hers. Vera waited until after the boys ate dinner, watched some TV and went to bed. Bobby sat in his recliner for another whiskey. Vera went into her bedroom, came back with a handful of hairpins, and smoked a cigarette. Vera's favorite ashtray hung just outside her bedroom door. It was a Mother's Day present from Freddie. It had a hook, a fish, and three little chains came from the fishtail to hold the tray.

"What are you looking at?" Bobby said.

"I'm lookin' at the no-good ass of a man I married," Vera said.

Bobby was jolted. "What did you say?"

"You heard me asshole," Vera replied.

Vera went and held her hand above the ashtray beside Bobby's chair, and let her handful of hairpins drop. Bobby thought about charm, but as the hairpins tinkled into the glass tray he recoiled.

"I'm tired of it Bobby," Vera continued. "I've been tired of it a long time, and it's got to stop."

Bobby looked at the pins. "Those are your pins girl."

"They most certainly are not," Vera stated. "They were deep in the carpet."

"But Bootsie," Bobby tried. "Those hairpins musta been in that carpet all year. You musta just stepped wrong an' found 'em."

Bootsie was Vera's nickname as a girl, and Jinny, Moody and Granny used it often. Bobby also called Vera that while courting her, but now, when Bobby said it the name simmered with anger and regret. Vera narrowed her eyes and took a drag of her cigarette. After she flicked her ash into the fishtail, Vera pulled a pin from her hair.

"Do you really think I'm that stupid?" she asked and held it up. Vera moved her cigarette to her left hand, and she held up the hairpin to study it.

"What's that?" but Bobby's question answered itself.

"This is one of *my* hairpins you snake!" Vera growled. "If you could tell your women apart, you'd know there was more than one kind," and Vera was beyond hot, and didn't care who heard her.

Bobby was cornered, so like any snake he struck. He stood abruptly and hit Vera across the face. But Vera was ready and took it. She also didn't move back, which fueled Bobby's rage.

"What the hell are you talkin' about bitch," Bobby snarled.

"I get my pins in West By God Virginia," Vera sneered and waived what was hers. "They have a twist in 'em you don't see around here. In fact, they don't make 'em anymore. So the whore you talked into comin' here into *my* bedroom, 'cause you couldn't go to hers, probably 'cause she's as low as you, well, she must be a more modern woman, 'cause the pins in the carpet were straight!" and Vera put her cigarette out and mashed the evidence into the ashes. Bobby grabbed Vera's right hand.

"Let me see that!" he screamed, and Bobby held Vera's hand up, looked at her pin and growled.

Bobby's pride was bashed, so he kept her hand and bent it backwards. He kept going, and Vera's wrist went as far as it could go, but Bobby kept going. When Vera had to drop the pin from her hand, Tracy appeared in the doorway of his bedroom with his bow and arrow. Neither his mother nor Bobby saw him. Tracy arched the bow high above his head, and brought it down the axis of his face. He drew the bow the way Granny taught him, and his eyes were fixed on Bobby's black heart. Then, as Tracy held his breath and brought the bow down, it was like a sheet of paper obscured his view.

"This is not for you," the Tall Shiny Silver Figure said.

He stood in front of Tracy, which clouded his mother and Bobby. Then it was as if He pulled Tracy aside. At first, Tracy wasn't sure he had heard Him. Tracy had stopped talking to his imaginary friend years ago, for all the trouble He caused with the dogs. Now, the Tall Shiny Silver Figure's voice was distant. But His light was there, even though it was shrouded, and He stood in the way of Tracy's target.

"You know I can shoot right through you," the sixth grader said.

"This is not your destiny," He said, and Tracy understood more of what He meant:

The choice was Tracy's. Either he could do what he wanted, and kill the thing he most hated - and Bobby personified hate while breaking his mother's wrist; or, Tracy could repent - change his mind - and leave it to Him. Tracy held the bow another moment and time waited. Everything was paused for this crossroad, and Tracy felt the Tall Shiny Silver Figure's patience. His light was warm - like a ground fog in spring, swirling on a warm breeze.

Then, as Tracy felt His image, Tracy remembered and relented. Besides, Tracy didn't want to take the chance of hitting his mother by mistake, so he released the tension of the bow. Once Tracy made his choice, He took over and time resumed.

As Bobby pushed down on Vera's wrist her head was turned, and she was shown her son. Tracy stood with the bow and arrow her mother had given her, which was now drawn against her husband, and that sight almost hurt Vera more than the physical pain inflicted on her. Then, the end of Vera's fingers almost touched the top of her upper arm, and Bobby bent farther against all that was good.

The break was loud to Bobby, but dulled for Vera and Tracy. The pain was quickly followed by adrenaline. The fog present from Him also helped Vera, and forced Bobby to let go. Then Bobby got his coat, went out the front door, and left his mess behind him. Vera slumped into Bobby's chair, and Tracy ran to lock the door. He ran for the phone as his mother tried to ask for it. Vera's wrist was limp, but after she caught her breath she got up and went to the kitchen for ice.

"Get a sandwich bag," Vera managed. Tracy did and put ice in the bag. When Vera put it on her wrist, Freddie appeared at the ready.

"Get Mom a small towel," Tracy said, and Freddie was gone. Vera sat down at the kitchen table.

"Momma Ro?" Tracy asked.

Vera nodded and Tracy dialed. Freddie came back with a towel, handed it to his mother and sat at her feet. Vera wrapped the towel around the ice on her wrist. Once Tracy heard the phone dialing, he held the receiver to his mother's ear. Rosetta answered during the first ring.

"I did it," Vera said, "an' ya need to come get me."

"Oh my Lord!" Ro yelled. "Are ya ok?"

"I'm pretty sure he broke my wrist," Vera said.

"He broke her wrist," Ro yelled to Charlie.

"I'm on my way with the gun," Charlie yelled back.

"No Ro, he left out." Vera said. "Just come an' get me to the hospital," and Momma Ro listened, but Charlie was also talking.

"Wait a minute," Ro said to both. "No, Charlie, he's gone out, an' Bootsie needs to go to the hospital. Now you hold on shug, an' we'll be right there. Charlie, get the car ready," and there was a brief pause. "Not the Camero," and Ro was annoyed now. "Bobby's left out, an' this is no time for a manhunt."

"Tracy had my bow an' arrow set out," Vera said through the pain. "He was ready to kill him."

"Charlie!" Ro screamed. "Tracy was gonna kill the bastard - with Vera's arrows!" and Ro laughed, but quickly followed with, "Oh Jesus. I'm sorry for that outburst, but ya know what I meant," and Ro was pretty sure the Lord forgave her. Then Tracy heard Charlie laugh out loud - a very unusual sound, and Tracy cried a little as he held the phone, but from pride.

"The boy's a man now!" Charlie gloated. "Come on Ro-Ro, let's get over there."

56

Chapter 8

- Tracy at 12 years old

After Bobby broke his wife's wrist, things were different. Vera was changed and Tracy was done with him. Vera told everyone in the high-rise she fell down the stairs, but Tracy wouldn't have it. When someone asked about Vera's cast, and she began to explain about 'her accident', Tracy interrupted.

"That's not true Mom," Tracy said. "Bobby broke your wrist."

Charlie was right – Tracy was twelve and becoming a man. He was vindicated about Bobby and what an asshole he was. But as hard as Tracy tried, he still wet his bed. He tried everything: no liquids after an early dinner, running around after dinner, and finally no liquids at all except milk in his cereal. None of it worked. Tracy's issue was the scout trip, which Vera had planned since he joined the troop. What was pure dread for Tracy was a bright spot for Vera. She was nostalgic for the Wanderers, and now her son was a member of the national organization. Vera put Tracy's camping gear on layaway until the end of September.

One evening they came home with his tent, canteen, stove, mess kit and sleeping bag. By this time Tracy ate his cereal dry, and lay awake so he could get up every few hours. Tracy was also on edge because the high-rise was noisy with too many people. The door slams were the worst, which were constant and at all hours of the day and night. Scars of safety chains etched the back of every metal door as a reminder of the trap they lived in.

A week before the camping trip, Tracy lay awake in his bed. As Tracy's mind wandered he realized how exhausted he was. He couldn't understand why the camping trip was such a big deal to his mother. Tracy didn't associate with many of the kids. A lot of kids couldn't afford camping gear, so they were bringing blankets and pillows from home. Even the scoutmasters weren't very interesting. Besides, they were only going to a park on the other side of D.C. So actually, they weren't going camping, they were just pretending. It wasn't like they were going on trip to the farm with fishhooks, moose, or Miss Odell.

Tracy was wide-awake and stared at the ceiling. Freddie snored a little eleven-year-old snore, which would have been cute to a father. It was annoying to Tracy, although not as annoying as Freddie's sleep talking. Freddie talked in his sleep since he was little, and Tracy could get him going. Tracy asked him questions, and Freddie would answer. Usually what Freddie said didn't make sense, but his words were quite understandable.

Unfortunately, Tracy told his mother about the phenomenon. One night, as Vera checked on Tracy, she heard Freddie talking.

"Is he doing it?" Vera whispered.

"Yup," Tracy said, and Vera was intrigued.

"It won't work," Freddie said, and he was frustrated.

"Why won't it work?" Vera said, and she gently sat on the edge of Freddie's bed.

"You don't wanna do that Mom," Tracy warned.

"Shhhh!" Vera hushed.

"Mom, I'm tellin' ya. Ya don't wanna do that," Tracy repeated. "Don't talk to him."

"Why not?" Vera asked.

"You never know what's gonna come out of his mouth," Tracy explained. But Vera was enthralled with her little boy dreaming his dreams, and telling her all about it.

"It's just so hard," Freddie said, and frowned with his eyes closed.

Vera stroked Freddie's hair. "What's so hard baby?"

"I can't get it to work," Freddie said.

"What are ya doin' baby?" Vera asked.

"I'm trying to play tennis," Freddie said.

"Playing tennis," Vera repeated, very impressed. "Are you winning?"

"No, it's too hard to hit the balls."

"Mom," Tracy warned. "I'm tellin' ya," and he shook his head. Vera shot him a look.

"Why is that honey?" Vera asked her littlest angel.

"I can't hit the balls hard enough to get them over the net," Freddie explained.

"Why is it so hard to hit the balls over the net?" Vera asked.

"Because the dildo won't work," Freddie said.

Vera scowled at Tracy before she stormed out of the room. The next morning, Tracy ate his cereal as Freddie came into the kitchen. Vera was making brownies for them to take to school. When she saw Freddie, she beat the batter hard with her wooden spoon.

"What's wrong Mom?" Freddie asked. "Wouldn't it be easier to use the mixer?"

"I suppose you'd use a dildo," Vera exploded.

Freddie's jaw dropped and he looked at Tracy.

"I'll explain it to ya later," Tracy said, and dove back into his cereal.

Now, Tracy smiled at his reverie as Freddie snored. Tracy went to the bathroom again. By the time he got back his mind was swimming with worry. All his remedies had hit a wall. There was nothing new to think about, no other possible work-around. Tracy was stuck and he knew it.

"Why not ask me?" the Tall Shiny Silver Figure said.

Tracy ignored Him but sarcastically thought, 'How could you possibly help me?' Tracy felt the Tall Shiny Silver Figure smile. His fog was gone even though He was with Tracy fully, just without His light. Tracy knew the light was there - he just couldn't see it, he only felt it.

'Oh no,' Tracy thought indignantly. 'You were the one who got me in trouble the last time.' There was no response. "You remember," Tracy said aloud like a twelve-year-old. "The dogs an' guns. Everyone runnin' around Rand, an' makin' everyone think I was crazy? No, I think I've had enough of that."

There was no response, and the Tall Shiny Silver Figure waited. Freddie snored.

Somehow, Tracy knew this was just between the two of them. Tracy knew nothing he said or did would wake his little brother, and he stared at the ceiling. The Tall Shiny Silver Figure who loved Tracy stood next to him and waited. Then Tracy's thoughts came back to the camping trip. Immediately, fear and dread came over him like a thick dark blanket.

"Why not ask me?" the Tall Shiny Silver Figure repeated.

"Ask you what?" Tracy said, but knew the answer. Then he thought, 'How?'

"Just ask Me for My help, and I will give it to you."

Tracy thought that was a little too easy. There was nothing easy about his Mom marrying an idiot bully who moved them to D.C. There was nothing easy about living in a high-rise with all these people slamming their doors, or having to go on this idiotic camping trip his Mom was so crazy about him going on. Maybe she should go, Tracy thought. Then he stopped, because Tracy felt another smile from Him that was gentle, and wanted to hold him.

"Why not ask me?" the Tall Shiny Silver Figure asked a third time.

"How?" Tracy asked aloud.

Tracy meant how he should ask, but he also didn't know how the Tall Shiny Silver Figure could possibly make him stop wetting his bed.

"I will if you let Me," He answered.

Tracy still didn't know how to ask, but thought he wanted to.

"Just ask Me to help you," the friend said.

"Ok," was all Tracy actually said, but Tracy released his doubt and accepted His help.

Instantly, Tracy's mind was changed. His body followed as Tracy felt his repentance, and he was fixed. Tracy knew he wouldn't wet his bed that night. Then Tracy felt such joy he didn't think he could ever go to sleep. This made the Tall Shiny Silver Figure smile again, which made Tracy realize the Tall Shiny Silver Figure *was* peace. So, Tracy *would* be able to sleep, which was a marvelous puzzlement. Then, Tracy felt the Tall Shiny Silver Figure go while His presence stayed, and there was a deep quiet where Tracy's heart was. Because Tracy knew he was fixed, he slept well.

In the morning, Tracy bounced out of a bed that was bone-dry. He went to the bathroom, came back with a swagger, and changed into his clothes without a shower.

When Freddie saw this, he got up and rubbed his eyes. "What's with you?"

"Nothin'," Tracy said, like a character wearing a fedora in a black-and-white movie. "Nothin' at all my good man." Tracy went to the kitchen and hugged his mother. She sipped her coffee and vaguely watched the news. Then Vera looked at her son, who was so radiant it hurt her eyes.

"It's over Ma," Tracy said, and skipped to a cereal bowl and poured.

"What's over honey?" Vera asked.

"You'll see," Tracy said.

Freddie arrived very sleepy. Vera looked to see if he knew, but her littlest man just shrugged his shoulders.

"Was everything ok last night?" Vera asked.

"Right as rain my good woman," Tracy lilted, but realized what he said. "I mean, there was no rain, no water, no nothin', and there won't ever be again."

"Tracy," Vera said sharply. "Is it wet or not?"

Tracy stopped fooling around and went to hug his mother again. "That's what I'm trying to tell you Mom, it's over. I'm through wetting my bed."

"How do you know that?" Vera asked.

"Yeah," Freddie blurted. "How?"

"I just know," Tracy stated. "It will be ok," and both Vera and Freddie were ok with that for the moment.

But that night, Tracy wanted to pluck Bobby's nerves. Tracy knew he would be fine, so as soon as he got home he drank all the juice in the refrigerator. Then he started on the soda. By dinnertime Tracy drank gallons of water, Freddie was more than skeptical, and Vera became perplexed.

"Don't worry my dahling mothuh," Tracy said in a vintage 1930's accent. "It is most certainly over, and there is simply nothing anyone can do about it," and he toasted his glass and guzzled more.

Vera did love her old movies. She and the boys watched them every Saturday while she did laundry. But this was a little much, and Vera was still concerned about Tracy's upcoming camping trip.

"You really aughta consider what you're doin'," Bobby growled quietly.

Tracy drained the rest of his glass before he looked Bobby straight in the eye.

"Oh we know what we're doin'," Tracy said.

"We?" Freddie asked.

Tracy looked at his brother and Mom and smiled brightly.

"Don't worry," Tracy assured them. "We got this," and they did.

Tracy was dry as a bone the next morning, and the morning after that. There was no issue with his scout trip, and Tracy had a new friend and confidant.

When he got back from camping, barely a week had gone by before Tracy had his next visit.

"Do you remember the vision I gave you when you were three?" the Tall Shiny Silver Figure asked.

Now, Tracy had a better idea of who He was, even though Tracy still didn't know His name. But somehow, since Tracy put his faith in Him, Tracy knew he could share anything with Him, say or think anything, and talk to Him as best friends do.

"What vision?" Tracy asked, as he got ready for bed. Tracy remembered the dogs, guns and the posse, but he was a little hazy about what caused the commotion in the first place.

"I will give it to you again in a dream," He said, *"and tomorrow, I want you to draw the vision in art class."*

"Ok," Tracy said.

'Paint the vision and make it plain,' were the instructions given at the end of the dream, but not before Tracy was reminded of all he had experienced. Tracy remembered his three-year-old self being taken up before the doctor put his body in the ice water. Tracy relived the sheer majesty of being in His full presence as he sat in His lap, and He showed Tracy the picture book. At the end, Tracy saw the marvelous page when He stopped and said, *"Remember this Tracy. Just get here!"*

When he woke, Tracy came back to his twelve-year-old self abruptly. The metal doors of the apartment building banged, and the chains swung and clawed at each other. Tracy missed the bliss of being three, and loathed the skeptical presence in the room. So Tracy lay in bed, something he usually didn't do, and held the vision for as long as he could before he had to get up for school.

"Come on man!" Freddie insisted and tied his shoes. "What's with you today?"

Tracy made it to school, and in art class the teacher introduced a new project. It was November, and the sixth graders got to work.

'You better quit it, or your gonna get me in trouble again,' Tracy thought.

"But you do not understand depth perception," the Tall Shiny Silver Figure said.

"I don't understand depth perception?" Tracy repeated aloud.

"There is no talking in class," the teacher said without looking.

'See,' Tracy exclaimed inaudibly. 'There you go again.'

As Tracy drew, the Tall Shiny Silver Figure spoke in Tracy's ear. This was strange, because they had never had a conversation in a public place before. No one could hear the Tall Shiny Silver Figure, which was the norm. But He was insistent, and Tracy had a hard time answering Him silently. His instructions also came fast and furious because the Tall Shiny Silver Figure was very excited.

"What tree roots grow over rocks?" Tracy huffed.

"Mr. Staples," and the teacher looked at Tracy this time. "Is it possible for you to create art without consulting your muse aloud?"

'Yes Ma'am,' Tracy thought.

"Did you hear me?" the teacher asked.

"I mean, yes ma'am," Tracy said. Then he thought, 'See, you're gonna get me in trouble again, just like the first time.' Yet Tracy continued drawing a tree with autumn leaves in the foreground. Water flowed in front, and a house was behind to the left. But, He insisted the tree's roots grow out and over the rocks before they reached the water. Tracy had seen trees that grew next to the river behind Granny's house. They were at the water's edge like at the lake in Virginia, and there weren't any big rocks. But Tracy did it anyway.

"Now," He said. *"Cut the ends off the roof of the house."*

Tracy had never seen a house with its roof cut off at a forty-five degree angle on the ends, although Tracy knew exactly what He meant.

When the Tall Shiny Silver Figure spoke, He simultaneously showed Tracy. However, cutting the ends off the roof made no sense whatsoever.

'Won't it leak?' Tracy thought, and then he got smart. 'Didn't You design the ark? Did Noah cut the corners off the roof on the ark?'

"Cut the ends off the roof Tracy," He said.

Tracy reluctantly got his eraser and fixed the roof. Tracy knew He was pleased, but He wasn't done.

"Now, put a mountain in the background to the right," He stated.

'But I just drew the fence right below the sunset,' Tracy argued.

"That is fine. That is where the fence is. Just put a mountain in front of it."

Tracy didn't understand, but felt it had something to do with depth perception.

"Exactly," He confirmed. *"The fence is there, you just can not see it from this vantage point."* So Tracy drew a light brown mountain in front of the fence. Then he reached for dark brown to work on the tree trunks.

"There are no trees on this mountain," He said.

"What mountain doesn't have trees on it?" Tracy yelled out.

"Mr. Staples!" the teacher shouted.

"I'm sorry," Tracy answered, but he really wasn't. Tracy tried to calm down to get this over with, but he knew it wouldn't be until the picture was finished. The problem was Tracy actually didn't know what his friend meant, even though he was shown.

"I want you to make it flow like wheat grass," the Tall Shiny Silver Figure said. Tracy felt His motion as He undulated side to side, which made Tracy smile. Then Tracy mimicked Him, and started a sideways dance move.

'Flow like wheat grass...' Tracy thought, and kept doing what looked like 'the snake'. Unknown to Tracy, his classmates noticed his music-less gyrations.

"Like this," He said.

Out of the corner of his eye, Tracy saw the Tall Shiny Silver Figure move back and forth. His image was unclear, as if Tracy was riding his bike on a hot day, and waves of heat from the road distorted His figure. Then the Tall Shiny Silver Figure took Tracy's arm, pressed Tracy's hand down to the paper, and made a series of flowing strokes. Tracy's arm felt wonderful and full of life. Tracy felt the pressure and temperature of the wind against the grass waving in the crisp fall air. Most remarkably, it seemed the motion and feeling Tracy experienced actually created the grass on the page.

'What is that?' Tracy asked, referring to the marvelous feeling in his arm.

"That is possession," He said, and Tracy realized that if he asked more questions, he got more answers.

'What is possession?'

"Possession is nine tenths of the Law," He said, which went over Tracy's head. Tracy thought of the next.

'What's the first tenth?'

"The tithe," He said. As they continued, Tracy knew all of their conversations were for his education. Later, the Tall Shiny Silver Figure brought Bible verses to Tracy's mind to prove His point. But from this moment on, Tracy knew he wanted to understand all the wisdom given to him.

At the moment, Tracy and the Tall Shiny Silver Figure had been undulating for a while. This inspired his classmates to do 'the snake' too, but silently. All Tracy felt was the warm power of His love, which inhabited his arm while they created the flowing grass.

"Ooooh," Tracy said. "That feels great!" and Tracy heard the echo of his loud moan.

Tracy looked up, and the whole class was undulating and giggling. His teacher was baffled and too amazed for words. Then the Tall Shiny Silver Figure laughed, which tickled Tracy to laugh, which caused the whole room to let out their joy. They laughed and laughed, most not knowing why, but there was a good reason – love was there.

"Ok class," the teacher eventually said. "We all have our own way of creating art, but let's get back to work."

'See,' Tracy laughed. 'I knew You would get me in trouble.'

But both Tracy and the Tall Shiny Silver Figure knew it was a triumph. They had shattered that skeptical presence, and brought the joy from the dream of the vision onto the page. Then, Tracy and his friend finished the mountain of grass in front of the fence. Tracy made the angle of the setting sun, and he thought the picture was done.

"Now put a cross in the distance," He said gravely, and Tracy was shown the size and shape of the cross he was to draw, just to the left of the house with the cut off corners.

'Oh,' Tracy thought smartly. 'I ride the yellow bus home from school.'

There was no answer. His friend's mood was changed, and He was very serious.

'Sticks and stones might not break your bones,' Tracy thought, 'but they might break this sissy boy's bones on my way home.'

There was no response.

'Do You really want me to be made fun of for puttin' a cross in my picture?' Tracy asked.

"I did not want to do it either," the Tall Shiny Silver Figure answered, *"but I did."*

Tracy felt this, even though he didn't fully understand. It was a matter of 'obedience' and the 'greater thing', which was a hard-sell to a twelve-year-old. But Tracy looked for the right color, and gray caught his attention. It was more colorless than black or white. Gray hung in between, just like the cross.

Tracy began drawing the cross in silence, and the Tall Shiny Silver Figure took possession of Tracy's arm again. This time the urgency, motion and excitement were absent as they colored it in. When the cross was finished, He left Tracy's arm and a peaceful quiet remained. Then the picture was complete, and with that, the vision was made plain.

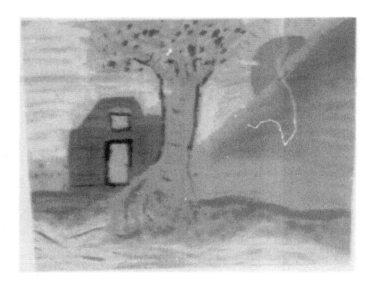

- the vision

Chapter 9

- Tracy and his
6th Grade Art Teacher

Tracy was a new person waiting for the next thing. When Vera and the boys went to West Virginia for Thanksgiving, Bobby stayed home. After dinner, Moody wanted to hear about Bobby breaking Vera's wrist. So Tracy went to the basement with Moody to 'do somethin'.

"The fuckin' bastard," Moody said.

"I was gonna kill him," Tracy said. He was going to tell Moody the Tall Shiny Silver Figure stopped him, but it wasn't time yet. "I guess I just thought better of it."

Moody grunted. "Well, I'm not sure I coulda controlled myself."

"The arrows didn't work," Tracy said, "so I tried another way."

"Ya don't say," and Moody perked up.

"A couple a weeks later I was doin' the dishes," Tracy said. "I was doin' them because Mom couldn't. But ever since I saw "Jaws", I hate doin' the dishes."

"Why's that?"

"All that soapy water, an' not knowin' what's underneath? Don't ask me to take a bath," and Tracy gestured to his torso. "Showers only," and Moody laughed.

"But the bastard knew it," Tracy said, "an' always makes me do the dishes. Bobby laughed about it with Freddie. I was thinkin' about that, an' Mom's broken wrist, an' I opened the cabinet to put away the Tupperware. There were Bobby's pills, sittin' right there above the sink. The label said to keep them away from moisture."

"Not the smartest place to keep those pills was it," Moody concurred.

"Nope," Tracy said. "So that cap came off and bloop, right into the dishwater. Then I rinsed them off, dried each one carefully, and back into the bottle they went."

"You want to see that man explode don't ya?" Moody said.

"I figured that's why they call it nitroglycerine," Tracy stated, and they clinked their glasses – Moody's apricot brandy and Tracy's coke bottle.

Then Moody got concerned. "You really wanted to kill him, didn't ya?"

"Still do. It's either gonna be him or me," Tracy stated.

"Well just hold on there Tracy. Nothin's worth all that, especially at your age. An' especially for somethin' as worthless as Bobby," but Tracy didn't see the problem with it. "Bobby is truly a horrible, good for nothin' weasel of a man."

"Ya got that right."

"But you shouldn't have to be doin' nothin' like that, at least not now. Besides, for some unknown reason, your wonderful mother don't wanna do anythin' about it. So, we can't."

Everything in Tracy wanted to argue with his grandfather's truth, but he couldn't. He wanted to fight. The very name Tramele meant to fight. It meant to separate right from wrong, and everything about that situation was wrong.

"That don't mean there ain't another way," Moody stated, and Tracy cooled a little. "I'll get ya outa there Tracy," Moody decided. "Just give me a little more time," and he took another sip. "But I'll get ya out," and that was enough for his boy.

Then, because the boys were staying in D.C. for Christmas, Granny took the boys and got matching jogging suits for them and Vera. They wrapped them up and the boys took them to D.C., but Granny didn't get Bobby one. So before Christmas, the boys and Vera went to pick out a sleeping bag with arms for Bobby. Christmas morning, the peace offering was opened and Bobby liked it, but for a different reason.

"Ya know," Bobby said. "I didn't get anything for my father for Christmas," and Vera's jaw dropped. "How wrinkled is that wrapping paper?"

Vera got apoplectic and went to get coffee. Tracy went to his room, and Freddie and Bobby were left to fend for themselves. Later they went to 'Grandma's house', Bobby's mother, with Vera's gift, and Bobby gave it away in front of his wife. Vera didn't speak to Bobby for weeks.

In April there was a bright spot. Tracy's art teacher informed him that his drawing of the vision won an award. Tracy had won awards for citizenship and participation. But an award for artwork - something he actually liked doing - that surprised him. Unknown to Tracy, his art teacher had entered his picture of the vision in a national competition. It won, and Vera was beside herself.

Before he knew it, Tracy was taken out of class with his art teacher. Vera took off from work, brought a suit for Tracy to change into, and whisked him into D.C. for the national ceremony. Afterwards, the new visionary was taken to Rock Creek Park for pictures. Vera memorialized the event as Tracy held the picture he was instructed to draw. Tracy didn't know it at the time, but it was the photograph holding the picture of the vision with his award that recorded the truth.

But that was the only highlight of the school year. When Tracy graduated sixth grade he was 'more than done'. After the ceremony, Granny asked where Tracy would be going the next year. Vera drove them past the middle school, which was just as dirty as his elementary school. It was also in a worse neighborhood and had no windows - not one.

"That looks like a damn prison," Granny stated, and she knew this for a fact.

Tracy went with Granny to visit her brother James a few times. He was never in jail for long - usually just until his drunk wore off or whatever happened could be sorted. But the prison and middle school were carbon copies of each other.

"And they don't have books," Tracy said.

"Now that's not true," Vera answered.

"It most certainly is," Tracy said. "I've been there many times for stuff, and there are no books in that school," and Vera was silenced. "Granny, you ever been to a school with no books?"

The next day, Tracy packed all of his clothes into his suitcase, an extra suitcase and part of Freddie's. Then Granny took the boys to Rand for the summer. That weekend it rained, so Tracy and Moody had to have their 'meetin" in the basement.

"I'm not goin' back Pawpaw," Tracy said. "I can't learn in a school without books, and I can't live with that asshole of a man," and to Tracy's surprise he was in tears. "I can't Pawpaw, I just can't!" Tracy stiffened. "Because I really will kill him!"

"I know boy," Moody said, and opened his arms. Tracy fell into them. "You're stayin' here Tracy."

Tracy sat back in his chair to look at Moody, and he was serious. Then Moody gave him a sip of his brandy, and Tracy's tears changed meaning.

"Me an' your Granny's been talkin' 'bout this long an' hard," Moody said. "Now, we might lose a daughter in the deal, but ya can't go on like this. Maybe your mother'll figure herself out too, but she's grown," and Moody looked at Tracy. "But you're not, at least not grown completely, an' you deserve better."

"I love you Pawpaw!" and Tracy hugged Moody. Then he began to laugh because it was over. It was actually over.

The summer started, and so did a whole new life as far as Tracy was concerned. Tracy moved into what would be kept as his room until Granny died. He reveled in the fact that he was not going back to D.C., although Freddie didn't care either way. He liked the high-rise as much as he liked 'hangin' with his father's family down the street. But by now, Freddie was a certifiably disgusting, adolescent creature. For instance, Moody and Granny loved The Commodores' "Brick House". The boys sang along in the back seat until Freddie got an idea. He asked Granny to turn up the radio, and graveled out the word "HOUSE" into Tracy's ear every time it was sung - every single time.

But Freddie's most annoying and possibly creative work was a variation of the classic, "Chicken-butt".

"Tracy?" Freddie would ask, and Tracy knew not to answer. "Tracy?" Freddie asked again, and poked him. "Tracy!?!" Freddie shouted.

"What!?!" Tracy shouted back and took it:

"Chicken-butt! - Take a slice and eat it up - two-cents a cup - don't try your luck - Chicken-butt! - Say what!?!"

The other option was almost as bad. The boys shared a room in Moody and Granny's house as usual. But now, Freddie was not only a new breed of smelly, he was proud of it.

"Hey Tracy," Freddie would say.

When Tracy looked, Freddie crooked his leg up sideways to crack a fart. And he could do this at will, twenty-four seven. Eventually, Tracy got so tired of him Granny let Freddie move into the basement. Tracy fully moved into 'his room' and lived in the house he called home until he graduated high school.

The Moody house was dug into the side of a hill. The driveway went into the basement where Granny parked her car and Moody had all his tools. The other side of the basement was finished for entertaining. Up the wooden stairs with a tricky step to the left, was the meridian blue kitchen. Granny's recliner sat in the living room next to the kitchen. That way she could talk on the saffron rotary phone that hung on the kitchen wall, or gossip on the cream Trimline phone on the end table. After sundown, Granny would sit and call the women of the neighborhood to make sure all the kids had 'got home safe'.

Out the front door was a high cement porch and front walkway lined with Granny's hostas. The backyard was house-width down to the riverbank. Across the river were train tracks and the turnpike. The steep vee of the mountains magnified the rumble, or carried the whistle of coal barges down the river. The Kanawha River frequently rose all the way to the backhouse. Sharp curves and strong currents made the depth fluctuated wildly. There were rumors the deepest channels were un-recordable. Occasionally, there was an accident on the turnpike.

Tracy remembered a rescue mission headlined in the "Charleston Gazette". A diver went in to find a car and bring back the remains. Reportedly, huge lips of what might have been a carp large enough to swallow the diver emerged from the murk. Future rescue missions were scrapped. From then on, if a loved one's car missed the mountain that was that. There were other rumors of prehistoric beasts snatching children from the river's banks. But more likely, the young swimmers were swept into the undertow first, and then eaten by monsters.

William Russell and his wife lived in a 1970's rancher across the street from Granny's house. Their living room had a massive wrap-around blue velour couch, which matched the stereo system. Most Fridays at four-thirty Granny heard Motown blasting. She'd fix herself a drink and go out on her rainbow carpeted cement porch. William Russell would soon be on his. The two caught up by shouting across the shallow valley of the road. It was faster to yell up or down the street than dialing, which may have been why West Virginia had 'hollers' in the first place.

The topography also made it easy to know what everyone was 'about'. That summer, Granny was 'all about' keeping the boys busy. Once Tracy and Freddie moved in, she decided they needed a hobby.

"What kind of hobby?" Tracy asked. They were in the kitchen, where all business took place.

"Somethin' you're good at, an' you can do into your old age," Granny said. "I got my bowlin'".

"I like bowlin'," Tracy said.

Granny had taken the boys bowling since they could lift a ball. The boys wanted to put the bumpers up, but that wasn't allowed. 'There are no bumpers in life!' Granny had said, and now she was even more indignant.

"Ya can't have bowlin'," Granny snapped. "That's mine," and she sat back, and proudly crossed her legs despite the pink rollers in her hair.

"Why not Granny?" Freddie asked.

"Many have tried," and she looked at Freddie and wagged her head sadly. "Don't be a casualty."

Granny referred to Jinny. When they were one short, Granny's team took Jinny on. The Bowlerette Ebonettes of Charleston were infamous, both in the lanes and off. Jinny was beside herself, 'gettin' to bowl with her Momma'. Tracy and Freddie overheard the story on a rainy day when Queenie came over to 'yak it up' with Granny. She was an Ebonnette from the 'git-go' and a 'fire-rocket'.

"Remember that time with that cop?" Queenie began. "I thought we'd be bailin' you outa jail for sure." Granny just lit a menthol. "An' when you turned an' swung that ball around, you almost took him out!"

The incident was during Granny's Impala days, which easily held all four Ebonettes. Granny had a few drinks before she left out, and they were late getting to the alley. There was just one parking space out front, which was a few inches shorter than it needed to be. But no matter, Granny pulled up parallel and backed in. Between the gin and her lit menthol, she was a little rough when she hit the rear car's bumper. She had all the power steering possible, so she pulled ahead until she 'touched' the front car's bumper. It took a while, but after a few 'nudges' she was parked.

"Jackie, you pulled into that car behind you and bam!" Queenie shouted. "Then you pulled into the car in front," and Queenie made a motion with her hand to represent the car, and she moved Granny's car back.

"Bam!" Queenie popped, and she moved Granny's car to the front to reload. Then she moved her hand back.

"Bam!" she repeated, and then Queenie couldn't go on for laughing.

"I did not see that police man," Granny laughed.

"Oh he was there girl! At first he was in his car, just sittin' there. Then he got out an' was leanin' on it, waitin' for ya to get done."

Once Granny turned off the car the Ebonnettes got out, got their balls from the trunk, and proceeded to the bowling alley. Granny had her bowling ball bag in her right hand, and her half-full plastic cup of gin and tonic in the other.

"Ma'am," the policeman said. He had walked across the street by then, and was behind the Impala to note the license plate number. Granny kept walking and pretended not to hear.

The cop followed. "Ma'am," he said louder.

Granny turned around sharply and said, "What!?!"

But the centrifugal force of her bowling ball took her around another time before she could regain her footing. After another spin, she got everything to stop without spilling anything. Then Granny straightened up, wobbled, and straightened up again.

"What!?!" Granny repeated, and took a sip.

"Do you know how many times you hit that car?"

Granny looked at the officer, looked at the car, looked at the officer again, and then she had it:

"Well, it's not an accident if you back in to it!" she screamed, and took off into the bowling alley cackling away.

- Granny on her porch

Chapter 10

- Tracy's Sousaphone

The next day Freddie decided football was his hobby, which coincided with his all-time favorite – girls. Tracy didn't have the same interest in girls, and consequently had more friends that were girls, which puzzled Freddie. Tracy liked Kung Fu, and he and Moody loved to watch Martial Arts movies. So Granny called Granny Betty, Squeaky's mother.

Squeaky was Jinny's first husband. By this time, Jinny had gone through two husbands before she married Alvin. But Granny continued her relationship with Granny Betty. Granny Betty was also an original member of the Wanderers, who loved to fish for bluegills. Tracy never saw such a small fish make such a grown woman happy.

It so happened that Granny Betty also knew Geoff, who taught Kung Fu. So by September, as soon as junior high let out, Tracy was at the YWCA to practice Martial Arts. Freddie was on the football field, and neither of the boys was 'runnin' the streets' as Granny designed. But there was one thing not right, at least for Tracy.

Granny attended the Baptist church in town. Now that the boys lived with her, Granny introduced the boys to the congregation. Tracy certainly knew about God, he met Him. But Tracy felt uncomfortable at Granny's church, and not without reason. After breakfast, he decided to talk to her about it.

"Granny?" Tracy asked, but the front door opened.

"Hang on Tracy," Granny said, and Granny Betty stepped into the living room. "No smokin' in the house today Betty."

"You must be bakin'," Granny Betty said, and took off her coat.

"Yep," Granny replied. "Rum cake an' bourbon balls - it's volatile."

Granny Betty took a seat. Granny Moody got the bottle of rum from under the sink.

"Now ya got to be careful with this part," Granny instructed, "or the whole place could blow," and she poured the 151 proof into the saucepan, took a swig and stirred. "I think we're safe now," and Granny grimaced from the rum. "Now, what is it Tracy?"

Tracy was unsure with Granny Betty there, and Granny Betty realized she walked in on something.

"It can't be that bad," Granny Betty said. "We'll understand."

"Ok," Tracy said. "I don't think I want to go to your church."

"Why not?" Granny asked, and she was nice about it.

Granny Betty was appropriately horrified.

"I just want something more," Tracy said.

Granny stirred her rum, and Granny Betty patted Tracy's hand.

"And I heard the story," Tracy finished.

"Oh," the Grannies said, and Granny Betty's hand retreated.

Once Tracy went to middle school, it wasn't long before he was 'jonesin' with the other kids at the lunch table. They weren't high. At the time, they thought 'jonesin' meant 'crackin' an' tellin' 'Your Momma' jokes:

"Your Momma's so big, she can't wear a Malcolm X t-shirt, 'cause helicopters try to land on it."

"Oh yeah, well your Momma's eyebrows are so arched, people keep honkin' their horn at her to order fries an' a shake, because they think they're at McDonald's."

In the fray, Rhonda told the story about Granny's church. Rhonda was the 'boy-girl' of the neighborhood, and her father ran all the clubs in town. He wasn't home much, but loved to spoil his daughter. Rhonda always had the newest dirt bike, and the white boys were jealous. But that was ok, because she could 'beat the crap out of 'em' if they gave her any trouble. Rhonda also didn't fit in with Deena and May, who vied to be valedictorian of Tracy's seventh grade class.

Unfortunately, at this particular time, Deena and May decided to have the same boyfriend. Well, May's Mom found out that her daughter called Deena a slut. May's Mom didn't do anything about it, and somehow Deena found out. The tinderbox exploded on a Sunday. After church, Deena confronted May's Mom as they left the vestibule. From the sanctuary, there were large swinging doors, a short hall, and open doors that led to the tall brick steps up to the church. May and her mother were at the top step when Deena ran to catch them.

"I tell you," Rhonda said, "Deena blew by Pastor, swung the doors open an' beat it to the steps. Next thing ya heard was, 'I am not a slut!' Then a pair a glasses flew back through those doors before the second swing!"

"You mean?" Tracy asked.

"That's right!" Rhonda confirmed. "Little Miss Goody Two-Shoes popped May's Mom so hard, that woman's glasses flew right back into church!"

So neither Granny could really say anything. Their church was often a 'mess a things'. Everyone lived so close, and even Moody talked about the Deacons like dogs. As a preacher's kid himself, the hypocrisy of Granny's church was too much so Moody didn't go. Of course Freddie went for the scandal, because that was obviously where the nice, 'bad girls' went. Regardless, Granny Betty called her daughter, Aunt Z, and later that afternoon Granny called Tracy into the kitchen.

"Aunt Z's pickin' you up for church Sunday," and that was it, no hard feelings.

There were several small, house-sized churches in the tiny town of Rand. Two were Pentecostal. The one behind William Russell's house was a full-bore 'snake handlin', strychnine drinkin', sign followin' Church of God'. Tracy knew Aunt Z was afraid of snakes, so they wouldn't be going anywhere near that one. The other Pentecostal Church was four blocks from Granny's house, and Aunt Z picked Tracy up on Sunday.

As Tracy approached the door of the church, he had an odd feeling. Then he was literally pulled across the threshold. Once inside, Tracy was enveloped by love, not by the people as much as the atmosphere. He was instantly comfortable. Granny's church was scripted: scripted announcements, scripted sermon, even scripted hymns that everyone knew to skip the third verse. Aunt Z's church was led by something unseen. They sang praise music with tambourines, and Tracy felt at home. At the end of the next week's service, the Pastor made an altar call.

"Does anyone want to come forward to receive the Holy Ghost?" the Pastor asked.

Without thinking Tracy stood, and Aunt Z went with him to the altar. Once Tracy knelt to the floor, he couldn't move. The church came up and prayed over him. Then Tracy began babbling, and had an out of body experience. Tracy looked down, and he saw himself knelt to the floor speaking gibberish. Then church was over, the congregation left, but Tracy still couldn't move.

Aunt Z and the Pastor stayed with Tracy another hour until he stopped babbling. To Tracy, the experience finished as fast as it began, and he got up refreshed. Aunt Z explained he was kneeling for an hour praying in tongues. Tracy didn't understand, and Granny wasn't too sure either.

"Boy, you ain't playin' with the Holy Spirit are ya?" Granny asked, because Tracy and Aunt Z had missed lunch by a mile.

"I'm not playin' Granny," Tracy said, and gave her a big hug. Then he looked at her with concern. "Granny, is there anything I've done lately?" and Granny didn't know what he meant. "I mean, ever," Tracy explained. "Is there anytime I ever made you feel bad, or hurt you? I mean, not just now, but ever?" and Granny was dumbfounded. "Well if I did," Tracy decided, "I'm sorry," and he was sincere.

The next day, Tracy felt differently toward everyone else too. At school he apologized to everyone, and made sure he didn't owe anyone lunch money. He also had a new awareness not to offend anyone. When he had a strong urge not to hang at the 'jonesin' session', Tracy began to understand:

While Tracy knelt at Aunt Z's church, a deposit of love was made. Afterward, Tracy had an overwhelming sense of joy and not a care in the world. Being filled with the Spirit made Tracy lose his eagerness for this world, and Tracy realized a profound peace. When he received the Holy Ghost, a standard was set. It was a standard Tracy would go back to time and again, which translated to success in his endeavors and opened doors for him.

The first was that November, when Tracy's Kung Fu teacher asked him to compete in Ohio. Tracy was so surprised he had to borrow a uniform. He competed using a Northern Shaolin Long Fist Form. To everyone's amazement except Geoff's, Tracy won. At the meet, Tracy met Ron, who also taught Kung Fu in Charleston. Ron introduced Tracy to Jean, who was a student in his class. Both invited Tracy to visit their studio when they got back, and the whole thing was a triumph. By the time Tracy returned home, Vera was at Granny's for Thanksgiving.

"Where did ya get that?" Granny asked. Tracy held up his trophy.

"Did ya have to fight someone?" and Granny walked around her grandson looking for cuts or scrapes, but there was no evidence.

"Well," Granny determined. "I don't think I'll know what it's for, even if ya tell me."

"Come here baby," Vera said, and admired the trophy. "This is remarkable Trace," and she looked at Granny. "Where you gonna put it?"

Granny's bowling trophies were stacked on the shelves over Moody's hifi stereo. Granny went over, squished some in the middle to make space, and put Tracy's hardware in the center.

Vera was astonished, but was more taken by how much her little boy had changed. Tracy's move from D.C. made him a different person. He wasn't angry. Instead, her boy was confident, gentle, and most of all, happy. Vera was glad, but at the same time, the fact she was no longer raising her boys gave her mixed feelings. The previous summer, Momma Ro had the same question.

Vera was deciding whether Freddie should stay in West Virginia with Tracy. School was starting, and Vera went over to Ro's to talk about Granny and Moody keeping her boys.

"Well shug," Ro said. "I don't know which way to go on this one."

"I don't either," Vera answered.

"You certainly can't blame Tracy for hatin' Bobby," Ro decided.

"No," Vera agreed. "It was horrible, seein' my baby tryin' to shoot down my husband with my own bow and arrow."

"Well, you know where I stand on that score."

"But now, they want to keep Freddie."

"I know it's hard, but you shouldn't split 'em up." Ro took Vera's hand and pleaded with her. "Don't let Bobby split those boys up. They're so close. You shouldn't let that man do that to them."

So Vera didn't interfere, but not without reservations. This wasn't the first time Granny significantly altered Vera's life. Granny had a big part in why Tracy didn't know his father. But it was Moody who wanted to raise Tracy, so Vera relented, and Tracy thrived. Although in the end the boys didn't stay together, at least not in the same house. By the following spring, Freddie's conversion to monster was complete. He didn't do chores or listen to Granny. One day, Freddie came home with a sassy white girl on his arm from a holler that was home to the Klan. The girl was not only white, she was the most rebellious kind of white Freddie could find.

When Granny heard the front gate open, she was at the front door by the time it was re-latched. To her horror, Granny saw Freddie walking his racist girlfriend up the walk beside her hostas.

"You will not be bringin' that shit to my house," Granny stated, slammed the door and called Jinny.

So Freddie was moved down the street to live with Jinny and her three girls. In short order, training under Uncle Alvin and Aunt Jinny began. Alvin was an ex federal agent, and Jinny was on her way to becoming a private investigator. Once Freddie moved in, boot camp was initiated and Tracy was amazed.

On Saturdays, Tracy voluntarily got up at seven, had breakfast, mowed the lawn, washed Granny's car, and Moody's if it were there. Then he headed down to Uncle Alvin and Jinny's to see what Freddie, Demi, Mia and Marie were up to. But Freddie and his 'runnin' cousins' were asleep. They had been up before dawn and had already cleaned the house, done the dishes, weeded the garden, mowed the lawn, mowed their neighbors' lawns - three deep on each side and across the street, and washed Alvin and Jinny's cars. By eleven o'clock, they were back in bed and fast asleep.

As for Tracy, he liked having his own room and living with Granny and Moody. He went to Aunt Z's church whenever they had service or Bible study, and he loved working out. He went everyday if he could. The first time Tracy went to Ron's studio, the Kung Fu hook went deeper.

Jean was working out when he got there, and Ron was playing with his sword. Tracy watched as Ron's sword made an amazingly loud noise – first in rapid circles, then over his head, then side-to-side. Ron added footwork and backed Tracy up to the wall, and stopped with his sword an inch from Tracy's torso.

"Trust yourself, trust your students, but don't ever trust anyone," Ron said, and walked away.

Tracy had no idea what that meant, but thought it was definitely cool. From then on, Tracy worked out Monday, Wednesday and Friday nights, and Saturday mornings at Ron's studio. There he met Jim Charlie, another in the Martial Arts family, and trained with three teachers at once. He began a routine of brewer's yeast and protein to gain weight and muscle. From there, Tracy's Martial Arts family continued to expand, but that wasn't enough for Granny.

Shortly after school was out, Tracy came home from church and Granny was pacing in the living room. Without a word, she motioned for him to sit on the couch. She examined him as she studied and paced, and took another drag before she pointed her menthol at him.

"You need some responsibility," Granny stated, paced, examined and smoked.

"You need something to care for, and something that cares for you," and Granny did another lap before she turned in pre-aha moment and stared at Tracy.

"That's it!" Granny yelled, as if Tracy answered her question, although Tracy hadn't said anything because he was hungry, and was actually thinking of a ham sandwich.

"You need a dog." Granny decided, and circled her cigarette at him to confirm her findings. "Research what kind of dog you want, an' get back to me," and she went into the kitchen to start dinner.

Granny and Moody always had field dogs, usually three, and Holly the Collie had saved Tracy a few times. When he was in diapers and left alone for a second, Tracy ran for the front gate and tried to open it. When the dogs heard the latch, they thought it was the mailman. When Holly saw it was Tracy breaking out, she grabbed his diaper. Little Tracy held onto the gate, but Holly was stronger and dragged him back up the walk.

However, by the time Tracy was given his assignment his decision was easy. One of Tracy's favorite movies was "The Doberman Gang", not to mention the other Doberman movies of the 1970's, or reruns of the "Rockford Files" that had a Doberman featured every other episode. Tracy also wanted a dog that had the qualities he strove for in his Kung Fu training: sleek, aware, highly trained and a protector. Granny loved the idea, because the training would fill the rest of Tracy's free time. Besides, Moody always wanted a guard dog.

Bonnie, named after Bonnie and Clyde from "The Doberman Gang", was born in April, probably on Tracy's birthday. Tracy got his new puppy as summer ended. In September school started for Tracy. School also started for Bonnie with her obedience classes Sunday afternoons. Tracy also joined band his eighth grade year. The marching band needed a Sousaphone player. Tracy could get it off the ground, which was the only pre-requisite.

So with Kung Fu, band practice, and Bonnie's obedience classes, Granny's plan was complete. Tracy had no spare time, didn't care, and Bonnie and Tracy became quite a pair. Tracy taught her fancy tricks from the movies and tracking, using Freddie as bait. By the time the band played at football games, they had a system. Tracy always cut through the baseball fields to come home, and as the days got shorter, Granny became concerned.

"Aren't you afraid walkin' home in the dark?" Granny asked.

"Don't worry Granny," Tracy said. "I'll have Bonnie come get me."

Moody put down his paper. "Not a good idea to train the guard dog to jump the fence."

"I got that too Pawpaw," Tracy answered. "I'll train her to do it only when I whistle for her."

When Tracy came out of the band door he would whistle. Bonnie jumped her fence and ran to him, and they walked home. Once they got that routine down, Tracy did one better. Bonnie walked Tracy to school. Tracy said, 'Go home' and Bonnie went home, jumped her fence, and Granny gave her a treat. Then Bonnie stayed there until Tracy whistled for her in the afternoon.

So Bonnie and Clyde had nothing on Bonnie and Tracy. Bonnie was one of the most reliable friends Tracy had, to the point of almost freezing herself. Late in the fall the band had a Friday night away game. It had snowed, and Tracy wouldn't get home until after midnight. At sunset, Bonnie escorted Tracy to the band door and went home as usual. After midnight, Bonnie heard her whistle and ran to the band door.

But Tracy wasn't there. Because of the late hour the school was locked up, and Tracy had whistled from the front door of the school. Then Tracy walked home, because he figured it was too late for Bonnie to come for him. The next morning, Granny noticed there weren't fresh tracks in the snow around the doghouse. If she wasn't in her doghouse, Bonnie lay across the front door. Granny checked, no Bonnie. When Tracy got up, Granny asked.

"Tracy, where's your dog?"

"I thought she was here," Tracy said. He looked out the kitchen window to the doghouse, and Granny figured it out.

"Did she walk you last night?" Granny asked, and Tracy nodded. "Then she's probably at the band door. That's the last place she saw you."

Tracy ran out and whistled, but Bonnie didn't come. When Tracy was almost to the band door he saw footprints in the snow. But the prints only came around the corner before they retreated back to the band door. Tracy whistled again, and pointed ears peeked around the corner. When Tracy came around, Bonnie saw him and ran wagging.

"You know your dog was out there all night waitin' for ya," band members said on Monday.

"I know," Tracy said.

That's when Tracy realized why Dobermans were called Velcro dogs - because they were so loyal to one person. Tracy had never known such friendship, and soon, through tragedy, Tracy would begin the deepest relationship with his most important friend, and Bonnie would help him too.

- Bonnie

Chapter 11

- Moody, standing

Granny Betty's boys were firemen who lived two blocks from the firehouse. Granny's church was another two blocks. When they got the emergency call, Granny Betty's boys ran into church to tell Granny on the way. By the time she got to Starling Drive, Granny had to park by Jinny's because of the emergency vehicles. When she got to her gate, Moody had already been loaded into the ambulance.

It happened a year after Tracy got Bonnie. The boys were in D.C. visiting Vera after school was out. Moody was by the river working in the garden, and a tree branch threatened to shade his tomatoes. The offending branch wasn't thick, but like all trees by the river, it was tall.

Sunday was Moody's only day off. So once Granny was off to church, Moody got the ladder and chainsaw from the backhouse. He headed down the bank and climbed about twenty feet up the tree. Moody liked doing things like this, perhaps from his days in the Pacific stringing electric lines through the jungles of Guam. Moody had sawed halfway through when the branch gave way. Then the limb swung back and hit the ladder out from under him. Moody was careful to throw the chainsaw out and away as he fell. He landed on his feet, but the impact broke Moody's back.

Bonnie and Sandy sounded the alarm. Barbara, who lived next door, found Moody sprawled out at the bottom of the bank with the chainsaw running. The dogs wouldn't let anyone near him, trying to protect him. Eventually, Barbara's husband talked Bonnie and Sandy down, and the paramedics got Moody onto a spine board. Moody was in rehab for the next year. Then Tracy got a housemate who was always home. The veteran's group put a lift on the front porch for his wheelchair, and Tracy helped Moody with his exercises.

In time, Moody got so he could stand and walk with crutches, but he got ahead of himself. Alvin took him to the farm in Virginia. As Moody showed his father how well he was doing, he fell and landed on a rock. From then on, Moody was afraid to use the crutches. He had feeling in his legs and might have walked again, but he resigned himself to the chair, and part of Moody's acquiescence may have been the timing.

When the accident happened, Moody was two months away from retiring. Moody and Granny had been saving and had gotten a new camper and boat. They planned some long trips for September. Tracy was old enough to take care of the house, and was safe with the dogs. But when Moody fell at the farm, he gave up. The upshot was Tracy had all the time in the world with his new best mentor, sounding board and friend.

Because Moody was also a preacher's kid, he and Tracy had a unique connection. During summer trips spent at the farm, Tracy remembered Moody's father sitting in the sun by the outhouse in his white metal chair. Except for an occasional conversation with one of the cats, the great Mr. Moody read his Bible. This transferred to his children. Great Pawpaw Moody taught his boys to pray, study the Bible, and they all received the Holy Ghost. When Tracy was taken up and shown the picture book, Moody immediately recognized the change, which was where Moody excelled.

Whereas Granny shot her mouth off first and asked questions later, Moody observed and asked for clarification, or he was referee. More than that, and perhaps because of his connection with God from his father, Moody was a careful guardian of Tracy. From the time Tracy stood at even height with the stereo speaker, and knew all the words to "Oh Happy Day" from hearing it in heaven, Moody believed him.

Back then, the only time Moody had to spend with Tracy was bathing his three-year-old on Saturday nights before he tucked him in. They knelt beside the bed and said the "Now I lay me down to sleep" prayer. One night, after they blessed everyone in the family, Tracy wanted to know if he could mention the dogs.

"They're God's creatures too," Moody said.

"And God bless Sandy, King and Holly," little Tracy said, and Moody agreed with his "Amen."

From that time on, little Tracy woke up when Moody came home from his second job. When he crept past the bedroom to go to the bathroom, Moody would be on his knees praying. Sometimes, Tracy joined him so his Pawpaw could tuck him in. But sometimes Tracy went back to bed, because Moody looked so tired. Either way, once Tracy heard Moody's snore he was comforted and went to sleep.

When Tracy received the Holy Ghost, the two had a few conversations about the encounter. Moody didn't have experiences like Tracy did, but he was fascinated. During his visits to the farm Moody shared this information with his brother, Dris. Moody's younger brother was close to him, like Tracy was with Freddie. At the farm, Dris also asked if Tracy wanted to read the Bible with him, if he wasn't running down the hall scaring the him with rats.

When Moody moved back home after the accident, Dris stayed for a week to get Moody acclimated. Since Tracy could remember, Dris carried an old shoebox full of praise and worship cassettes. He got up first thing in the morning, and spent a few hours singing and worshipping God. By the time Moody came home in his wheelchair, the box was about to disintegrate. Tracy teased Dris as they worked the lift on the front porch to get Moody into the house.

"Hey Dris," Tracy said. "You need another shoebox?

"God will keep it together," Dris said, and once they got Moody on the porch he looked at the teenager. "I heard you got the Holy Ghost."

Tracy didn't know what to say.

"You got an adventure in front a you boy," Dris said.

At the end of the week, Dris went home to Virginia. Then Moody was home for good, and the full transformation took place. Moody sat in the kitchen reading the Sunday comics as usual. But there was something different, so Tracy studied Moody. Of course the chair was new, Tracy thought, but something was missing.

"Pawpaw," Tracy said. "You're not smoking your cigars."

Moody put down the paper and looked at Tracy. "I always hated the damn things."

"How?" Tracy stammered. "You've smoked your cigars since I've known you."

"Doesn't mean I liked it," Moody confided. "I only smoked 'em to piss off your grandmother. I hated cigarette smoke worse, so I smoked cigars in self-defense."

Tracy remembered when he was a kid with little Freddie. The heavy puffing created dueling clouds of smoke. The cigarette smoke from the kitchen, and the cigar smoke from Moody's room battled it out for scraps of oxygen left in the living room.

"But I only puffed 'em," Moody explained. "That shit'll give you cancer. Besides, I hated the taste of 'em. I never inhaled 'cause I was scared I'd throw up. That's all I'd need was for your Granny to start cacklin' all over the phone about that, an' I wasn't gonna give her *that* satisfaction. But it usually kept your Granny at least a room away, so it was worth it," and Moody began to laugh. "An' everyone knew," Moody said. "At least all the men in the Wanderers Club, especially Henderson with that pipe of his. I could stand the smell of that even less. He'd run me around the room, churnin' smoke out of his pipe like a locomotive," and Moody sat back.

"But your Granny never knew. I just kept bringing back whiskey-cured tobacco leaves from the farm." Moody laughed again, and hit Tracy's arm. "Ya know, I never knew it was illegal until they told me why they couldn't get any. We always had it at the farm, along with the moonshine."

"You mean your tomato wine," Tracy said.

"Nope, I mean my moonshine," and Moody clicked his Errol Flynn mustache.

"I just told ya it was tomato wine," Moody admitted, "because I knew how much ya hated tomatoes," and he winked. "That way, I knew you'd stay out of it," and Moody looked at his boy.

By now, Tracy was a young man halfway through high school. Moody rolled his wheelchair back from the dinette table, backed up to the sink, opened the cabinet and got a large pickle jar. In it were small brown ovals that were obviously not pickles.

"Get me that glass up there," Moody said. "You know, the one I like."

Tracy got up and reached into the cabinet above the stove. Moody opened the jar of moonshine steeped with apricots.

"You want some?" Moody asked.

"Sure," Tracy said. "Why not," and when Tracy sat down he realized this was the new place for their ritual to accommodate Moody's wheelchair.

"Organic eggs," Moody said, and chuckled to himself.

"What?" Tracy asked.

"There was a sign at the grocery store today. It said, 'Organic Eggs'." Moody turned to Tracy. "You ever see an egg that didn't come out of a chicken?"

"No. Maybe I can see the sign next time," Tracy said, "or maybe I can drive you."

"That's right," and Moody was surprised by the year he lost in rehab. "You need to start drivin'."

"An' you need to get those hand controls you've been stallin' on gettin', if you're gonna teach me how to drive."

"You're absolutely right," Moody said, and he did.

Tracy goaded Moody into an electric garage door opener too, and it wasn't long before Moody had his independence and became a celebrity. He'd take off in the morning for the store or post office, and would talk with anyone about organic products, or other interesting observations. Moody wouldn't come home until he picked up Tracy from whatever practice he had.

But it was in the kitchen that grandfather and grandson were converted to best friends. Nothing was off the table. They talked about everything – God, the Holy Spirit, Moody's war experiences, Vera and Bobby, Jinny and her kids, Granny, or Moody's plans for the farm. The two new best friends got a lot off their chest, and a lot of truth was dropped at their evening ceremonies, but neither of them knew Tracy's father was about to drop in.

- Tracy, Moody and Vera

Chapter 12

- Uncle Alvin

On the first Sunday of February 1981, Granny answered the phone and called for Tracy. He appeared in the kitchen while Granny was still on the phone.

"Go down to the basement an' get a screwdriver," she said quietly, still listening to the earpiece.

"What…" Tracy began.

"Just get a screwdriver boy," Granny said, covering the mouthpiece, "an' take it down to Aunt Jinny's." Tracy looked at her. "I don't get it either," Granny said to Tracy. "Jinny needs a screwdriver to fix her dryer," and she uncovered. "He's on his way," Granny said loudly. "Yep, right now," and she hung up the phone.

"Do you know what *kind* of screwdriver she wants?"

"I don't know what she wants," Granny said, "or what makes her think she or Alvin can fix a dryer, just do it. She's on fire for somethin', so git down there an' bring it back!"

Tracy got a screwdriver and ducked out the garage door. Tracy knew to return the exact same screwdriver, because tools disappeared down to Aunt Jinny's at an astonishing rate. But as Tracy approached the house, Uncle Alvin was in his car and rolled the passenger side window down.

"Git in," Alvin said, "an' hurry before Granny sees!"

As soon as Tracy got in, Alvin spun out and high-tailed it down the road talking a blue streak.

"Now ya can't tell your Granny about this," Alvin said. "An' me an' your Aunty, we've been talkin' 'bout this for a long time. But a boy needs to meet his father."

Tracy thought Alvin was right about not telling Granny. If she saw Alvin peel out, she'd figure what direction he was going and try to follow him. At the time, Alvin had a silver Mercury Cougar XR7 with a super-charged V-8 engine, and a jacked-up rear-end with mag wheels. So in reality, Granny couldn't possibly tail them. But Alvin took no chances, and took the first corner so hard he spilled the drink in his lap.

"We're late meetin' your Dad," Alvin said, and caught up as much of his cocktail as he could. "But I'm gonna try anyway," and he squealed onto the highway.

As it turned out, Tracy's other real grandmother lived in Vandalia all along. Tracy had passed her house all the time on his way to Kung Fu practice. Then, Tracy remembered that he saw her once. Vera drove her Camaro, and little Tracy sat in the back seat. His Mom took a turn down an odd street, stopped at the next intersection, and rolled her window down.

"Lean up," Vera said, and she meant business. Little Tracy unfastened his seatbelt, leaned up, and looked over his Mom's shoulder. There was a white Cadillac next to them at the intersection, and a well-to-do black lady drove it.

"Look at that woman," Vera said, and the woman in the Cadillac rolled her window down to see better. Tracy looked at her closely, and thought the woman looked like another Granny Moody if she 'had her hair on'. The woman instinctively looked back directly at Tracy, and their eyes locked for a moment.

"Who's that Momma?" Tracy asked, but Vera yelled into the Cadillac.

"This is the grandson you never wanted to meet!" she screamed.

When the woman in the Cadillac realized it was Vera, she floored it and steamed across the intersection.

Now, Alvin was hell-bent for Vandalia, and Tracy got nervous.

"Ok listen," Alvin said. "Don't be scared. Your father loves you. He loves you very much. This is the first time you're meetin' him, but it's not the first time he's seen you. There was a lot goin' on. Now I know you love your Granny, so I don't wanna say too much. You'll understand more later, but a boy's got to meet his father. Your Dad's in town because his mother died, your other grandmother. Lucille's funeral was yesterday, and we have to catch him before he's got to go back."

'Lucille,' Tracy thought. 'The lady in the Cadillac, her name was Lucille.'

They pulled up to a house Tracy had been by a thousand times. Out of it came a tall black man with a broad chest, and a complexion darker than Granny's. This was odd, because everyone in Tracy's family was light-skinned except Granny, and Tracy wondered how this man could possibly be his father.

"Well finally," the man said. "We meet."

Tracy's father looked at his fifteen-year-old son with a large smile before he spoke to Alvin, who called him Harry. His father spoke well, Tracy thought, like he had studied in school. His voice was quiet and serious when the matter called for it. But when he got excited, for his size, the man's voice went surprisingly high. Then Harry laughed a carbon copy of Tracy's laugh, and even Alvin noticed.

"Goodness, you sure laugh like Tracy," Alvin said, and he turned to Tracy. "Now, you ask your father anythin' you like."

Tracy was unable, so his father did it for him.

"Our stories of growing up are quite similar," his father said, and he spoke in a slow deliberate way. "You'll understand more later. I'm sure you've heard stories about why I wasn't in your life."

Tracy hadn't actually, so Alvin intervened.

"Tracy's not gonna ask," Alvin said, "but let me. I know there are two sides to every story, an' I know there's a man side."

Harry looked at Tracy. "I don't want you to think of your Granny differently. I don't want you to break your plate."

Tracy smiled, because it seemed an odd thing for his father to say. He was so formal, and 'break your plate' was a country expression. But Harry didn't want Tracy to lose his meal ticket with Granny. Harry smiled at himself as well. Then he drew in a breath and looked at his son squarely.

"I didn't do the responsible thing at the time," Harry said. "There were too many women's voices involved. I couldn't make a man's decision before the decision was made for me. I'm not going to hide anything from you son. Moody offered. He told me I could stay and live there while I went to school. But your mother couldn't live there with her mother. Your other grandmother, Lucille, didn't want that to happen either, and let's just say your Granny's relationship with her wasn't the best."

Alvin laughed out loud, because Granny thought Lucille was the biggest hypocrite there was. She went to the bigger Baptist Church across town. According to Granny, Lucille had no problem running around town in her Cadillac, quoting scripture and looking down on everyone. But when her son got Vera pregnant, she wanted everything swept under the rug. Sure, Granny smoked, drank and cussed, but she didn't hide it from anyone. She wasn't going to hide Vera and Harry's situation either. Tracy found this out later that afternoon.

Everyone had seen Lucille's obituary with the possible exception of Granny, because Moody kept the newspaper from her. Once Granny went down to her mother's house, Tracy and Moody ended up in the kitchen with the sink cabinet open.

"Well," Moody said. "I was surprised your Granny went for that screwdriver crap. But I guess a dryer is the best they could come up with," and Moody looked at his boy. "Are ya relieved?"

"In some ways," Tracy said. "In a lot a ways it doesn't change anything. But now I wonder," and Tracy felt some anger. "Maybe I wouldn't have had to put up with that asshole Bobby this whole time."

"Your father's a good man," Moody stated.

"Everyone keeps sayin' that," and Tracy looked at Moody. "An' both Alvin an' my father said they don't want me to think of Granny differently," which made Moody sip his 'shine and apricots hard.

"You still got that screwdriver?" Moody asked.

Tracy had forgotten about it, but it was still in his pocket so he nodded.

"I'm not sure I'm the best one to tell ya about that," Moody decided. "Why don't you see if your Aunty and Alvin got that dryer fixed."

"Ok Pawpaw."

"I'll keep your Granny busy, in case she comes back."

So Tracy went down to Jinny and Alvin's, who were expecting him. Jinny had sent the other kids out of the house and cooked greens and cornbread. The ribs were almost stove-done before Alvin would throw them on the grill. It was February, but they were Tracy's favorite. Then the two sat down with Tracy to explain. Tracy's father was a few years older than Vera when they dated in high school. They got in trouble when Harry was about to go to college. Lucille didn't want her son to jeopardize his future, and Granny and Moody wanted him to do the right thing. Vera still had one year of high school left, and Moody offered.

"You can stay an' live with us while ya go to school," Moody had said, "free of charge. I can help ya find a job while ya go to school, an' we'll help with the baby."

"To hell with that," Granny had said. "He should become a man, an' live up to his responsibilities."

"Shut up Jackie," Moody had said. "I'm talkin' man to man here, so you ain't involved."

"Oh, I know how to get involved," Granny warned.

"Aw shit," Moody said, which was how the issue came to a head.

Granny had a relation she called 'Cousin Texas', who had police officers under his command, and he kept a close eye on Granny's girls. If Granny called, Cousin Texas had his squadron search for the boy who had either girl out too late. If he couldn't find them, he dispatched more forces from the state.

Fortunately Harry got Vera home on time, but she was a minor. Granny threatened to charge Harry with statutory rape if he didn't marry Vera, and Cousin Texas could have made that happen. Beyond that, Vera couldn't live in the same house with her mother, a new husband and baby, where everyday a look from Granny would be judgment on her mistake. So Tracy's father left West Virginia, and Moody took care of Vera and her newborn. A year later, Vera was married to the wrong man. But Tracy got Freddie out of the deal, so there was a silver lining.

-Tracy and Freddie in Rand

Chapter 13

- Tracy his Junior Year

Granny Berger died the week before Mother's Day after a long battle with lung cancer. Granny was devastated, and telling Vera had to be done gently. Vera was close with Granny Berger, and had recently bought her grandmother a necklace for Mother's Day. No one could find Bobby for a while. When he finally called back, Bobby told Granny to 'wait till his shift was over'. Granny slammed the phone onto the wall and got Tracy. By this time, Vera was an administrator at the hospital. They called Beverly who was a nurse, and a good friend of Vera's. Her shift was almost over, so Tracy asked Beverly to go to Vera's desk before he called. Beverly collected the other nurses on the floor and headed for Vera while Tracy dialed.

"Hey Mom," Tracy said. "How are you doing?"

"Hey Trace," and Vera was surprised he had called her at work.

"Is Beverly at your desk yet?" Tracy asked.

Vera was distracted but said, "Yeah, she just got here," and Vera saw Beverly's face and screamed, and Tracy heard his mother sob. Tracy listened as Beverly hung the phone up for her, but knew his mother was surrounded with comfort.

The Monday after Mother's Day they buried Granny Berger in the necklace Vera had gotten her. Then, the mantel of matriarch fell on Granny with weight. Granny became unrecognizably serious, and her brother got more depressed. He lived in the area and was an alcoholic loner. His depression became chronic after his mother died.

By October he succeeded in drinking himself to death, and Granny stood resolute as the only one left of her family. Moody also became uncommonly quiet after Granny Berger's funeral. His wife's mother recognized what Moody did by stepping up to raise Jinny and Vera. If Granny had agreed to move to the farm their lives would have been very different. At the time, Granny Berger was all for it. She dreamed with Moody about sitting on the porch as they sipped moonshine, but her daughter liked to bowl and hang out with her girlfriends too much. So even though they didn't win, Moody had a confidant in his mother-in-law. Granny Berger was always in his corner and helped fend Granny off. Now that she was gone, Moody was a lone pilgrim where his wife was concerned.

For Tracy the summer barely registered, and he became serious as well. He quit band to focus on his college prep classes. He kept up with his Kung Fu, but Tracy's childhood was over. Then, even though his junior year started slowly, it gathered steam with dizzying speed. By the following Mother's Day, Tracy was off to D.C. in a professional capacity. He had entered a contest to attend the Washington Congressional Seminar sponsored by Union Carbide. The black senior girls had goaded Tracy on, because they didn't want to miss representation at a national level.

"You're the only black person entering this essay contest from our school," the girls explained, "an' we're gonna help ya win."

The young black women conspired to collectively help Tracy write his essay. The teachers who graded it were also co-conspirators, but not just because of Tracy. Some of Tracy's teachers taught Vera and Jinny. Back in the day, Vera was beloved almost as much as Jinny was infamous. When Tracy began high school, his teachers asked him *whose* he was at point-blank range. When Tracy asked Granny and Moody about this, he got the whole story.

Vera and Jinny were similar to Tracy and Freddie in terms of temperament and scholastic interest: Tracy was a good student who kept his head down, and Freddie went to school to meet girls. Likewise, Vera's teachers loved her, while it was difficult to keep Jinny out of jail. The disparity was partly due to the sisters' personalities, but some had to do with their appearance. Vera's was soft with hazel eyes that, along with her sexy voice got things done more easily with sugar. In contrast, Jinny's feisty green eyes snapped easily, but her biggest problem was that she looked white. Her hair was naturally blond, and Jinny's skin-tone was lighter than some of the Klansmen's daughters in her class.

The sisters hit high school in the early 1960's. From the 'git-go', Jinny was known as Queen Bee – 'sting first, ask questions later'. She had a short wick, a sharp wit, and the physical power to back it up. Early on in the girl's high school career, it was a particularly hot summer. At the time Glasgow, West Virginia, was a known home to the Klan, and had a 'whites-only' pool. So Jinny got a bee in her bonnet how to shut it down. She stirred up her hive of 'colored' accomplices, and they climbed into Granny's massively white Impala to head for Glasgow.

"Now Bootsie," Jinny instructed. "You stay here an' keep the car runnin'."

The girls had their swimsuits on, but they left their towels in the car. A tiny girl sat at the admission desk to the pool, who looked like she should be selling cookies. Silently, Jinny's group bum-rushed the girl, ran directly to the pool and jumped in, and splashed around yelling and laughing. Just as fast, every white body jumped out of the pool in disgust. They screamed the N-word and ran for their Mommies.

With the pool cleared Jinny's gang hopped out, ran back past the bewildered clerk, hopped into the waiting Impala, and sped off in a signature cloud of dust. Afterward, the pool was drained and scrubbed with bleach. That took three weeks, so the pool was condemned for the rest of the summer. The only option was for the residents of Glasgow to go to one of the integrated pools outside of town. They weren't about to do that, so Jinny's mission was accomplished.

But perhaps Jinny's greatest work was at a football game. She was a senior and was going out with Squeaky, her first future ex-husband, who was the star quarterback. During a particular game a white girl sat at the top of the bleachers with her redneck friends. She wasn't as pleased with the notoriety of the school's winning team of black athletes. Jinny sat in front by the flagpole with the other girlfriends of the players. As Jinny and her gang cheered their men on, the white girl began taunting Queen Bee.

"Hey Jinny," she said between gum pops. "Why don't you come on up here?"

Jinny ignored her, but everyone heard.

"I got a bet goin' on up here," she explained. "Come on up so we can settle it."

Then Squeaky came in from the field, and Jinny leaned down to him. "Keep an eye out," Jinny instructed. "There might be some shit," and Jinny faced the top of the bleachers.

Word went through the team as Jinny stood, and Vera got ready. "What do you want?"

"We need you to come up an' settle somethin' for us," the white girl said, and her gang sniggered.

All eyes were on Jinny as she climbed to the top of the bleachers. The game continued, but the kids watched the show playing out beside them. When Jinny reached the top, the white girl took off her sandal, put her foot in Jinny's face and smirked.

"The only thing darker on me than you is the bottom of my foot," she said, alluding to the dirt collected from her open sandals.

Jinny snatched that foot. She dragged it from the top of the bleachers to the bottom, and didn't care about the screaming body attached to it. When Jinny reached the bottom, the football team rallied and formed a circle around her. Then Jinny and Vera commenced to 'givin' that girl a Seven Sons of Sceva whuppin', and ripped clothes flew everywhere. The football team surrounded the flagpole until the wrath of Queen Bee was satisfied. But, it wasn't long before the white girl was strung to the flagpole by the back of her bra, and hoisted up for all to see.

Ironically, years later after Jinny and Squeaky married, had three lovely girls and were divorced, Jinny tried to kill the very same quarterback. Granny Berger was knitting in the living room. She had one eye on the TV, and the other on the large picture window. Squeaky got drunk and decided to test the restraining order. It was dark outside, but Granny Berger saw him working his way up the driveway. Jinny was in her bedroom.

"Jinny," Granny Berger said. "Squeaky's on his way up here."

"Ok Granmomma," Jinny said.

"Jinny, he's gettin' closer."

"I know Granmomma," and Granny Berger heard a drawer open in the bedroom.

"Jinny?" Granny Berger asked.

"Yes Granmomma?" Jinny answered.

"Squeaky's pickin' up a lawn chair an' staggerin' toward the plate glass window."

There was no answer. About the time Squeaky managed to lift the lawn chair toward the window, Jinny appeared with her pearl-handled revolver. She jumped into the living room, squatted into position, and fired off a round of shots through the plate glass.

Then she ran to the front door, opened it, squatted and fired off another round in every direction before she yelled.

"Come on Granmomma," Jinny said. "Help me look for the body so we can drag it into the house!"

But Granny Berger didn't move from her chair. Instead, she put her knitting down, and looked through the broken window at Jinny running around the yard in a panic.

"It's self defense if we drag him back into the house," Jinny panted. She shot one more round down the driveway, but Squeaky was long gone. Only a tossed lawn chair, murdered plate glass window, and disappointed Queen Bee were left.

By the time Tracy reached high school, the only thing his teachers wanted to know was which one of 'the girls' was Tracy's mother. An audible sigh of relief was released when it was Vera. The upshot was the same teachers graded Tracy's essay for the Union Carbide contest, which helped Tracy become one of seven students to attend the seminar from West Virginia. The weeklong seminar was at Marymount College. Tracy expected the seminar to be a kind of vacation, and thought he would finally be able to go into the buildings he drove by so many times as a child. Then Tracy planned to visit Vera for Mother's Day.

But the experience was eye opening, and the world became a much bigger place for Tracy. This was the first time he met such a wide variety of academically alert students his age, which was thrilling and shocking. As one of a handful of black students, Tracy saw racism plainly visible. He didn't expect this in such an educated group, and didn't realize there could be 'smart bigotry'. On the bright side, Tracy's newly formed friends were more broad-minded, and the revelations cut both ways.

Tracy's roommate was named Dean, who was from North Carolina. He was the first white person Tracy ever shared a room with. From Tracy's vantage point, and hearing Granny talk about cleaning white folk's houses, his assumption was that white people were dirty. Tracy brought shoes for the shower because, as every black woman who ever cleaned a white bathroom knew, all white folks had athlete's foot. As it turned out, Dean was the farthest thing from dirty. Tracy also thought he was handsome, was impeccably tidy and nobly polite.

On the other hand, when an aspiring girlfriend wannabe showed up, she proved Granny's point. The girl who thought Dean was cute was definitely from the bigotry camp. She also wore un-kempt clothes and her hair was a nest, perhaps of several small animal species. When she bounced in, Tracy and Dean were studying in their room. She sat close to Dean on his bed and said hi. Surprised, Dean said hi back, as southern gentlemen do. Then the girl looked at Tracy, and back at Dean.

"Does he have to be here?" she said, rolling her eyes toward Tracy.

"This is his room," Dean answered.

"Oh," and the girl was confused for a moment. "Is that ok with you?"

"Why wouldn't it be?" Dean answered.

Tracy sat on his bed watching them talk about him.

"Well," and the girl sounded obvious. "Because he's…"

"Because he's what?" Dean pressed to make her say it, but she bounced up and looked into one of the closets instead. She picked up a bottle of shampoo.

"This is nice," she said. "Whose is this?"

"Mine," Tracy said, which startled her.

"Why are you using our shampoo?" the girl asked.

"*Our* shampoo?" Tracy asked.

Dean looked at Tracy and tried not to laugh. Then the girl ran out of the room before Dean and Tracy fell apart from the ludicrous exchange.

"I kinda wanna sterilize the room now," Tracy said, which made them laugh harder.

"I guess I should see how she's doin'," Dean said, and left.

As Tracy placed his shampoo back on the shelf he thought of Granny. He kept silent and let the girl hang herself on her own words, just like Granny would have done. Tracy also knew he had a good friend, and Dean and Tracy remained friends for years after.

A few days later, Tracy met a more pivotal person in his life. On Thursday, the students went to Capitol Hill to spend the morning with their respective senators. Tracy's was the longest serving congressman at the time - the Honorable Robert Byrd of West Virginia. The senator was expressly interested in shaking Tracy's hand, and both were proud. When Mr. Byrd started out he was a champion for the Klan. Over the years he did a one-eighty, as did his disposition. Even after decades in Congress, the senator became younger, lighter, and acted like a kid in an old suit. Senator Byrd was also a cut-up. On his tour he rode the kids on the little train under the capitol until his secretary had to come find him.

"Are ya doin' this again?" she yelled with a twang. "Get on upstairs now!" she scolded.

"Yes ma'am," the senator answered, and the kids laughed.

That afternoon the group watched congress from the gallery to prepare for their mock congress on Saturday. Then the long, hot, political day was done. The busses headed across Memorial Bridge to Marymount at sunset. About the time they rounded the Lincoln Memorial, "Candy Girl" by New Edition came on the radio. Immediately, an effervescent light-skinned young man stood up, and proceeded to dance down the center aisle. He was Tracy's height with a big Afro, and a shocking sense of himself. He began to strip, which made the bus driver notice the commotion and turn the music up.

Working the crowd, the skilled performer knew all the words and took his time throwing his coat, tie, and eventually his starched shirt into the crowd. It was as if a bottle of pink champagne was popped, and the bus became a bubbly, cool mass of laughter and refreshment. Tracy was more than captivated and secretly observed the young man, who kept an eye on Tracy. The introduction happened during dinner.

"My name is Justin," and he held out his hand, and Tracy shook it. Without hesitation, Justin pulled a chair up and sat next to Tracy.

"Today was pretty cool, don't ya think?" Justin said, not allowing an answer. "I thought the congress was a little sluggish. They could have cut some time with a properly placed objection. But all-in-all I think it was good day," and he took a small bite of his burger. "At least we got the bill passed," and he swallowed and hit Tracy's arm with his elbow. "Hey, I lost my mother's camera up on the hill today. She'll kill me if I don't bring it back," and Justin turned to Tracy. "You want to help me look for it tomorrow? It's our free day."

Tracy wasn't sure if this was a rhetorical question, but he nodded in the affirmative.

The next day after breakfast, Justin and his groupies headed for Capitol Hill. They retrieved Justin's camera, and with nothing better to do, they went for lunch in Georgetown. Justin was uncharacteristically low-key, but that was because he was preparing. That evening was the culmination of the seminar. When he introduced his bill, Justin's performance was spectacular.

"I know you guys recognize me," Justin said, and spit out a little Bobby Brown from "Candy Girl."

Suddenly, the student congress tasted pink champagne and broke into applause. Then, Justin's command of the room shocked everyone. He cut the conservative camps off at every turn, and their points fell to Justin's procedural mastery. This led to a heated debate with a judge from Union Carbide. A ten-minute recess was called for the judges to discuss the merits of Justin's unorthodox use of Robert's Rules. When the congress reconvened, Justin won the night, and the next day the seminarians headed home. Justin caught up with Tracy to exchange numbers, and invited Tracy to come to his home in Connecticut. Tracy agreed, but that wasn't to be until the following summer.

When Tracy returned to school, he was a hero to the senior girls. But his accomplishment was short-lived, because a rumor surfaced Tracy was getting a D in English. The next morning, Granny sat outside the principal's office. The small, skinny white principal had been Vera's history teacher back in the day. Jinny went with Granny 'in case there was some shit'.

At ten a.m., Tracy was called to the Principal's office over the P.A. system. The women entered the office and sat in front of the principal's desk, and Tracy took a seat along the wall behind them. Once the principal hung up he started in.

"Well, hello Miss Mud," he said, referring to Granny's skin color.

Granny lunged across the desk, but Jinny caught her by the waist.

"You know my name," Granny snarled.

Jinny looked at the principal, and her green eyes snapped like a welding torch.

"You remember me too," Jinny said quietly, and stared at the pasty little man who was in a closed room protected only by a desk. "I aughta let her go."

"Please," the principal said warily, and gestured kindly for the ladies to sit. Granny thought of Tracy sitting behind her, and relented. Jinny let go of her mother's waist and they sat down.

"It seems this was a misunderstanding," the principal continued.

"Ya think?" Jinny said.

"It seems Tracy's English teacher didn't tell him about the test his class was given while he was at the seminar," the principal said.

"Seems the teacher also failed to mention the test was 50% of his grade," Granny barked.

"And that I was excused from all of my classes for the seminar," Tracy stated.

"Which means he should be able to take the test," Jinny concluded.

The room fell quiet as the racism of generations sat there - from Tracy, to Vera and Jinny, to Granny and Granny Berger - even from the time in elementary school when Tracy asked Granny Berger about her family history for an assignment. Back then, his great grandmother slapped him before she knocked him down, and smothered little Tracy with a pillow.

"Don't you ever mention Alabama again," Granny Berger shouted. "Ever!"

Three generations of struggle and injustice sat, and looked at the skinny white man behind the desk. Mentally, Tracy drafted a letter to his good friend Robert Byrd, who told Tracy he could call his office at any time. In her mind, Jinny sized up the principal's weight, and figured she could get him halfway up the flagpole if she used his belt.

"Well," the principal finally said. "This does seem to be a misunderstanding," and the women let him finish. "And seeing as Tracy represented the state and this school so admirably with Union Carbide, I will see to it he can take his test so this can be straightened out."

"Huh," Granny said.

Without so much as a goodbye Granny got up, and Jinny followed her out with Tracy. He took his test, received an A in English, and Tracy's junior year was done. Then, things got complicated, as Tracy's horizons were both broadened and clouded until he graduated high school, when God would fully launch Tracy into this world.

102

Chapter 14

- Tracy's graduation

Tracy went to spend the summer with Vera in D.C. as usual. Before he left West Virginia, there were rumors of a new division starting for the 1984 summer Olympics - Chinese Wu Shu. Tracy's teacher said it was the chance of a lifetime, and suggested he train at a weeklong workshop in D.C. The cost was $150 up front, and Tracy asked Vera for the money. She said no, because Bobby had told her not to pay for it. Bobby also wouldn't let Tracy use any of his cars to get to the practices.

"Why you wastin' your time with this stuff," Bobby said, and his tone was caustic. "You know this. You know you ain't gonna amount to nothin'. You might as well get used to it now. Forget that college talk, an' go out an' get yourself a good-for-nothin' job."

Tracy stared back because he knew the truth - Bobby didn't want Tracy to get better at Kung Fu for his own safety. Granny was incensed and sent Tracy the money, but not until she laid Vera out.

"I truly do not understand why you put up with that man," Granny began.

"I just don't have the money right now," Vera said.

"Bullshit," Granny snorted. "You got that good payin' job at the hospital now, an' ya seem to be able to pay for that big ass yacht of yours. You just don't wanna go against that asshole husband of yours."

Vera had a whole arsenal about how badly Granny treated Moody, but knew that wouldn't go anywhere. Granny had a reason for everything, no matter how thin.

"I spent all those years drivin' Tracy around to his practices," Granny vented. "An' you're tellin' me you can't even manage it for a week? It kept him off the streets an' it will there too. It'll also give him somethin' to do in his old age." There was no answer, so Granny poured it on. "I drove him Monday, Wednesday an' Friday all those years, 'cross town an' back again. An' now Tracy can drive, he's got a chance of a lifetime, an' Bobby can't see to lend him a car?"

"He's usin' his car," Vera stated.

"So," and Granny had her now. "He drives all three at the same damn time?"

Bobby had three cars by this time, and his cab. His excuse was Tracy didn't have a D.C. driver's license. As an added insult, David, Bobby's actual son, drove Bobby's cars even though he had a Maryland license. So it was just like the Christmas when David kept his bike, and Tracy and Freddie had to load their bikes into Moody's truck, and watch them go back to West Virginia.

When Chris, Tracy's friend from grade school, heard the hard time Bobby gave Tracy, Chris's Mom said Tracy could stay with them. She also offered to give Tracy the money to piss Bobby off, but Granny had already sent Tracy the $150, plus money for food, subway and bus fare. Then Chris helped Tracy map out a route to the classes, which was a morning and evening combination of busses and subways. What could have been a forty-five minute drive became a two-hour commute, if all the busses and trains were on time. Tracy didn't want to be late, so he left at six in the morning. He didn't get home until nine or ten at night, which caused the cramps.

Training with Sifu Mfundi Dennis was awesome but grueling. Tracy learned new Wu Shu forms and techniques rapidly, and lost several pounds in a few days. He trained from eight in the morning until seven at night every day, while Tracy's classmates trained every other day. By mid-week, Tracy's cramps were so bad, he drafted Freddie to dig into the muscles he couldn't reach to pull them apart.

By the end of the week, Tracy was chosen to compete. He was the only competitor from West Virginia, and the only other student chosen from his D.C. class. In the end Wu Shu wasn't added to the Olympics, but talk of adding Martial Arts to the games led to the formation of NACMAF - the North American Chinese Martial Arts Federation. The organization built a network of teachers, many who were key figures in the Martial Arts. They appeared in Martial Arts movies, and became coaches in later mainstream films. As Granny designed, Tracy's Martial Arts family became lifelong friends, but there was another reason everything happened the way it did. While riding the subway tired and weak, Tracy heard Him again.

"It is going to be ok," He said, and His voice wasn't behind Tracy like when he was a child. It came to him as a still, small voice, as Tracy retraced the bus and subway routes yearning to sleep.

"There will be a lot of opportunities coming your way," the Tall Shiny Silver Figure said. *"Take advantage of all of them. You will mess it up, and you will learn from it, but it will come around again,"* and Tracy didn't know it at the time, but He was talking about the blessing.

Once the summer was over and Tracy got back to West Virginia, Granny decided Tracy needed a car. It was his senior year of high school, and college was around the corner. Granny was also still pissed at Bobby from the summer.

"We're not gonna have the asshole do that again," Granny decided. "No more car issues. Find yourself somethin' under ten grand."

Tracy did Granny one better, he thought, and found a car for three thousand. It was a 1960's Camero like Vera had when he was little, except it was fawn-colored with dual black stripes. Late in the afternoon, Tracy drove proudly into Granny's driveway, and she came out on her porch.

"Aw hell no," Granny said. "You can take that blond piece of shit back where it came from," and went back into the house.

It turned out the fawn-colored Camero was the skinny white principal's car, which he drove during Vera and Jinny's high school career. He gave it to his daughter, who tried to sell it to Tracy. Fresh from the confrontation over Tracy's grade the previous spring, the cursed car wasn't an option. Worse, the sight of it 'got Granny goin', and she decided to 'step it up a bit'. In Tracy's mind, he thought if he got a car for three thousand, Granny would have money to buy Freddie, and Jinny's oldest daughter Demi a car. That way, each of them could get back and forth to work, school, or whatever else the three musketeers might dream up. But that's not what happened.

That fall Isuzu came out with a brand-new Impulse, and Granny decided that's what Tracy had to drive to high school. Her pride wanted Tracy to show off for the principal, and the racist kids that plagued her family all those years. There was only one black Isuzu Impulse with red stripes in the entire state of West Virginia, and Granny and Tracy drove to Beckley to get it.

The next morning, the car had the desired effect. Tracy's classmates thought it looked like a Porsche. The Impulse also mimicked the car featured in "Risky Business". Most importantly to Granny, it was a much nicer car than the principal drove.

"How'd *you* get a new car?" the white kids asked.

"Do not get side-tracked," the still small voice said.

Tracy heard Him in real time as his peers ogled his car. So Tracy paid them no mind, and knew there wasn't time to bask in this small glory.

"I am opening up opportunities for you," He repeated, *"such that have never been seen before. You will blow it because of a lack of knowledge, but it will all come back to you later in life."*

Tracy came back to himself as his classmates argued over his new car, and they were bewildered at Tracy's disinterest when he left for class. From then on, Tracy knew his job was to minimize errors and take advantage of every opportunity placed before him, which included working at the steakhouse for gas money. But Tracy's first day at his first job wasn't what he expected. Donnie taught Tracy to work the potato bar with 'all it's fixin's', and help with the dishes. Mark's sister Beth worked the salad bar. Not so secretly, Donnie had a crush on her. At the end of the night, Donnie thought it a good idea to throw a dinner roll at Beth as she came through the double doors. If wet, the rolls exploded like a snowball when they hit the wall.

"That's not a good idea," Mark said. "She's a big girl, and weighs-in in more ways than one."

Donnie ignored him and wet a few rolls, but Mark was adamant.

"You shouldn't do this," Mark warned. "I know my sister, an' this ain't gonna end well."

It was after midnight on Friday. They were all tired, and Beth came through the double doors loaded with inserts from the salad bar. She struggled with the double doors, and was careful not to spill anything. Suddenly a roll whizzed by her head, hit the wall, and burst into a blizzard of flour. Beth stopped in her tracks, Mark disappeared, and Beth saw Donnie's mouthful of braces laughing at her. Then, Beth's eyes narrowed and seemed to change color as she transformed into a Kamikaze. Beth spied the steak knives to her left, dropped the tray, grabbed a blade for each hand and chased Donnie through the kitchen.

"Ya wanna play, huh?" Beth screamed.

"Mr. Matthew!" Donnie yelled, and tore into the dining room. "Oh shit, oh shit, oh shit!"

Beth followed Donnie into the girls' bathroom, because it was the only one that locked.

"Get yourself outa that bathroom you little girl!" Beth yelled and beat on the door, and then she turned nice. "Can't ya see I'm just playin'?"

When Mr. Matthew arrived, Donnie unlocked the bathroom door and presented himself. They went back into the kitchen to survey the damage.

"Scared him didn't I?" Beth whispered to Tracy with a wink.

"Who's gonna clean up this mess?" Mr. Matthew asked.

"Donnie is," Beth decided. "He's the one who threw the roll."

Mark's voice came out from under the plate warmer, "I told ya."

But this sideline job didn't distract Tracy, nor did he see it as his future. Tracy took classes half-day at the technical college to study electrical engineering, which was like breathing. It was fascinating, and Tracy intuitively knew everything about his coursework. He never had anything come so naturally, and by the end of the semester he decided his final project would be a car alarm. It was 1983, and car alarms were primitive. The few that existed were key activated and ran off the car's battery - a disarming flaw.

In his design, Tracy installed motion detectors with sensors attached to the doors, hood and hatchback. He created a circuit to disable the car battery when the alarm went off. Tracy had a separate battery to run the alarm system, along with relay switches that reset the alarm after two minutes.

To accomplish this, Tracy took out the seats of his brand-new Impulse, and ripped up the carpet to run the wires. In short, he took the car apart, installed his alarm, and rebuilt it. The fact Moody was a mechanic obviously helped, but Granny's mouth did not. Nonetheless, Tracy did it, and news of his project spread throughout the community. Tracy's teachers were amazed, and the seed was planted. Then came a misstep.

There was a bridge on the way to Kanawha City infamous for drag racing and playing chicken. It had a long high arch and the crest was sharp, which made it impossible to see the other side in either lane. Tracy made plans to meet up with friends who worked at a taco place, and the steakhouse gang left when they got off work. It was raining and they should have gone home, but the lure of fried ice cream was greater than the danger of crossing the Kanawha City Bridge when it was slick. When they crossed the crest there was a car stalled in their lane. Tracy managed to stop before hitting it, but the eight-cylinder Firebird that followed him couldn't.

When Granny heard about the accident and where they were, she figured Tracy was 'drag racin'. Moody fixed the Impulse, but that was it for Granny. After Tracy's graduation, Granny told Tracy to meet her at the dealership where she traded his Impulse in for her burgundy, first edition Dodge Daytona Turbo.

"This is *my* car," Granny said, as her matching painted burgundy fingernails caressed the hood, and that was that. Although in the end, Granny's new car got her back a little. There was a glitch in the first edition's dashboard that only the tachometer and gas gage worked. Three tickets later, Moody figured it out and sat Granny in her car.

"What dial are ya lookin' at for your speed?" Moody asked.

Granny pointed to the tachometer. "I can't get this car to go over thirty."

"Aw hell Jackie," Moody laughed. "No wonder you're passin' everybody 'cept the cops."

So Tracy's first car was gone, but the Impulse's purpose wasn't to get him back and forth to work. Through God's intricate plan, it was the vehicle that got him into college.

Tracy and Granny began looking the previous fall. Tracy took the SATs and didn't do so well. He applied to colleges, but was turned down because of his scores. By January, Tracy prepared to retake his SATs but he got a letter.

Tracy had kept up with his college prep courses, and worked out three times a week with Ron. There, he was reunited with Jean from junior high. Now that the two worked out so often at Ron's studio, their friendship grew and they began dating. Unknown to Tracy, Jean's father was the fundraising executive for Union Carbide. The corporation not only sent Tracy to the Washington Congressional Seminar, they also awarded scholarships to colleges. One was N.C. State, and Jean knew about Tracy's famous car alarm.

Before Granny had a chance to trade the Impulse in for her Daytona Turbo, Jean arranged for Tracy to do a demonstration for her father. Tracy's invention worked brilliantly, however Jean's father only said he wasn't sure.

Then, as Tracy prepared to retake his SATs, he received an acceptance letter to N.C. State's Electrical Engineering Program without applying to the school. Vera wanted to visit the campus immediately, but Granny wanted to wait until the weather broke. So during spring break, Tracy, Jean and Granny headed to D.C. to pick up Vera. It was almost summer across the campus in North Carolina, but Granny and Vera were nervous. N.C. State was in the heart of tobacco country, and not the most welcoming place for folks of color. Then, as they approached the library they smelled it, and the aroma held them captive.

"What is that?" Vera asked.

"That's magnolia," Granny said.

"Where is it coming from?" Vera asked.

"There," Jean said, and pointed to a tree as wide as it was high. Its deep green leaves held brilliant white blooms as big as plates up to the sun.

Tracy was transfixed. He remembered the smell from the picture book, when he sat on His lap when he was three. Tracy remembered the warmth, the expanse of the brickyard before them and the sight of the library, but the smell was his confirmation. Tracy relived the sweetness of the scent programmed in his memory, when he saw in reality what he was shown as a tiny child.

"This is where I am supposed to go to school," Tracy stated.

Vera looked at her son, and recognized the expression she had seen so many times before. Ever since Tracy came home from the hospital, when her toddler stood at the glass storm door and asked his imaginary friend what he was here for, Vera knew that look. Granny looked at Tracy and saw it too, but God wasn't done yet.

When they got home, Tracy got another letter from In-Roads, a local teaching organization for black youth. They invited select college prep students for extra classes every Saturday, which were taught by previous In-Roads students. With curriculums in calculus, chemistry and physics, there was a high school, college, and graduate group that networked together.

Tracy always wanted to be chosen, but wasn't invited until he was accepted to N.C. State. There was just one caveat - Tracy needed to secure an internship with a corporate sponsor. Tracy kept walking. Dupont was up the river from Granny's house, and Tracy found out Dupont sponsored internships for college students. But Dupont was looking for chemical engineers, so he kept walking. Tracy moved on to IBM, interviewed with several different teams of people, and then forgot about it.

Meanwhile, Tracy worked at the steakhouse, trained in Kung Fu with Ron, and prepared for N.C. State. Before he knew it, Tracy took Jean to the prom. The next week the seniors practiced for graduation, and Vera and Bobby came to town. Because of the occasion, Moody allowed Bobby in his house.

Shortly after they arrived, Bobby was on his third whiskey, and Moody was two past his 'medicinal' shots of 'shine' to keep the peace. Moody also remained in the adjacent bedroom with the door open, and kept his gun loaded.

Late in the afternoon, Granny realized she had forgotten to get the mail. When she came back, Granny handed Tracy a clean white envelope.

"You got somethin' here," Granny said.

Tracy opened the letter. Without so much as a phone call or follow-up interview, IBM offered Tracy a high-paying internship for the summer. The offer included working at IBM for the same salary during his college breaks, in order to groom Tracy for a permanent position. They expected Tracy to report for work the Monday after his graduation.

"What is it honey?" Vera asked.

"I have an internship at IBM," Tracy said.

"That's wonderful," Vera said. "Will it take up a lot of your time?"

"It's a full-time job Mom," Tracy said, "and they want me to start Monday."

"What are you gonna do about your job at the steakhouse?" Vera asked, and Bobby chimed in.

"Ya might wanna keep that job in your back pocket, in case anythin' happens."

That was it for Tracy. All the years of Bobby beating him for no reason, abusing his mother, and degrading him were over. Tracy stood up.

"And you said I wasn't going to amount to anything!" and Tracy pointed his finger at Bobby.

"Not gonna amount to anything," Tracy repeated, and held the letter up. "Before I'm out of high school I've got a company job, I'm makin' more money than you are now, and I'm goin' to one of the top engineering schools in the fall!"

"Tracy!" Vera exclaimed.

"Let the man talk!" Moody shouted from the bedroom.

Tracy stood a moment to let the truth settle.

"That's all I've got to say," Tracy said and sat down, because suddenly he saw it. God had brought it all back together: Tracy had a salaried job, a future in college, and he had nothing to do with any of it but walk. Then, He reminded Tracy what He stated the previous summer as Tracy rode the subway...

"I am opening up opportunities for you," He said, *"such that have never been seen before."*

Tracy realized he would never have to deal with Bobby again, unless he chose to do so. Tracy also recognized what God had orchestrated over the past two years. The previous summer, Tracy had spent a week with his father, where Tracy gained a better understanding of his father and his own identity. That experience, combined with what his heavenly father had just proved, made Tracy a different person. As it turned out, Tracy was just getting started with his transition to adulthood, and his idea of family and identity was about to expand farther than he imagined.

Chapter 15

- Tracy and Bryan

Two things greatly affected Tracy on his path to college. The summer before Tracy's junior year he spent a week with his father in Columbus, Ohio. There he met Harry's wife Lynn, and his much younger brother Bryan. Tracy was also introduced to a new idea of religion. It was through Harry's bloodline that Tracy had met the Tall Shiny Silver Figure. The whole family was also involved in their non-denominational, extremely charismatic church.

However, Lynn's personality was something brand-new to Tracy. He had never heard anyone speak like her, correct like her, or give praise like her. Even though she grew up in Columbus, Lynn's family was from Georgia, so she was raised in the church and her family was from the south. Her mannerisms were a perfect blend of the two, which resulted in remarkable outbursts.

"The Lord said, 'Thou shalt not want', but I truly want another piece of that sweet potato pie," and she leaned into Tracy. "I hope He will forgive me," and Lynn took another slice. "But of course He will, because 'He forgives all our sins', although my hips might not," and she took a bite and broke into a shout. "Praise Jesus! He does love his little – well, hopefully I'll stay little – children!"

When Lynn met Tracy, she recognized the issue and neutralized it.

"We have no steps in this family," she stated. "Now, I realize you have your Mom and your Granny. So when you're comfortable, you call me whatever you want to call me, but it won't be stepmom. Steps are what you stand on. I am here to lift you up."

For Tracy, calling Lynn 'Mom' was uncomfortable at first, but it got easier because Lynn was so approachable. For all her scripture quoting, it was actually her natural thought process and not something conjured up to condemn. Lynn laughed easily, and her mirthful eruptions seemed to take her by surprise. Her soft toffee skin was framed by shoulder length, jet-black wavy hair. Her most common expression was 'What?' - only because she wanted to understand the entire meaning of what was said. As her children got older, many times her questioning was because of her innocence. But she enjoyed the joke once it was explained, and she asked Jesus' forgiveness.

However, it was Lynn and Harry's son that was a bigger revelation to Tracy. The newly acquainted brothers were more like twins, despite the age gap of twelve years. Unlike Freddie, who had a different father, Bryan and Tracy were the same, as Tracy was about to find out.

"Well sons," Harry said. "I have to go to work, so you two have the house to yourselves."

Tracy panicked before he looked over at little Bryan, and realized it was if he was looking at himself when he was that age.

"So what do you want for breakfast?" Tracy asked.

"Cereal," little Bryan said. Tracy smiled because that's what he wanted. Then he thought he would test his new little brother.

"What kind do you want?"

"Let's get Daddy's favorite," Bryan said, which Tracy thought would mean granola or worse, until he saw Bryan's crafty look.

"Is that because Dad's not here?"

"No, it's because you're older, and you won't get in as much trouble," and Tracy saw the resemblance to his brother grow.

"Which one is Daddy's favorite?" Tracy asked. Bryan pointed. "Teddy Grahams? Dad likes Teddy Grahams?"

"Um-hum," Bryan said and smiled so much like Tracy it scared him.

"Well, let's have a bowl," and Tracy poured two identical bowls.

Bryan looked at him. "You gave me too much boy."

Tracy laughed, because that was something he would have said. "Well, one day you'll be able to finish a bowl that size. Until then, do what you can."

"Alright," Bryan said, and the brothers ate their chocolate bears and watched TV.

After they finished, Bryan went down to the basement to play on his drum set. This made Tracy realize his new little brother was in tune with music. Tracy always played something in school, from his clarinet to his trumpet, and then the Sousaphone. When Bryan came back, the last revelation cinched it.

"What's that music?" little Bryan asked.

Tracy was on the living room couch watching "The Blob", the way he did with Vera when he was little. Bryan came and sat next to him.

"Are you sure you want to watch this old movie?" Tracy asked.

"I don't know," little Bryan asked. "What's it about?"

"Well, it's about this big blob of jelly that runs around town scooping up people."

"Can't they eat their way out?"

"It's too much jelly for them," which was good enough for Bryan.

So Tracy made them popcorn. As the movie progressed and the music intensified, Bryan grabbed a pillow and nestled beside Tracy.

"What's the matter?" Tracy asked.

"I'm scared," little Bryan said.

"It's just music," and then Tracy realized he could finally say what he was thinking. "And remember, Dad says we are to rebuke the spirit of fear, in Jesus' name."

"That's right," Bryan said, and grabbed a pillow for his big brother.

"What's this for?" Tracy asked.

"Because you're scared too," and Tracy knew he had a new home, and a new brother. Then, Tracy spent the next two years in high school, and continued visiting his father's family during the summers.

After Tracy graduated high school another curtain opened. Once the pink champagne was popped, it was impossible to put back in the bottle. Justin and Tracy had spoken at least once a month since they met at the Congressional Congress. In August, Tracy went to Connecticut for a week, and Justin picked him up at the airport.

Tracy had never been to New England, but he felt comfortable there. The family's large Tudor style house looked like a castle to Tracy. Justin's father was black, and owned the largest hearth store in the state. His mother was white, and was the first woman on the fire department, which inspired Tracy.

During his visit, Tracy also did things he had never done before. The two hopped a train to New York and saw the musical "A…My Name is Alice". They went to jai alai matches, and drove to Mystic to eat pizza, long before the movie came out, because Justin wanted Tracy to see the New England coast. Toward the end of the week they borrowed a bike from a friend. They rode into town to see a double matinee of 'red' movies: "Red Dawn" and "Red Sonja". When they got back they were exhausted, sore, and both took showers. Before they dressed, they stayed in Justin's bedroom, deciding whether to take a nap or eat something.

"That was quite a ride," Justin said. "I hope I don't get a cramp."

"I know just the thing for cramps," Tracy said.

"What's that?" Justin asked.

"It's a massage technique we learned in Wu Shu class," Tracy explained.

"Does it work?" Justin asked

"Lay down face down, and you tell me."

"Whoa," Justin exclaimed. "Not so hard!"

"Sorry," Tracy said. "I guess we're used to it."

Tracy eased off and Justin felt better. A few minutes went by, and Justin suddenly jumped off the bed with his back to Tracy.

"Did you hear that?" Justin asked, and went to the window to look.

"Hear what?" and Tracy quickly sat up on the bed.

"Did you hear that dog barking?"

"No," Tracy said, and looked at Kato. The German shepherd still lay peacefully on the floor. Tracy figured if a dog barked Kato would have at least looked up, but Justin kept looking out the window.

"Are you naïve?" Justin asked.

"No, I'm not naïve," Tracy said.

"You don't even know what that means, do you?" Justin said, half joking. Tracy did, but wanted to see where this was going. Justin's bookshelf was in his closet. He went to it, picked up his dictionary as he kept his back turned, and looked the word up.

"Naïve," Justin recited. "A person showing a lack of experience; innocent or trusting," and the statement lay on the floor for a moment before Justin continued.

"I really have a strong affection for you Tracy," Justin said, and replaced the dictionary. "But I don't want that to ruin our friendship."

"I understand," Tracy replied. "I have a strong affection for you too."

"No, I mean a really strong affection," and Justin turned around, and his excitement was clearly visible through his underwear.

"Me too," Tracy said, and stood to reveal himself. Justin came over and kissed Tracy, which was returned. Then Justin looked at Tracy to read his expression.

"Promise me," Justin said, "that whatever happens we will still be friends."

"I promise," Tracy said.

"Then let's go to bed, and maybe you'll feel differently in the morning." Justin decided.

"I don't think I will," Tracy said, and they went to bed. The next morning, Tracy didn't feel anything different except relief.

"Have you ever felt this way before?" Justin asked.

"Yeah," Tracy said. "All my life, but I never acted on it. Did you?"

"Yes, but it felt awkward," Justin said. "Did you ever read any books about it?"

"I read this one novel," Tracy admitted.

"Oh yeah? What book?" Justin asked.

"The Lord Won't Mind," Tracy said.

"By Gordon Merrick?" and Justin began to laugh.

"What are you telling me?" Tracy asked, astonished. Justin walked over to his bookshelf again.

"You mean this one?" Justin asked.

"This is really cool," Tracy shouted. "I can't believe you have it!"

"Have you read all three?" Justin asked. "This is one of a trilogy," and he led Tracy to the living room. Justin pulled out the other two books off and Tracy freaked out.

"You have these out in plain sight?" Tracy exclaimed.

"Sure," Justin said calmly. "My Mom read them too. She was helping me figure myself out. Although, she is probably more open to it than yours would be."

Tracy laughed. "You have no idea what would come out of my Mom's mouth, let alone Granny's."

"Well, Mom really likes you. My whole family does."

Tracy was still trying to process everything.

"In fact," Justin said. "We should talk to her about it," and Justin hesitated a little, "together."

After Tracy's initial shock they did, and the experience was different from anything Tracy had ever known. Justin's Mom suggested Tracy read the other books in Merrick's trilogy, and she was right, the books gave Tracy positive insight into himself and his sexuality. From then on Tracy knew he wanted to look for love, not just sex. Tracy also didn't hear anything from Him to the contrary, so it seemed the Lord didn't mind. Then it was time for Justin to take Tracy back to the airport. The two were off to start school at separate colleges, and they quietly contemplated that fact.

"So," Justin finally said. "You want to be mates?" and Tracy wondered what that meant, but it seemed appropriate he didn't exactly know. Then Tracy thought of N.C. State and Jean.

"Yeah," Tracy said. "At least until we get out of college, and we'll see where it goes after that," and Justin smiled because they were mates. Then Tracy put his hand on Justin's leg, and Justin reached down to hold Tracy's hand the rest of the way.

- Justin

Chapter 16

- Tracy at N.C. State

Between his visits with Justin, Tracy went to N.C. State for orientation with Granny, Jean, and Jean's Mom. Vera didn't go. She was fine with her son's decision once they smelled the magnolias, because Vera knew He was guiding him. The college orientation was ordinary enough to a point, with tours and long meetings that discussed enrollment. But on the last day the four went to the African Symposium, which was a meeting for black students and their families.

The freshmen were divided by curriculum. The engineering school had about one-hundred-and-fifty incoming freshmen of color. The black faculty introduced themselves, and discussed the black experience at N.C. State. Black fraternities were introduced, safe havens were discussed, and it wasn't uncommon for students to be called the N-word by students and faculty alike. The black faculty then listed names of professors who were known racists, described who to speak to if a new student was treated unfairly, and advised black students to be aware of their surroundings off campus.

Then they introduced a group of black upper classmen. It was explained that each new student would be teamed up with a mentor. They would guide the new student through their first semester, and help with tutoring. The new student was to check-in with their mentor at least once a week. If their mentor didn't hear from them after a few days they would reach out to find them, which was too much for Granny.

"Why the hell should my boy go here?" she yelled.

Another mother shouted, "Is it safe to send our kids here?"

Before uproar could start, the black faculty explained themselves.

"We know your concerns," the leader said. "Believe us, we know. But as difficult as it is for us, for you or your child, it will be ok. It is a fact some of them don't want us here, yet we're here, and we're staying."

"Will our kids graduate?" a mother asked.

"Yes. N.C. State is one of, if not *the* top engineering school in the U.S. That's why we're here, and yes it can be done, because we are graduates ourselves. N.C. State is how we got here."

After the meeting Jean's Mom confirmed this. There were a lot of systems in place, and her husband wouldn't support a bad school. But being a black student at N.C. State's Engineering School wasn't the most difficult part of college for Tracy - it was figuring himself out. Within the first month of classes, Tracy and Jean broke up, and it was mutual. They remained friends and soon, Jean dated the man she eventually married. Tracy also met a peer whose close friendship he treasured the rest of his life. It happened as Tracy prepared for his first test with a study group at a classmate's dorm. The rooms were in suites with a central study area.

Mid-way through the session, a stately man strode by. He was medium height with a barrel chest, and carried himself in impeccable manner. He wore everything Polo – his hat, coat, umbrella, briefcase and shoes. Looking more like a dandy than a sophomore, he was very dark, had a broad face, and sported a jerry curl as flawless as the rest of him. His walk was serious about success, yet he stopped short when he spotted the caramel stranger in the white study group. He looked at Jim - a small, energetic white guy with dirty blond hair, who obviously knew the gentleman.

"Hey Jim," the gentleman said. "I see you've got company," and his voice was quiet and confident, but with enough consonant emphasis to make you notice.

By the time Jim looked up, he was gone. He came back with two apples - one he was eating, and he held up the other and looked at Tracy.

"Do you want an apple?" the gentleman asked.

"Sure," Tracy answered, and the gentleman tossed the apple and Tracy caught it.

"Aren't ya gonna offer anybody else one?" Jim groused.

"No," the gentleman said, and returned to his room.

"Who's that?" Tracy asked, studying his apple.

"That's Todd," Jim said, and rolled his eyes. "He's a sophomore who lives two doors down."

"Huh," was all Tracy could say.

The study session ended and Tracy took his test, but Todd made an impression. Tracy thought Todd was empowering, and would be a great ally as an upper classman. Besides, Tracy needed a good friend, and it wasn't long before they were properly introduced. As Tracy and Todd's friendship grew, so did Tracy's success. Todd introduced Tracy to the black preppy culture of upperclassmen in the engineering school, and within months Todd gave Tracy a Swatch watch. Academically, Todd was an excellent role model, and Tracy observed his study habits carefully. As often as Tracy wanted to break loose and throw his books out the window, Todd helped keep him focused.

By the next year, Todd and Tracy had become such good friends they were roommates, and Jim lived down the hall. Todd and Tracy had their routine down, but one day Jim interrupted. The roomies were studying between classes midday, and Tracy was watching "ThunderCats". Todd allowed it, because Tracy was going to have to sit through two hours of "One Life to Live" and "All My Children". That's when Jim came in to talk.

"Hey Tracy," Jim said.

"Hey Jim, what's up?" Tracy said, who munched tortilla chips.

"I just wanted to hang," Jim said.

"That's cool," Tracy said. "Give me half-an-hour."

"Ok," Jim said. "I'll just sit here and be quiet," and he sat down on the couch, which annoyed Todd.

"Jim," Todd said. "Can you go back to your room and wait?"

"I'm not your company Todd," Jim stated. "I'm Tracy's," which made Todd get up.

"You should probably go," Tracy advised.

When Jim didn't leave, Todd went to physically eradicate Jim from the room. As Todd advanced, Jim backed into the sofa and pushed his feet out in self-defense.

"Don't touch me!" Jim screamed.

In a snap, Todd grabbed both of Jim's ankles in mid-kick, and lifted Jim to suspend him by his ankles. Because of the size difference Jim wasn't able to reach Todd, and Jim's arms and head easily cleared the floor.

"Put me down!" Jim yelled.

"Not yet," Todd said, and carried Jim out of the room.

Then Todd went down the hall with Jim dangling by his feet. He went into Jim's room where he instructed Jim's roommate: "Keep your trash in your own room," Todd said, dropped Jim on his head and left.

In the meantime, Justin and Tracy managed to keep seeing each other through their first year of college. They met secretly during breaks and scattered weekends, but it was no way to live. After Jean, other girls approached Tracy. He wanted to change and 'be normal', but Tracy knew that wasn't his path. Tracy also didn't want to mess up anyone else's life, or involve anyone in a falsehood, so Tracy kept dating Justin. Then, before he knew it, Tracy went home for the summer and resumed his paid internship at IBM. There he met Pete, who inadvertently made Tracy fully deal with his sexuality.

Pete was a computer science engineer who went to school in Cincinnati. He was from Charleston, but because of the Kanawha River and economic boundaries, he and Tracy had never met. But Pete was confirmation for Tracy. He was the first peer Tracy met from West Virginia who had a promising future, a serious manner, was white and gay. Pete was a year older than Tracy, had a handsome face, black feathered hair and a rugged body. He also had an abnormally low voice Tracy thought was sexy. Pete's father was president of the Chamber of Commerce and Wealth for the state of West Virginia, and lived in a grand house atop a steep hill overlooking the city.

The house had wide double front doors made of thick mahogany. Pete rang the bell, and opened both doors to reveal a cobblestone floor across a broad foyer. At the end was a swooping staircase with mahogany steps and matching railing. But everything else - the walls, trims and balustrades were shellacked white. The kitchen and dinette were hidden to the left, but the entrance to the living room was open. The long room of sofa sets went the length of the house, and was guarded by a full suit of armor holding a lance.

"His name is Lance," Pete told Tracy, "for obvious reasons."

At the end of the immense foyer was the formal dining room. Its entrance was tucked under the staircase landing. From it, a woman looking 'all the world' like "Auntie Mame" appeared. She wore an elegant gown and had a short hairstyle she changed frequently. Her cocktail glass clinked delightfully as she flowed down the length of the foyer, which unmistakably held a vodka tonic.

"Come in, come in," Betty sang, enthusiastically drunk.

"Mom, this is Tracy," Pete said.

"I know, I know!" she confirmed. "My name is Betty, and I feel I know you already!" and she hugged Tracy before twirling off into the living room, probably meaning to go to the kitchen.

"This is normal," Pete assured. "We do this all the time. You wanna beer?"

Tracy had never been offered a beer upon meeting someone's mother. However, he was about to get drunk with all of them.

"You need help with dinner?" Pete asked loudly.

"No honey," Betty yelled through the house, and she had almost found the kitchen. "I've got everything under control."

"Where's Dad?" Pete hollered.

"He's at a meeting," Betty said. "Or upstairs, or doing something."

But Betty didn't have anything under control. Her roast was in the oven hours later. By that time, Tracy had met Pete's father, John. Appropriately enough, he was an amiable bear of a man that looked 'all the world' like "Beauregard Burnside", and his personality filled his enormous house. Betty and John loved Pete and his gay self, which astounded Tracy. Just like Justin's parents, Betty and John loved Tracy at first sight too, and he was instantly part of the family.

In fact, later that July, Pete invited Tracy to watch the fireworks because he had an excellent view from the manse's roof atop the hill. Pete said it would just be the two of them, so Tracy went in shorts and carried a six-pack of beer for Pete. When he arrived, Tracy found out that Betty and John were hosting their annual Fourth of July bash. There was a string quartet at the formal garden party, along with the Mayor, and fifty members of the Chamber of Commerce and Wealth.

"Shouldn't we go in through the side door?" Tracy asked.

"Nah," Pete said, "let's take a look at this before we go to the roof."

However, Betty instantly spotted Tracy and grabbed him, and took off into the fray with Pete in tow. When she reached the back colonnade, she spun them around to face her elegant guests.

"Ladies and gentlemen," she bellowed, and the strings halted, and the company stopped. They turned to Betty in her pink sequined gown, which matched her 'Rose Kennedy' – a vodka soda, with a whisper of cranberry.

Then she proudly raised her glass to Pete and Tracy, who both looked 'all the world' like Mame's young ward, standing in their shorts and T-shirts, except they were the interracial version.

"This is my adopted son Tracy," Betty exclaimed with bravado. "Who is Pete's *very* close friend," which, appropriately enough, was followed by applause.

Now, as they waited for dinner, Tracy, Pete and his parents played scrabble on the dining room table. Betty may have been an absent-minded cook, but she was slaughtering them at scrabble. John went on about their vacations, and how much he loved the month they spent in Canada, or their month in Hawaii, or Africa.

'Who spends a month on vacation anywhere,' Tracy thought. 'Let alone on that many continents.'

Then, somehow the conversation turned to how Pete came out.

"Oh you were a mess dear," Betty said, "but then, so was I at first."

"It's true," Pete admitted. "It was finals week, and I was under intense pressure. I was on the brink of suicide," and there was a sobering silence. "I had to do something to relieve the anxiety. So I called home, and I told Mom I was gay."

Then, no one said anything. Betty moved a few scrabble pieces around, and John traded in a few pieces for his turn.

"So what happened?" Tracy asked.

"Oh," Betty realized. "Finally I said, 'Well, I don't understand why you have to decide anything right now. Why don't you finish college, and then decide?'" which made Pete and his parents laugh like they did that night. That was the statement that broke the ice so everything was out in the open, and they could deal with the issue.

"Then my mother turned gay," Pete said.

Tracy was caught unawares. "What?"

"Yessiree," Betty trilled. "I sure did. I joined PFLAG. I went to all the meetings, read the books, and I bought the T-shirts – all of them."

Tracy didn't know such an organization existed. As Betty explained about the gay parent group, Tracy marveled, and was shocked to meet a second family so at ease with their son's sexuality. Justin's parents were liberally progressive just by being a mixed-race family. But Betty and John were white civic leaders of the capital of West By God Virginia, who just happened to have a gay son. Then Betty turned to Tracy to ask.

"Have you told your Mom?"

"No," Tracy said sheepishly.

"Well," Betty said. "You should. It'd do everybody good. And if it doesn't work out, well, you can just move in here because you're family."

"I should probably start with Granny and Moody," Tracy decided, and the next evening he did. They three had finished dinner but no one was talking, not even Granny.

"Tracy," Moody said. "It seem's like somethin's on your mind. What's goin' on? You seem kinda heavy."

Tracy and Moody sat at the Formica kitchen table in the meridian blue kitchen, and watched the tiny TV. Granny was at command central in her recliner, hoping the phone would ring. She watched TV past Moody's head, and pretended not to be listening.

"I have something to tell you," Tracy said.

"Uh-oh," Moody replied. "Sounds like one of *those* conversations."

Moody backed his wheelchair up, and got his moonshine from under the sink. Tracy got the glasses and the ceremony started, but this was the first time Tracy had called it. Moody poured the shot. They did the first one 'medicinal' before Moody poured the second.

"An' we'll just sip this one," Moody confirmed.

Granny started smoking heavily, which made Tracy more nervous. But after some introductory small talk, he came out with it.

"I'm gay," Tracy stated.

"We ain't raise you like that," Granny exploded.

"Aw shit Jackie," Moody gruffed. "If ya can't handle the conversation get the hell outa the room!"

Technically, she wasn't in the room, but Granny stormed off to the side bedroom 'mumblin', stompin' and puffin'. Then she kept an ear close to the wall.

"Is she gonna be alright?" Tracy asked.

"Yep," Moody said. "This ain't new. We saw this conversation comin'," and Tracy was shocked. "We were waitin' for you."

"You're not surprised?" Tracy asked.

"No," Moody said, and sipped.

"You're not disgusted?" Tracy asked.

"No," Moody said. "This ain't my first time 'round the barnyard. I saw plenty of things during the war. Met all kinds a people, some like that. An' with all those differences, in the end we were all decent men, mostly, an' we got the job done."

"So it's ok?" Tracy asked.

"We just wanted to know that you were comfortable," Moody said. "We want ya to be happy, an' we don't want ya to be alone."

"I believe I'm ok Pawpaw," Tracy said. "I can't explain it, but I don't feel I'm making a wrong move."

Then Moody shifted gears. As he did, Tracy thought of Great Pawpaw Moody, and the fact that Moody was also a preacher's kid.

"What does your imaginary friend say about this?" Moody asked.

Tracy knew but listened. His eyes darted back and forth, and Moody waited. Then Moody saw his boy hear Him, and Tracy looked back at Moody.

"He said His grace is sufficient for me," Tracy repeated, and Tracy listened again and looked forward. "He said He would reveal His grace on the subject later," Tracy reported, "and that was all I need to know about it." Tracy paused. "And that I should be at peace," and Tracy looked forward again, and then back to his grandfather. "That's all He said Pawpaw."

Moody smiled and sat back, because he knew Tracy had His guidance. Then Moody thought of Granny and poured two more.

"We might wanna gulp these," Moody said, and they did another shot. "Your grandmother and I talked about this earlier. As long as you're comfortable with it, an' you know where you're headed, it's alright with me."

Tracy felt a relief he hadn't known since he sat on His lap looking at the picture book, because it was going to be all right. Then Moody got serious again, adjusted himself in his chair, and leaned toward Tracy.

"I just have two requests," Moody said.

Tracy leaned in too, because clearly a deal was about to go down.

"Now, this is no different than with all Jinny's girls," Moody said. "Number one is, we want to meet all your friends, an' everyone ya date."

The smoke had stopped billowing from the bedroom, and Granny was unusually quiet. Moody looked around and came in closer.

"Number two," Moody stated. "We raised you to be a man, an' we expect ya to find one, since a woman isn't your prerogative," and Moody stopped.

They both thought they heard Granny's slippers trying to glide through the living room undetected. Moody hunkered down farther.

"Which means this… Please don't bring home any queenie guys," and with that terminology, Moody let out a low chuckle.

"Aw shit," Granny muttered from around the corner.

"Jackie," Moody yelled. "Shut the hell up! This conversation's over."

With the backing of Moody, Tracy was set free to put himself first, and was released to be who he was born to be. Tracy still knew he needed to find out who he was with integrity, but he didn't need to date another girl, or worry about seeming 'normal', or care about who knew except for one.

"Now, you better tell your Momma," Moody said. 'Cause this secret's strong - it could carry your Granny away if it's not out by sundown tomorrow."

"No worries," Tracy said, and for the first time in a long time, he had none. The next day, Tracy called Vera during her lunch break and told her.

"Mom," Tracy said. "Why are you crying?"

"I just don't want you to be alone," Vera sobbed. "All the gay people I know are lonely. I don't want you to end up that way - alone and unhappy."

Tracy didn't know what to say, and Vera tried to compose herself.

"Are you seeing anybody?" Vera asked.

"Yeah," and he realized he had never been asked that before.

"Who?" Vera said, clearing up.

"Justin," and it was a warm feeling for Tracy to tell his mother that.

Vera laughed a little. "Justin is gay?"

"Of course he's gay Mom," Tracy said, although Justin could be very professional, polite and the perfect diplomat.

"Well, that's a relief," Vera said, and Tracy felt the weight lift from both their shoulders. "In fact that's wonderful," Vera decided, and his Mom sounded joyful because her boy wasn't alone. "Can he come home for Christmas?" Vera asked, and Tracy thought he heard her smile.

"I'll ask," Tracy said, and they both wiped their tears.

Chapter 17

- Todd and Sabrina

"Are you on drugs or something?" Todd asked.

"What do you mean?" Tracy asked innocently.

Todd asked because Tracy returned to N.C. State a different person, sporting a high top fade with a wedge swoop. Tracy had decided to tell Todd he was gay, which didn't seem a hard sell. Todd's closet was stocked with Polo from underwear to tie pins, but he beat Tracy to the punch. During Tracy's first class, Todd picked the lock to the trunk in Tracy's closet. That wasn't difficult, although it took Todd a few minutes to decipher Tracy's diary. Todd was studying codes, but Tracy had turned his diary sideways, wrote his letters in capitals down the page akin to Chinese, and wrote from the left side of the page.

"You seemed different from last spring," Todd continued, "so I had to find out. I hope you won't be mad, but I broke into your trunk and read your diary."

"Was it interesting?" Tracy asked.

"Yes," Todd said, but wanted to say '*extremely* interesting', and Tracy wasn't mad. However, from this point on, Tracy stopped keeping a diary on paper and began one in his head. The first entry was when Todd pulled a small package from his desk drawer.

"But to make amends, I got you this," and Todd handed it to Tracy. He opened his second Swatch watch from Todd and smiled. Then Tracy turned the tables, because Todd's gift now seemed suspect in terms of Todd's sexuality.

"Todd," Tracy asked, "are you gay?"

"Yes," Todd said, "but I don't let it rule my life."

"How long have you known?"

"All my life, and I went through a dark period. But then I realized I wasn't that one-dimensional. I made up my mind it wouldn't dictate my life, and it doesn't."

"I knew I could tell you, and I would have…" Tracy said, "but I feel better that you know."

"I just don't get caught up in all the drama. We are still black men, and we have to be role models."

"I understand, but I guess I don't have to lie about seeing 'Stephanie' in New York ever again."

"No, and Justin sounds like a great guy who has things going on."

"He does," Tracy agreed. "Mom wants him to visit over Christmas."

"That's great Tracy, but what are you doing for Thanksgiving?"

"I'm not sure. What did you have in mind?"

"I think I want you to meet my parents," Todd said, and thought about it more. "Yes, and my friend Sabrina. I've known her all my life, and we're very close."

"I have a friend like that named Tori. Her Mom is Mom's best friend, Momma Ro."

"Do they know you're gay?"

"No, but Momma Ro probably does by now. Does Sabrina know?"

"No," Todd hedged, "or my parents. I'm not going to tell anyone until after I graduate." Tracy was skeptical. "I want to concentrate on my degree, and then I'll go there," Todd explained.

"Ok, I can deal with that," Tracy said.

"Do you still want to meet my parents and Sabrina?"

"Sure," Tracy said, and they did.

Todd grew up a few hours from campus. Now that Tracy was legal age, they took road trips on weekends. Todd's parents 'loved them some Tracy'. Sabrina and Tracy also became two peas in a pod, and the three had a blast dancing at the straight nightclubs. Then, after finals, Justin came to D.C. over Christmas break and Vera was delighted. On Friday night, Tracy and Justin went to D.C.'s oldest black gay bar. It was the first time Tracy had been there, or anywhere as gay man in D.C.

But as the couple made their way through a crowded corridor, Tracy heard a familiar voice. He turned and looked, but Justin stopped.

"I thought you've never been out in D.C.?" Justin shouted above the music.

"I haven't," Tracy said, and then he saw her. She had strawberry-blond hair, wore a red leotard onesie with a wide black leather belt ala Cindy Lauper, and was carefully balanced on black pumps. Tracy checked again to make sure, and then tapped her on the shoulder.

"Sabrina?" Tracy asked.

Sabrina whirled around and looked as if she'd seen a ghost. "Tracy! How ya doin'?"

"I'm…" Tracy started.

"Is Todd with you?" she asked in a panic, and scanned the crowd behind Tracy.

"No," Tracy said. "This is my boyfriend, Justin."

"Oh. Of course, of course," Sabrina stammered. "I just didn't know if Todd came with you too."

"You mean Todd doesn't know you're gay?" Tracy asked, although Sabrina's look was enough. Even though she and Todd had known each other since Kindergarten and both were gay, neither had come out to the other. So Tracy took Sabrina's hand, leaned in and spoke in her ear.

"I understand," Tracy said. "That's a secret best kept for the right moment," and Sabrina backed up to look at Tracy in the eye. "And it's yours to tell," but it wasn't.

Fast forward: Todd's college graduation:

Tracy made a special trip down from West Virginia in his Fiat. After Todd walked across the stage with his degree, Todd's parents came and went. The next day the three went to dinner to celebrate - Todd, Sabrina and Tracy. As they sat and made idle chitchat, Tracy was about to pop. Twenty-four hours had passed since Todd had graduated, and no one had dropped a hint about where they might go out after dinner. Tracy had decided three-and-a-half years of silence was enough, so he stood up.

"I have to go to the bathroom," Tracy said. "But before I go, I would like both of you to know something. I have been clubbing with both of you separately, and I'm tired of this. Tonight I want to have a good time with both of you."

Todd and Sabrina stared at the tablecloth in shock.

"So here's your topic," Tracy announced, and hit the table sternly three times. "You're both gay. Please discuss amongst yourselves," and he twirled with a flourish, and went to the men's room.

Now, after Tracy and Justin's visit with Vera for Christmas, New Years came and went. Then a series of events began to unfold that threatened to change the course of Tracy's life. At the end of the week, Tracy planned to drive back to N.C. State. By this time, Granny had gotten too many tickets in the Daytona. She traded it in for a Dodge Conquest, which wasn't really her cup of tea. The upshot was that Tracy took Granny's new Conquest to college.

However, the weather wasn't looking great in terms of ice. Vera worried about Tracy driving back to Raleigh by himself, and she suggested Justin drive with Tracy. She offered to pay the difference if Justin changed his plane ticket from D.C. The deal was done because Justin had something on his mind. The next day the couple was off to go back to their respective colleges, but Justin waited until they crossed the North Carolina line as Tracy drove.

"Tracy," Justin said. "We need to talk about something."

"Shoot," Tracy said.

The particulars to Tracy were a blur. In a nutshell, Justin tried to explain why he couldn't be gay anymore. He was studying business and political science, and at the time, Justin decided he needed a wife to have a political career.

"That goes against everything you believe in," Tracy said.

"I know," Justin said. "That's what my Mom and Dad said too."

"You, of all people," Tracy cried, "are the last one I thought would want to live a lie."

"I know." Justin said, "but I've started my internships and I see how things are done." Tracy stayed silent. "I just know this is what I'm supposed to do. I am a politician."

"Not a very good one for me right now," Tracy blurted out. "Not very convincing," and he began to seethe. "And you've known this whole time? We just spent our whole break together!"

"But I wanted to," Justin said, and he was honest. "I just know my career is more important, and I should make a clean break now." Tracy thought of Todd and his resolve, and drove through his pain. "You're not mad at me, are you?"

"I understand your reasons," Tracy admitted. "It just doesn't seem ethical. And yes, I'm mad at you, but I won't stay mad because I promised we would always be friends," and they did stay friends, but they were mates no longer.

As it turned out, Justin became a politician without ever getting a wife. He also raised two children. When his aunt and uncle died of cancer within a year of each other, Justin adopted their barely teenage boys. Among his other accomplishments in business and civic organizations, Justin served for a time as the country's only openly gay black state legislator.

But when Tracy dropped Justin off at the airport, it was the dead of winter. In his mind, Tracy thought he and Justin were going to college together, even though they attended schools in different states. Now that they weren't everything was changed, although Tracy wasn't totally alone when he returned to N.C. State.

"You're depressed," Todd said. "Here, this will bring you out of it really fast."

He tossed Tracy a small package. It was obviously Tracy's third Swatch watch, and it did help. In time Tracy snapped out of his funk, and was 'dancin'' and 'clubbin'' between 'studyin''. Then came a misstep that further complicated Tracy's life, and the dark saw how to use pride and manipulation to steer Tracy farther from his trajectory.

In February, Tracy had a term paper to write, so he didn't go dancing with Todd and Sabrina on Friday night. Instead, Tracy did his laundry as he worked, which he usually did with Todd. Because he was alone, Tracy met a cute and chatty fellow who put his things in the dryer next to his. Now that he was single, Tracy became interested.

The conversation inevitably turned to Krispy Kreme donuts, and, even though the roads were icy the two went clear across town to get some. After sliding down a hill the car went over a curb and into a tree. Tracy managed to get the car home at the end of the semester, but the wrecked car was all the ammo Granny required.

She had acted up since Tracy and Justin broke up. As far as Granny was concerned, the honeymoon was over with the 'gay thing'. She went on the warpath, and the Conquest was the first thing she could withhold to try and run Tracy's life. By this time, Granny had her Oldsmobile 98. The Dodge Daytona turned Conquest was actually Tracy's high school graduation gift.

But, when Tracy returned after the accident, Granny announced Tracy wasn't allowed to use 'his' car - it was to stay parked in her driveway.

"But it's still your car," Granny stated, "an' you have to keep up with the payments."

"So my graduation gift comes with strings, is that it?" Tracy asked, and he let belligerence well up. "How is this different than Bobby not lettin' me use his cars? It's not. It's just plain manipulation, which is why you bought me a car I didn't want in the first place - so you could show off."

Granny was silent and became more resolved.

"Just to make this plain," Tracy said. "I have to pay for my car, but I can't use it?"

"As long as you're in this house," Granny said.

"You shouldn't a said that," Moody mumbled.

Granny turned in a snap. "What?"

"You'll see," Moody said, and wheeled himself off into his room.

But Moody didn't want Tracy to move out and let pride have its chance. While Moody was incensed at Granny's conniving, he had no way to stop her. Moody knew he had to let it play out, which it did at the 'meetin' with the sink cabinet open.

"Aw come on boy," Moody coaxed. "You should stay an' fight this." and Tracy looked at his old friend. "Come on," Moody said with a whisper and a wink. "Don't leave me alone with her."

Tracy relented. "No worries Pawpaw, I'll take the bus to work," which he did. But in July, Beth, from Tracy's steakhouse days, made a date with Tracy to see a movie and picked him up.

"An' don't worry T," Beth said. "I'll get you back by eleven."

Tracy was shocked. "What are you talking about?"

"I know Granny's got you on curfew," Beth said, " an' I assured her when I called the other day."

Tracy knew nothing of this, because he was always home before the bus stopped running at eleven. But that was it - the damage was done. By August, Tracy decided he wasn't going back to N.C. State. He thought the school was too big, too competitive, and Tracy wasn't going to be caught in North Carolina without a get-away car.

Instead, Tracy found a roommate who lived on the bus route, and he moved out from under Granny's thumb. Then, Tracy transferred to West Virginia Tech in Montgomery, West Virginia, which triggered the next succession of events. When Todd found out, he drove up from North

Carolina to take Tracy back with him. When that didn't work, Granny decided stronger measures were necessary. She arranged a pow-wow with Vera and Tracy's father, but Tracy wasn't invited - he was abducted. He got the call Saturday morning.

"Good morning son," Harry said.

"Hey Dad," Tracy answered. "What are you up to?"

"Well, I'm supposed to pick you up."

"Pick me up for what?" Tracy asked.

"Your Granny called me and your mother into town to have a meeting," Harry said.

"Oh," Tracy said defiantly. "I get it," and Harry laughed quietly.

"She didn't tell you?"

"Nope."

"It sounds like I might know where this is going. I'll pick you up at your apartment in two."

"Ok," Tracy said, and began to panic. Tracy had told everyone he was gay except his father, and he wasn't sure how that fit in with the church, or his father's take on everything.

"Son?" Harry interrupted.

"Yeah Dad."

"I need to know the address of your apartment."

"Oh yeah," Tracy said, "and I'll be ready in two hours."

When everyone arrived at Starling Drive, Granny had her war-room setup. She sat in command central by the phone, put Vera and Harry on the couch, and Tracy sat in the corner recliner. Moody was in the opposite corner and watched, and it was odd to say the least. Vera and Harry rarely had pleasant experiences in Granny's living room.

A few years earlier, they had come for Tracy's graduation when, with the exception of Bobby, everyone was proud and tripped over each other with pleasantries. But this time was more like when Vera and Harry were teenagers, when they sat on the very same couch and Granny went to get her shotgun.

But Tracy's parents thought their son was in trouble, so they kept quiet. The first thing out of Granny's mouth was to announce that Tracy was gay, and that was why he was ruining his life. The second thing was her reason for taking Tracy's car away, which was because he was gay, which was ruining his life. The third thing was about him dropping out of college, which, was because he was gay, which was ruining his life.

This went on for a while, but Tracy got in a few points about why he didn't want to go back to N.C. State. He was still a junior in college at a reputable school, but the car issue was unacceptable. Besides, it was Granny's manipulation that caused Tracy to move out and live his own life in the first place.

Finally, Tracy's father had had enough. After all, this was the woman who threatened him with false rape charges. Granny was also the one who came between him and Vera in the first place, and Harry was not going to allow Granny to treat his son the same way. So, Harry reached into his suit jacket and pulled out his checkbook.

"How much is the balance on the car?" Harry asked.

"What?" Granny asked, dumbfounded.

"It seems the car is the issue," Harry said. "So, what is the balance due on the car?"

"I don't know," Granny lied. Suddenly, Granny was a lone warrior at her own pow-wow, and Harry knew how to end it.

"You must have a bill," Harry said, "or a payment book."

"I got it," Moody said, somehow without a snicker as he wheeled himself into his room.

Moody came back and read off the amount owed on the Conquest, and Harry wrote out the check.

"Now," Harry said, "you can pay off the car, and put it in Tracy's name."

Granny bristled. "I'm not puttin' it in his name, that's *my* car!"

Harry wrote the check, tore it out of his checkbook and held it up. "You will put the car in my son's name."

"To hell I will," Granny said, and with that, Harry carefully folded the check in half, put it back in his checkbook, collected his things and showed himself out. Tracy met Harry at his car.

"Dad," Tracy began, but his father cut him off.

"Don't worry son," Harry said. "I've seen your Granny do this before."

Tracy was surprised there was no mention of his sexuality, but was glad. "What about the car?"

"Well, it's seems pretty clear you're Granny wants to keep her car."

"I guess she does," Tracy guffed, proud of his father.

"But you need one, so find yourself something for a thousand dollars," and Harry reached into his jacket pocket again. Then he wrote out another check and handed it to Tracy.

"Stay in touch," Harry said, and hugged Tracy. "And remember, I love you son, no matter what," and he got in his car and left.

The fight was over, the pow-wow was ended, and Tracy bought himself a 1980 blue Fiat Brava. More importantly to Tracy, his father came through for him, even with the knowledge that he was gay. Tracy felt relief, and that he had reached another level of independence, but the arc of his trajectory had seriously been altered. At the moment, it was a comfort to Tracy that he left N.C. State, and had made a u-turn to West Virginia. But God's plans hadn't changed, so Tracy wouldn't be comfortable there for long.

Chapter 18

- Vera, on her yacht

During the summer of Granny's drama, Tracy worked at IBM with Pete. Tracy had returned to West Virginia alone - much like "Auntie Mame" constantly returned to Beekman Place without a man. As Tracy was now an eligible bachelor, he and Pete dated. By the end of the summer, Pete suggested Tracy transfer to Cincinnati instead of continuing at West Virginia Tech, but Tracy wasn't sure that was his path. Besides, Tracy thought, Cincinnati was only a two-hour drive. Pete also came home often, and took care of the manse while Betty and John were off somewhere actually traveling with Mame.

Moody liked the match because Pete enjoyed being gay while not embracing the stereotype. Moody also liked how Tracy talked about Pete. However, it was Pete's actions that spoke volumes. Once the fall semester began, Pete and Tracy couldn't see each other until fall break. By then, Tracy was so revved to see Pete he locked himself out of his Fiat Brava. Pete was waiting for Tracy in Charleston. The plan was for Tracy to go home and they would go to dinner. Instead, Pete got a phone call.

"Where are you?" Pete asked with his deep voice.

"I'm still at school," Tracy said. "I was in a hurry, and I locked my keys in the car."

"I'll be in Montgomery in an hour," Pete decided.

"Are you sure?"

"Yeah, I got this."

"But I already called Granny, and Moody was gonna come up."

"Not to worry," Pete assured. "Call Granny and tell her you're fine, and you're staying with me."

"What about dinner?"

"Get yourself changed. That way you'll be ready to go to dinner by the time I get there."

"Ok," Tracy said, because now the circumstance sounded like an adventure rather than an inconvenience. Within the hour, Pete drove up in his 1984 black Toyota MR2. He hopped out like Bond when he drove the Lotus Esprit submarine in the "Spy Who Loved Me", only Pete wore dark sunglasses even though the sun was almost set.

"Where's you're car?" Pete asked.

Tracy pointed. "What are you gonna do?"

"Get a new set of keys made," Pete said, popped the trunk, and pulled out his toolbox and Slim Jim.

"How you gonna do that?" Tracy asked as they walked to his Fiat.

"Stand back," Pete said with a smile, "and time me."

Without rolling up his sleeves, Pete popped the door open with the Slim Jim and got a screwdriver. In three minutes, he had the steering column free, had pulled it out and laid it on a pre-placed piece of cardboard in his trunk.

"You're scaring me," Tracy said, but he loved it. "How do you know how to do that?"

Pete just smiled, gathered his tools, and threw Tracy's book-bag in his trunk. "How'd I do?"

Tracy looked at his Swatch. "Five minutes."

"Not too bad," Pete said.

Then they hopped in the MR2 and in Tracy's mind, sped off as the orchestra reached the crescendo of 007's theme music.

"What do we do now?" Tracy asked.

"We're going to dinner, and then a movie as planned," Pete said. "Then you're staying with me at the house. John and Betty are in Tonga. Tomorrow we'll get the keys made."

After breakfast, Pete and Tracy went to Judy's Locksmith and got the serial number off the steering column. Within half an hour the keys were made, and an extra set for Pete. By midmorning, they were back at Tracy's car where Pete re-installed the column. They were back in Charleston by noon and after lunch, they went by Moody's garage, and he checked that the Fiat's column was solid.

"Yep," Moody said. "You boys are ready go. So where ya headed?"

"Pete has some electrical work to do at the house," Tracy said.

"Yeah," Pete said. "I need to show him how to change the ballasts in the kitchen lights, and a few fuses need replacing," Then Pete shook Moody's hand. "I'll bring him back tomorrow Mr. Moody."

Yep, Moody 'liked him some Pete'. He wasn't a 'queenie guy', and after that episode, Pete was Tracy's knight in shining armor.

Then, things got harder over the next year, and darkness crept through the crevices. Tracy's transfer from N.C. State made him ineligible to continue his internship at IBM. The following summer, Tracy could only find a part-time job, which was a further defeat. Tracy's decreased cash flow convinced him to move back in with his grandparents. The move was also a blessing, because Granny needed more help with Moody. Then, life slowed to a lull. A season of quiet came over the three, as if God was preparing them for something. But as fall came, the quiet was stirred into aggravation.

Tracy's classes had suffered the past two semesters, and as Thanksgiving approached things came to a head. Tracy wasn't sure of the issue, but something was wrong with more than his grades. Granny and Moody argued all the time. Likewise, to Tracy, everything became difficult, sluggish and gloomy. Vera was coming for Thanksgiving because everyone was going to her house for Christmas, but even that was complicated. Bobby stirred the pot by buying a used van. He wasn't sure if it would make it from D.C., but he was hell-bent on driving it to West Virginia, and everything was strife.

"I don't see why he don't take the Lincoln," Granny groused.

On the day before Thanksgiving, Granny became more uncommonly bossy. She ran around the house cleaning and decorating at the same time. She wanted everything to be just right, but made everything all wrong. Moody stayed in his room, and wasn't to be trifled with. Tracy was outwardly quiet, but disturbed in his spirit. He spoke to God about it constantly, but He was silent too. Tracy kept praying and waited for an interruption, and kept asking if he was in the right place or not.

The next morning, Tracy sat in the kitchen and ate his cereal. Moody and Granny were still at it, and both talked to themselves with expletive pops. Most of the strife was unintelligible to Tracy. Moody stayed in his room and muttered, and Granny carried on in the kitchen as she made a pie.

When Moody finally came to get breakfast, Granny immediately turned and yelled at him. Moody yelled back, turned his wheelchair around, and finally said the first thing Tracy had understood in days.

"I'm gonna take care of this right now," Moody stated, and went back to his bedroom.

Granny continued muttering as she kneaded her dough. Then she threw the flour down before she kneaded the hell out of it again. She stood by the sink, and looked out the window with her back to the living room.

Then, Tracy and Granny heard the distinctive click of a gun barrel closing, and there was a pause. Tracy looked forward over his cereal bowl. Granny's cigarette smoking stopped, as did her pie making. As Granny looked into the living room her cigarette dropped into the sink. Almost simultaneously, Granny turned around with her pie dough in one hand, and a handful of flour in the other.

In the small diamond mirrors that went down the meridian blue walls, Tracy saw Granny scream as the dough flew behind his head. Granny followed with a lunge through the doorway, and left a cloud of flour in her wake. Then Tracy heard Moody's wheelchair tip over. His grandparents hit the floor with a thud that shook the house, and they wrestled to try and kill the other one first. Tracy jumped up, and once the flour fell, Tracy made out Moody's empty wheelchair tipped on its side with the top wheel spinning. Tracy couldn't tell where one ended and the other began, and Granny and Moody struggled too hard to make any noise. But the gun was thrown aside, so Tracy grabbed the phone and dialed Jinny and Alvin.

"You got to get up here," Tracy panted.

"What's wrong?" Jinny asked.

Alvin was already out the door and running from a block away.

"I don't know," Tracy said. "I've never seen this before," and he couldn't describe it. "I, I don't know," Tracy repeated, "but I can't do this."

In no time, Tracy saw his aunt and uncle come through the front door, and they managed to pull the two apart. Jinny got Granny to her room to get cleaned up, and Alvin got Moody back into his chair. They got the gun put away, and then, all four sat in the living room and wept quietly. Tracy felt removed as he watched them cry. He never found out what the fight was about, and Tracy never saw Moody and Granny do anything like it again.

Vera and Bobby arrived for Thanksgiving the next day, and it was as if nothing happened. Even more oddly, nothing was mentioned. Everything was perfectly lovely, just as Granny wanted before the mangled altercation. The following day, Tracy gave Vera a hug before she left. As she walked to Bobby's van, Tracy finally heard Him.

"O death, where is thy sting? O grave, where is thy victory?" He quoted.

'What does that mean?' Tracy thought.

"Look it up," He answered gently, *"and find Peace."*

Chapter 19

- Vera

When Tracy was in junior high, Vera took a trip to Nassau. She took the vacation as a gift for herself before her surgery - a routine hysterectomy that required a blood transfusion. That was how Vera contracted lupus. Subsequently, she lost her job and insurance. Then Vera was told she had three months to live, and she prepared to die. But the doctor who diagnosed Vera developed a soft spot for her.

Lupus was a relatively un-researched disease at the time. Her doctor decided to champion the effort to fight it. He refused to take another patient unless Vera was given a permanent job at the hospital. With his persistence, Vera got a job, and she got covered under the hospital's private insurance. After a few scares, Vera's doctor stabilized her condition, and she went into remission for eight years. Vera became her doctor's success story. He wrote about Vera in medical journals and books, and pushed for reforms in testing blood for lupus.

As for Vera, from the time of Granny Berger's death to Tracy's freshman year in college, she had worked herself up from an administrative assistant to the Director of the Radiology Department. Vera never missed a day of work, and became beloved by the entire hospital. After eight years, Vera's doctor decided it was safe for him to go on vacation. He took his family to Venice, and left his staff to keep an eye on Vera.

By this time, Vera and Bobby had lived in their split-level rancher for years, which was down the street from Momma Ro's. Vera was excited the whole family was coming, because Bobby's Christmas present to Vera was finishing off the basement. Vera decorated it to the nines and put up a huge tree. A few days before Christmas, Granny and Tracy drove the Oldsmobile to D.C.; and, even though Moody stayed home because of Bobby, the family had a lot of surprises lined up for Vera.

Jinny's middle girl, Mia, had her first child after her husband was transferred to Germany. Now that Mia's newborn was old enough, she planned to fly out from D.C. so Vera could meet her first great nephew. Freddie had joined the Army two years earlier. For his surprise, he flew in from Germany on leave for Christmas. When they drove to Dulles Airport, Tracy realized the timing was perfect.

As they dropped off Mia and her newborn, Freddie stepped off his plane and brought Vera to tears. Everything was aligned, the murk of Thanksgiving was replaced by blessings, and Tracy felt His nudge. The next day, the family went shopping at the mall. They went into a shoe store where the manager had forgotten to take old sale signs down before he put up new ones. This meant Granny got four pairs for the price of one, even with her odd feet. That night, Tracy, Freddie, Tori and Bunky went to the movies. It was the first time the four had been together since high school, and they acted like it watching "I'm Gonna Git You Sucka." Christmas morning was wonderful, and Vera's radiance out-shone any animosities from the past. Her entire family was in her new basement, and her children were grown and successful. Vera gave Tracy the new "Art of Noise" cassette, and a sweatshirt that spoke louder.

Earlier that fall, Bobby Brown came out with "My Prerogative". The song played non-stop in the gay clubs for obvious reasons. When Tracy opened his sweatshirt a peace came over him. The sweatshirt acknowledged his Mom wasn't afraid anymore, because she knew Tracy wouldn't be like the lonely gay people she had known.

Later that night, Tracy asked Granny if he could borrow her car and go out. He put on his new sweatshirt stating it was 'his prerogative', grabbed the keys and headed down the split-level's stairs. But when Tracy touched the doorknob, he got another nudge from Him.

"Goodnight," Tracy said. Vera and Granny chatted at the kitchen table.

Vera turned and said, "Goodnight honey."

Tracy opened the door and looked back at them. From the lower elevation and the lighting in the kitchen, the pair looked like they were on stage. With Freddie home and everyone together, Vera had a warm spotlight on her as she finished the dishes and got teacups. Tracy was moved and shut the door. Then he went back upstairs and gave Granny's keys back.

"Ain't ya goin' out?" Granny asked.

"I think I want to stay here with you," Tracy said.

So Granny, Vera and Tracy sat at the little round kitchen table into the wee hours. They ate cinnamon toast and sipped milk tea. As it happened, Vera had never heard Helen Keller jokes, and Tracy knew a lot of them. Vera laughed until she had to jump up, and bend to hold her nightgown in front of her.

"Stop it Trace!" she screamed, and ran down the hall giggling.

"You always could make your Momma wet her pants," Granny mused. "Just like that time with Freddie an' the cake batter."

"Yeah," Tracy smiled. "That was a good one."

When Vera returned she got more tea. Then Tracy re-enacted the childhood drama, pantomiming the beater licking, bowl sniffing, and the crime itself.

"Mom, when you saw Freddie with that batter all over his face," Tracy screamed, and the veins throbbed in his neck from laughing, "you fell on the floor, and laughed so hard you peed yourself!"

"I can't believe you remember so clearly," Vera said. "You two were so little," and she sighed. "I'm so proud of you, both you and Freddie, and I love you so very much," and Vera sipped her tea. "We've been through a lot, but we're still here."

The next day, Granny and Tracy left for West Virginia in the Oldsmobile, and it was an abnormally peaceful ride. Granny didn't even gripe about Tracy's speeding, because that antagonistic entity was nowhere to be found. The second day, Tracy unpacked the car, Granny did her laundry, and she checked that Moody had gotten enough to eat while they were gone. Then, Tracy and Moody had a recap with the sink door open. On the third day, Tracy got up and fixed Moody pancakes. It was an unusually warm and breezy day for December, and there was an uncommon dew on the grass like spring.

"What are ya doin' today?" Moody asked.

"I'm goin' over to Beth an' Aunt J's," Tracy said. "Aunt J is making mix-tapes for New Years, an' we're all gonna play Pictionary," and Tracy did.

After lunch the phone rang. Aunt J picked up the phone, but a strange expression overtook her face.

"Who is this really?" she asked. Then she called for Tracy. "It's your Granny," Aunt J said, "but she doesn't sound herself."

Tracy took the phone and it was Granny. She told Tracy his Mom was dead. Vera, the one Tracy had through it all was gone.

Selah.

It took thirty-minutes for all of them to get back to Granny's house. When they got there, Granny sat in the middle of the living room floor. Her legs were spread in a wide vee as she rocked back and forth, which made the phone line stretch and release from the kitchen wall.

"My baby just died," Granny sobbed, and repeated it over and over.

Tracy took the phone from her hand. "Who are you talking to?"

Beth and Aunt J got Granny into her recliner and got a cool towel.

"Hello?" Tracy said to the phone.

"Are you ok?" Justin asked.

"I guess," Tracy answered. "But how...?"

"I just happened to call," Justin said. "I had no idea."

"It's ok, neither did I," and Tracy couldn't go on.

"Are you alright?"

"Yeah - a little numb, but I'm not sure what's next."

"From talking to Granny, it sounds like you're going back to D.C."

"I haven't even unpacked."

"Can you pick me up at the airport in D.C.?"

"Sure," Tracy said, and was amazed at what a good friend he still had in Justin.

The next day Granny, Tracy, Jinny and Cuz Demi drove to D.C. in Granny's Oldsmobile. Alvin and Moody followed in the camper, because there was no way Moody was going to stay in Bobby's house, especially now that his daughter was dead. But the Oldsmobile was where the strategic planning went down. There were a lot of questions surrounding Vera's death. Her doctor had given Vera a clean bill of health before he left, and had systems in place in case anything happened. Bobby and Freddie were the only ones at home with Vera, and their stories didn't match. The plan was to separate the two from the 'git-go' and get each of them to say what happened, because even though it was awful to think about, Bobby's history was well known.

"Freddie will tell me the truth," Jinny decided.

"I could tell when Bobby was lyin' since the day I met him," Tracy said coldly.

As soon as they arrived, Jinny and Demi herded Freddie off into his room. Granny and Tracy took on Bobby, and the witnesses definitely told two different stories. Bobby's expression was also odd, because he looked scared and no one knew why. Freddie was also upset, but that made sense. It was his mother who died, and he was still pretty jet-lagged from his flight from Germany. The issue was that neither took the appropriate action.

Through the course of the night Vera passed out three times - two times from convulsions. Each time she woke Vera asked for more water, which was a clear sign something was wrong for someone with lupus. The odd thing was, both Bobby and Freddie said they went back to sleep after the first two episodes. Even though Vera didn't recognize them and she had more convulsions, they waited until morning to take her to the hospital. Even with that, they only called the ambulance because Vera had passed out on her way down the stairs.

By that time, Vera was so bloated Bobby and Freddie couldn't lift her, so they were forced to call the EMT's. To make matters worse, when Vera was finally admitted the doctors told Bobby to call the family in. That was at six-thirty in the morning, and Bobby didn't call Granny until one that afternoon.

"That's six-and-a-half hours," Tracy yelled, but Bobby could barely comprehend the issue.

"Granny an' I can get here easily in six," Tracy said. "Justin an' I have done it in four!"

"In whose car?" Granny demanded.

"Never mind!" Tracy cried.

He was incensed neither Bobby nor Freddie had called. He thought he could have gotten to D.C. to be with his mother before she died. Then, Tracy heard Him again, calmly, and as a gentle reminder:

"O Death, where is thy sting? O grave, where is thy victory?" He said softly, and Tracy was stopped.

Immediately, Tracy was made to understand injustice was done, but knew that it would be made right. He understood the unexplained was not understandable. Tracy also knew he could only be comforted by His presence, and could only find peace with the circumstance at His word.

The next day, Tracy picked Justin up at the airport. The following day, Justin helped Tracy get Moody up the stairs of the funeral home in his wheelchair. When Tracy entered the vestibule, Granny and Jinny were beside themselves.

"Tracy!" Jinny hissed. "You got to get in there!"

The door was locked to the chapel, and there was a woman sitting at a desk to the left of the door.

"Why?" Tracy asked.

"They're makin' the decision whether to have the casket open or closed," Jinny said.

Tracy looked through the small yellow-paned window in the chapel door, and only Freddie and Bobby were at the casket.

"You need to get in there an' have your voice heard!" Jinny exclaimed. "They're only lettin' in Bobby's immediate family."

Tracy knew to go over to the woman at the desk who was busy with her register.

"Excuse me," Tracy said. "I need to be let into the chapel."

The woman didn't look up. "You have to be immediate family."

With those words, something inside Tracy came through. Tracy hadn't felt this since He took control of his arm, and he drew the flowing wheat grass in the picture of the vision during art class. But this possession was different because it was urgent. Tracy was pushed aside - literally pushed out of his body. Then, Tracy watched Him while floating next to his body, and saw Him say these words through his mouth:

"I am the first-born," and His magnificence turned and winked at Tracy.

An immediate fear came over the woman. She wasn't old, but she got up slowly. She kept her eyes to the floor and knees bent as if prostrate, except she had to open the chapel door. She also trembled as she backed up, and was careful to stay facing Tracy. Eventually, the woman got the key into the lock and opened the door. He and Tracy passed through, and she shook as she closed and locked the door behind them.

"What did Tracy do to that woman?" Granny muttered.

"I can't rightly say," Jinny said as she stared.

Tracy stood inside the chapel. He looked down the aisle where Bobby and Freddie were by the open casket. Then Tracy got a frustrated feeling, because he didn't know what was about to happen. As Tracy walked, the aisle telescoped longer and longer, which made his mother seem farther away. Then a cloud enveloped Tracy, yet he saw through it like a ball of mist - or a fog that shimmered in the morning sun as it evaporated. But the cloud was bright from the inside. It was so bright it lit the room, and because the cloud was crystalline it made tiny rainbow prisms shoot out in every direction. Tracy turned around in awe, and the cloud disappeared as quickly as it had appeared.

'What just happened?' Tracy asked Him.

"That is Shekinah," He said. *"I will explain it to you later, but for now we will just have fun with it."*

Then, because he had turned around, Tracy saw Jinny's face pressed to the little yellow glass window with her hands cupped to see in. Tracy walked back to the chapel door in complete amazement.

"Did you just see that cloud?" Tracy asked.

"There ain't no cloud," Jinny said roughly. "Now get down there so we can git in."

Abruptly, Tracy turned and walked up the aisle to his Mom's casket. Freddie and Bobby were crying and Tracy looked in. Vera's ears were totally enclosed and undefined, which made her head twice its size. She had bruises where they tried to drain the fluid from her face. Septicemia had set in, which made her skin discolored and splotchy. But as Tracy looked at her, God allowed him to look beyond her physical appearance. Much like Tracy had just been out of his body, he saw Vera as she truly was - at rest and beautiful. Then he pulled a peach colored rose, Vera's favorite, from the arrangement next to the casket. He put the rose in her hair and said,

"You are my beautiful Lady."

After a moment Tracy turned, and he went back up the aisle to let in the rest of the family. After they closed the casket, Tracy put his mother's picture on top. It was the last picture taken of her, and Vera stood outside her church surrounded by her friends, and she was beautiful by any measure. She was the successful woman she dreamed of becoming so many years before, when she moved into the D.C. high-rise with her horrible husband and two toddlers.

That night, the tradition was for the entire family to gather. Everyone brought his or her choice of beer, wine, moonshine or smoke. They gathered to remember the person they were to bury the next day, and it didn't take long. Stories, funny stories came out, offensive to some, but all got over it for the sake of Vera, Mom, Auntie, or Bootsie, depending on who spoke.

The company sat in the upper level of Vera's split-level rancher. As the evening progressed, so did the drink, smoke and 'shine. The kitchen's L wall obscured a few, but most could see from the dining room into the living room, or across the stairwell into the smaller living room. Because of the odd assortment of loved ones, the subject turned to how everyone knew Vera. The first question came from Tracy's stepbrother David. He couldn't help but notice Justin, who hadn't been introduced. Bunky also noticed the stranger on the couch next to Tracy, and Tori had made googly-eyes at Justin all evening, which wasn't missed by Granny.

"So, who's your friend Tracy?" David asked, but no one said anything. "I mean, I was just wonderin' how he knew my step-mom."

"Oh," Granny piped up. "That's Justin. He's been in the family for years. He called me an' Bootsie almost every month since he an' Tracy met," and Granny caught Tori shoot Justin a wink, and saw her opportunity to 'stir somethin'. "Isn't he hot Tori?"

"Granny Moody!" Tori protested, and everyone laughed. "I mean, he's cute an' all."

"Does he make your panties wet?" Granny asked, and there was an appropriate chorus of 'aw shits', but Granny held up her drink to finish it.

"Well that's good," Granny said and sipped. "Because he's gay."

"He's gay?" Tori screamed.

"He's Tracy's old boyfriend," Granny cackled. "So there ya go," and the house erupted with laughter, and Justin laughed so hard he almost did wet his panties.

The next day, Vera's funeral was monumental. Few of Tracy's family realized how many lives Vera had touched through her work at the hospital. When they arrived at the church, there was a police escort four rows deep assembled in front of the hearse. In the parking lot another group of ambulances, fire trucks, and a second police escort waited to follow her procession.

Easily one hundred cars lined the side streets filled with friends from Vera's church, along with nurses, doctors, past patients and co-workers. Members of county government, and colleagues from the healthcare community acquainted with her famous case also came out for Vera. After the funeral, the procession closed streets from one end of D.C. to the other, but that wasn't important to Tracy. As he traveled home in Granny's Oldsmobile there was only one thing he cared about - Tracy thought he missed his mother's last words.

"You did not," He answered. *"You heard them spoken over milk tea and cinnamon toast."*

Tracy smiled. Suddenly he was grateful, and recognized the opportunity given him. As they drove, Tracy remembered sitting at the kitchen table and hearing his mother's sweet, sexy voice. He heard Vera's laughter, saw her smile, and smelled the cinnamon toast. Then, for the moment, Tracy was at peace with his Mom's passing.

Chapter 20

- Lynn, Tracy, Bryan and Harry

Vera was buried in the first days of 1989 when Tracy was twenty-two years old. Then, for the next year, Tracy couldn't hold onto anything. He grabbed at school and jobs, but everything eluded him. The only solace he found was visiting his Dad, Lynn and little brother Bryan in Columbus, and they became important to Tracy during this part of his life. No one could replace Vera, and Tracy wasn't looking for that. Besides, Tracy had spent most of his childhood with Granny and Moody. But no distance of geography or time can change losing one's mother. Yet, after Vera died and Tracy's path was unsure, his father and Lynn played their part in getting him back on track.

The only friend Tracy had made at West Virginia Tech was Mo. He was quiet and easy going, studied computer science and was black, so Tracy had a comrade against the racist faculty. But Tracy's real connection with Mo was Kung Fu, and the two became good friends over the next year. By the following January, and what should have been Tracy's last semester of college, he got a letter.

Tracy lost a lot of credits transferring to West Virginia Tech, he wasn't close to graduating, and he was now on academic probation for the spring semester. Classes started on Monday, and Tracy sat in his room at the same maple desk he sat at in junior high.

When he didn't go to campus, Mo called and asked if he was ok. Tracy wasn't. He didn't want to be a burden anymore, didn't want to go back to school to fail more classes, and was totally submerged by darkness. It may have been the desk, but Tracy felt exactly the way he did when he was about to go camping with the scouts. Back then, Tracy tried everything he knew in this world. With no way out, that's when He said, *'Why not ask me?'*, so Tracy tried again.

"Lord," Tracy said. "You know what I'm supposed to do. I know I'm not supposed to be leaning on my grandparents - they should be leaning on me by now."

The Tall Shiny Silver Figure listened, but Tracy hadn't asked.

"So," Tracy decided. "I'm just gonna sit here until you say something," and Tracy muted the television and waited. He was at the end of himself, bowed his head, and gave himself up.

"Go to the newspaper stand on Capitol Street," He said. *"Get the Sunday "Columbus Dispatch" newspaper. In it will be an advertisement for a career fair. Call your Dad, and tell him you are coming to go to this."*

"Did I just hear that?" Tracy said aloud.

"Yes you did," He answered quickly.

So, Tracy went to sleep with no other plans except to do what He said to do. Tracy woke up early Tuesday, and got his cereal as Granny had her coffee.

"Granny," Tracy said, "somethin' strange happened last night."

"What?" Granny asked.

Tracy muted the tiny TV on the kitchen table, and repeated what he was told to do word for word. As he said it, Tracy saw himself do it. When he finished, Tracy came back to himself. Granny hadn't moved. She was frozen with her cigarette in front of her cocked hip, the ash had burned halfway down to her fingers, and her mouth was open.

"Granny?" Tracy asked.

Granny flipped her ash in the sink, which she never did.

"I've been waitin' for this!" Granny exclaimed. "I've known for the longest time. He said He was gonna do somethin' with ya, an' I've been prayin'. I just knew He was gonna do somethin'!"

Then Granny looked at Tracy, and wondered why he was still there.

"Well go on," Granny said. "Go down an' get yourself that paper. Take the car!"

Tracy took Granny's Oldsmobile and went to Charleston. He parked in front of the newsstand and asked the guy at the counter.

"Do you sell the Sunday "Columbus Dispatch" newspaper?"

"Funny you should ask," the clerk said. "We were gettin' ready to throw it out, seein' as its Tuesday. We got one left," and the clerk had it in his hand.

Tracy took it, opened the paper in front of the clerk and saw the ad for the career fair. Tracy bought the paper, thanked the man, and went home to show Moody.

"Out of all these companies listed," Tracy said, "someone at that fair is lookin' for me."

Then Tracy called his Dad and told him what happened.

"Wow son," Harry said. "Let me know when you're coming, and I'll do some praying on my end."

"I will Dad," Tracy said, although he didn't know how he would get to Columbus.

Tracy still had his Fiat, but it wouldn't make it to Ohio. Tracy didn't want to take Granny's car either. Before Tracy could ask if his father could come get him, Tracy got an impression to go to the bus station, and he told his father.

"Well son," Harry said. "If it's the Lord, he'll make a way for you to get here."

"This was His idea," Tracy agreed. "I'll let you know."

Tracy looked in his wallet, which only had change from the twenty he used to buy the paper. In the back, Tracy kept a credit card that had expired two years earlier. So Tracy went to the bus station to get a one-way ticket from Charleston to Columbus. He handed the clerk his old card and it went through. Tracy didn't know how, but he got out of there and ran home to show Granny his ticket.

"I thought ya said you didn't have any money?" Granny said.

"I don't," Tracy said, and he showed her his expired credit card.

"Yup," Granny said, "He's up to somethin'. You'll be alright."

Tracy got the scissors from the kitchen drawer and cut up the expired card, because he knew its use was only for that one time. When Tracy called his Dad to tell him the story, he agreed.

"I get in Thursday evening," Tracy said. "I'll pack up tomorrow."

"Is your résumé updated?" Harry asked.

"I'm working on that, but I only have one copy."

"Don't worry about that son. When you get here, I'll take it to school and make copies. How many will you need?"

"I have eight companies picked out from the list in the ad."

"That sounds good son. I'll pick you up tomorrow."

That night, Tracy packed his only department store suit that mostly fit, finished his résumé, and put it in a blue pocket folder. He arrived in Columbus the night before the career fair. It started at noon the next day, and ended at seven. Harry had to teach at the high school until three, so Tracy had to wait for his résumés.

Tracy and Harry got to the hotel by four. Companies had tables set up on balconies overlooking the lobby. There, Directors and Division Heads from high-tech companies conducted on-the-spot interviews in front of their hotel rooms. When Tracy and Harry walked in, an army of tailored suits rushed by with briefcases. Their cufflinks glittered off the newly minted engineers vying for the same positions.

"This is exciting!" Harry said, and his voice was elevated with enthusiasm.

Harry was not at all put off, and was thrilled with what God was doing for his son. Tracy looked over the crowd and was less convinced.

"I guess God is gonna make me shine all by Himself," Tracy said.

"I guess so," Harry said. "So let's pray son," and Harry prayed over him. "I'll be here in the lobby."

There were three hours left, and Tracy went down his list. Between interviews, Tracy saw his father speaking with other applicants. As a teacher of computer science, Harry easily struck up conversation with the other attendees, and Tracy went to check in with his Dad midway through.

"All these people have degrees son," Harry said eagerly. "I've seen their résumés, and yours needs updating. A lot of these folks already have work experience."

Tracy almost became deflated, but that wasn't what Harry meant.

"This is exciting! Imagine what the Lord is about to do for you, especially if He has you in this crowd!" and Harry hugged his son. "So exciting!"

Tracy went back for his next interview and finished, but was snagged by three more companies. It was close to seven-o'clock when Tracy came down the escalator. Harry saw Tracy and waved. Tracy thought he was done, but he heard Him again.

"I have one more place for you to visit," He said.

'But I don't have any more résumés left,' Tracy thought, but there was no answer. Tracy got off the escalator and told his father what He said.

"Well," Harry said, "it's almost quittin' time, so you better get back up there."

"But Dad, I only had eleven résumés - the original, and the ten copies you made. I spoke to eleven companies, and gave each one a copy."

Harry looked off into the distance for a moment. His eyes darted around a bit - the way Tracy's did when He was speaking. Then, his Dad came back to himself and gave Tracy a smile.

"Look again son," Harry said with a soft wink.

Tracy opened his blue pocket folder, which was definitely empty when he came down the escalator. In it, there was one copy left. When Harry saw it he clapped his hands and rejoiced.

"Wow, this is so exciting!" and he looked at Tracy. "Go! Go back up the escalator. Go! Go!"

Tracy went back up the escalator. The Department Heads that were left were packing up their things. Tracy didn't know what he was looking for, but he went down a hall he hadn't noticed. The tables were cleaned off, and no one was in sight. Halfway down, a sign caught Tracy's attention. The logo had "B & W" in blue letters printed on white cardstock. At first, Tracy wondered why a car company was there. Then he realized it wasn't an "M", but an "&" in the middle.

As Tracy deciphered the logo, the door suddenly opened like in the "The Wizard of Oz", when the little green man with the big face and curled mustache opened the round portal and asked who rang the bell. But this man's head peeked out by the door handle, and he looked at the table to his left. When he looked to his right, he was surprised to see Tracy from the waist up, standing in his department store suit holding his blue pocket folder.

"Oh," the man said. "Hello there. How are you doing?"

He stood to shake Tracy's hand. This man had a round face like the little green man, but was jovial like Santa. He also seemed laid back, which helped Tracy relax.

"I just came out to see if we left anything," the man said. "Were you coming to talk to us?"

"I guess so," Tracy said.

"Oh good," he said. "What's your background?"

"Electrical engineering."

"Really?" and his voice had a lift.

"Yes sir," and the man looked at Tracy with knit eyebrows, although he still looked like Santa, and that suggested he liked to be tickled.

"Do you know anything about electromagnetic fields?"

"I knew enough to fail the class twice before I passed it," Tracy said, and Santa laughed.

"Well come in, come in," the man said.

Suddenly, Tracy was in his hotel room with the standard queen beds, and another man spoke on the phone.

"I have our info packet here," the man said, and rustled through his things. The other man ended his call, and Tracy's host looked up to make introductions.

"Hey Nate," the man said. "This is," and he looked at Tracy. "What's your name?"

"Tracy," Tracy said.

"This is Tracy," he said. "This is Nate. He's head of our engineering department. My name is Carl."

Nate came over and shook Tracy's hand. The opposite of Santa, or the little green man, Nate looked like the man voted sexiest of the year, and Tracy was standing in his bedroom.

"How ya doin'?" Nate asked easily.

"Good," Tracy managed.

Carl kept looking for an information packet.

"What can you tell me about eddy current?" Nate asked.

Tracy answered a lot like the scarecrow after he got his diploma: "It's an undesirable when it comes to magnetic field theory, but you can work around it."

"Is that the right answer Nate?" Carl asked, rifling through his bag.

"I'm gonna call Dale," Nate said, and got Dale on the phone. He was eating dinner. From what Tracy overheard, Dale spoke country like Momma Ro.

"Do you have time to talk with this gentleman?" Nate asked. Dale said sure, and Nate handed Tracy the phone.

"So my wife just fried me some chicken," Dale said, "with mashed potatoes."

"I love fried chicken," Tracy said. "Did she use a cast iron skillet?"

Dale laughed hard. "That's the only thing my wife uses!"

"Well, she's right about that," Tracy said.

"I've got to see you," Dale decided. "Can you come up Monday?" But Dale didn't wait for an answer, once he finished his mouthful of mashed potatoes. "Put Nate on the phone Tracy, an' oh, enjoy yourself this weekend. An' if you're worried about anythin' don't be. They'll do a drug test, but just tell 'em you had poppy seed cake," and Dale laughed again. "My wife makes a mean poppy seed cake, an' I'm plannin' on havin' some after dinner, if ya know what I mean."

"That sounds good sir," Tracy said, who couldn't hide his smile.

"Just call me Dale Tracy, an' put Nate on the phone," and Tracy did. Then Nate and Dale spoke a few moments before he hung up.

"Have you got a car?" Nate asked.

"No," Tracy said, "but my Dad is downstairs."

"Can we meet him?" Nate and Carl asked in unison.

"Sure," Tracy said, and Carl finally handed Tracy the info packet.

The career fair was over by this time, so the three were easy for Harry to spot coming down the escalator. Then Carl and Nate introduced themselves.

"Nice to meet you Harry," Nate said. "We can have the company plane come down from Barberton to pick him up Monday, if that's alright with you."

Harry didn't expect that statement.

"Think about it," and Carl and Nate went to check out.

"What did you say in your interview?" Harry asked, and his eyes were twinkling.

"I'll tell you later," Tracy said quietly, "but it's all good."

"Well it's God," Harry said loudly, "so it's better than that son!"

Carl and Nate came back with their luggage in tow.

"Would it be ok if I drove him up?" Harry asked.

"Oh sure," Nate said. "No problem. We'll send you all the info, and reimburse both of you for your hotel, meals and travel," which was what Harry wanted to hear.

"Did you give them your résumé son?" Harry asked.

Carl laughed. "Oh yeah, we might need that!"

Tracy gave it to them, and they shook hands and left. When Harry and Tracy got home they told everyone. Their friends at the church were ecstatic, and marveled how fast things transpired. Then Lynn rolled up her sleeves, and the next day Lynn had the opportunity to do her most favorite thing – shop. She bought Tracy a new suit, shoes and overcoat. They were home by mid-afternoon, and Tracy put on his new uniform.

"Here's a pair of your Dad's cufflinks," Lynn said, and Tracy put them on. "Now sit here," she instructed, and she got her tray. "From what your father tells me, none of these men ever did any hard labor. This shine will fit you right in."

Lynn polished Tracy's nails, and she went through a round of mock interviews. Lynn's questions were rapid and coarse as she buffed, and she got right to the point.

"Now stand up and get your new coat," and Tracy did as he was told. Lynn took it and put it on. "When you go into your interview, take your coat off like this," and Lynn seamlessly dropped the coat from her shoulders. She reached behind through the sleeves, and folded it in half while inside out. Then she halved it again over her arm and stood there.

"And never sit down until you are asked," Lynn said. "This way you can hold your coat in your lap," and she demonstrated. "And don't let your back touch the back of the chair, otherwise you look too relaxed." Next, Lynn explained how to order lunch so Tracy could answer questions. "You can chow down later when you go out with your father. That's why they gave you an expense account." Finally, Lynn instructed Tracy to take notes: where he was, who showed him what equipment, and to write down all names, and how to spell them.

On Monday, Harry and Tracy went to Akron where Tracy interviewed all day. He got an entire notebook of names, addresses and equipment notes, and they came home. Tracy sent out detailed thank you notes to each of his interviewers and then, nothing happened. It was the middle of January in Columbus, so it was overcast and snowed every day. Tracy sat in his father's house all week before the rejection letters poured in, but his parents were undaunted.

"Well," Harry said, "we might as well send for your clothes from Granny's."

"Dad," Tracy said, "didn't you see the three rejection letters today?"

"Did you buy a one-way ticket from Charleston son?" Harry asked.

"Yes," Tracy answered, which kept his mouth off his worry.

"No child of mine will ever work at a fast-food restaurant!" Lynn screamed into the ceiling. "I come against that in Jesus' name!"

"Amen to that!" Harry agreed, and sealed the confession.

"Now, let's start believing for your salary," Lynn said, and Tracy looked at her as if she had three heads. "If they were going to say no, they would have said so by now."

Tracy saw Lynn's eyes and thought, why not. After all, He started this, so He had to finish it.

Three days later, Tracy got his acceptance letter from Babcock and Wilcox. He was to start February first in Barberton, Ohio, and Tracy's salary was five thousand dollars more than the figure he wrote down with Lynn. In the letter, Dale also remarked how impressed Tracy's interviewers were with the polished gentleman he had introduced to them.

"And that's the way it's done," Lynn said.

"Yes," Harry agreed. "This is so ex*ci*ting!" because God had gotten Tracy back on track.

Chapter 21

- Freddie in 1990

Harry was a minister with his family's church in Columbus. He recently met an elderly woman in a nursing home who had just moved in, and had all her things in storage. They included a sleeper sofa, dishes, pots and pans, and all the necessities to start a new life. In contrast, Tracy had left Granny's house with a one-way bus ticket and nothing but faith. So Tracy bought some of the church lady's home goods. That weekend, Tracy, Harry, and Bryan loaded them into a rental van and headed for Akron to find an apartment to put them in. This wasn't easy to do in one day, particularly in February, so they put everything in storage there. Lynn followed to take Harry and Bryan back home, and they had an early dinner. Afterwards, lake effect snow surrounded them as they drove to their hotel, which seemed foreboding.

"Well," Harry said, "we leave in the morning, and you start work on Monday."

"That's true Dad," Tracy said, but didn't catch his point. His father's calm was also disconcerting, given the silent barrage of snow that assaulted them. Then, Tracy was hit with a similar unvoiced ferociousness, as he realized he was about to be marooned in Akron.

"Hey Dad, what about transportation?"

"I thought about that too son," Harry said, which wasn't an answer. "Let's see what the Lord will do," Harry decided. "He's done much more than I could, and I don't want to interfere. They know you don't have a car, but I am here if you get stuck."

The next morning, Harry, Lynn and Bryan left for home, and God had things lined-up for Tracy's first professional job. As Tracy reviewed his Welcome Packet, Amy called. She was his liaison, and got Tracy a ride with a fellow recruit staying at his hotel. Then, Tracy spent the week getting acquainted with his job, and most importantly, Dale. He was Tracy's Department Head, and they were two of a kind. In fact, Dale was originally from Charleston, and had hung out at some of the same neighborhood bars Tracy had.

Dale was a little man who looked hunchbacked, but only because of his carriage. A lot like Moody, Dale was a 'cussin', smokin', drinkin' guy', who happened to get into 'nucler' when it started. Dale's jaw was permanently clenched, his breath was consistantly fresh with bourbon, and clucks of damns that usually involved God punctuated every phrase.

"Now when ya get to Lynchburg for trainin'," Dale said, "you're gonna meet Paul." As they walked, Dale showed Tracy the huge warehouses where they assembled and inspected the pristine inner workings of nuclear reactors.

"He's the guy who set all these fandanglin' systems up," Dale explained. "He's gonna teach ya. That way he don't have to come up here every gongalingin' time somethin' thinks about goin' off-line," and Dale turned to Tracy. "An' don't ya worry 'bout a car."

Tracy didn't know how Dale knew, but that seemed to be the way things worked in this new season: God not only showed up, He showed off.

"By the time you're done with your trainin', you'll have had two paychecks an' not time enough to spend 'em. That'll git ya started on a down payment. Now come on, let's take a break."

As much as Dale kept Tracy engaged, Amy worked everything out behind the scenes, a lot like Bond's "Moneypenny". On Monday morning, Tracy was packed and ready for his training. As he waited outside his hotel, Harry called to check in.

"Hey Dad," Tracy said.

"How are things going son?" Harry asked.

"Things are good. I'm leaving for Lynchburg to train for two weeks."

"That sounds good. Did they give you a car?"

"They said they were flying me."

"Goodness! What airline are you flying?"

"I don't know. They just told me to hand them this piece of paper."

"Is it a boarding pass?"

"No, and there are no markings on it other than my name."

"My, my," Harry mused. "How are you getting to the airport son?"

"They said they were sending a car," and as Tracy finished, a limousine pulled in front of the hotel.

"You mean a cab?" Harry asked.

"No Dad," Tracy reported. "It's a limo," and Harry's voice went extremely high.

"A limo!"

"Mr. Staples?" the driver asked, who seemed a lot like Bond's Q.

"Yes," Tracy answered, and he showed the driver his piece of paper.

"Let me get those bags for you," Q said, and loaded Tracy's luggage.

"I have to go Dad," Tracy said.

"This is so ex*ci*ting!" Harry said.

Unlike when Pete acted like Bond with the steering column on the Fiat, this was the real deal, and Miss Moneypenny (aka Amy) didn't disappoint.

"Have you had breakfast Mr. Staples?" Q asked. "If not, they have food waiting for you when you get there," and he continued as he drove. "We had trouble getting you a rental car Mr. Staples, because you are not yet twenty-five. We couldn't do it legally, so Dale called the president of Hertz. They worked out a deal, and the company co-signed. The car will be waiting for you when you land. The address of your hotel is in the Training Packet that I put in the front compartment of your luggage."

They arrived at the airport, and drove down a side road to a hanger with the Babcock and Wilcox logo painted on it. The limo stopped, and Q got out and removed Tracy's luggage. But there was no one in sight. They stood on the tarmac in silence until Tracy looked at him, so Q turned to answer.

"You are taking the company jet," Q explained. "Dale didn't want me to tell you."

Tracy looked around. "What do I do?"

"The pilots will be here in a moment," Q said. "I am waiting so I can hand you over to them," and at the mention, the pilot and co-pilot appeared from an adjacent building.

"Gentlemen," Q introduced. "Meet Mr. Staples," and Q shook Tracy's hand goodbye. "Have a good time."

The pilot went into the hanger to prep the jet for take-off, and the co-pilot followed with Tracy's luggage. Once the plane was out of the hanger Tracy went up the small steps. Tracy was seated, and the co-pilot went to the service area and came back with a box.

"Amy heard you liked chocolate covered cream-filled donuts from Krispy Kreme," the co-pilot said, and opened the signature white box with green polka dots. Tracy was speechless. It was a full dozen and his favorite.

"Do you want one?" Tracy asked the co-pilot.

"No, I'm fine," and he shut the door to the cabin.

Tracy did another check and saw only empty seats. "Who else is coming?"

"Just you," the co-pilot said. "As soon as we get the plane level I'll get you a drink."

In Lynchburg, the rental car waited at the hanger. On the front seat was another packet of information about Tracy's classes and local restaurants. In two weeks, Tracy completed his nuclear training without a hitch. Then, he was flown back to Akron. As Dale predicted, Tracy had enough money for a down payment on a car. Instead of a new one, Tracy bought a used Subaru for $1,000 and called it a day. In another week, Tracy had an apartment that was the entire third floor of an elegant old house, with bay windows that overlooked the city, and Tracy marveled at God:

In less than two months since getting instructions to get the Sunday "Columbus Dispatch" newspaper, Tracy had a great job, a car and magnificent apartment – a far cry from sitting at his childhood desk contemplating failing college. Tracy's life was made anew, and, as he would find out, the plan included saving Freddie.

For now, at work, Tracy became Dale's right-hand man. For the next two years, Tracy donned astronaut-worthy clean suits, and climbed up narrow gaps in generators the size of trailer homes. Technically, Tracy ran the robotics equipment to test for imperfections before a reactor left the plant. He also traveled off-site if there was an outage, discerned the cause, and made sure everything was safe to be put back into service.

Unofficially, Tracy was the liaison between the programming heads who couldn't get their ties dirty, and the union workers who couldn't hand him a screwdriver without checking their contract. The suits worked on one side of the street, the union guys worked the other, and Tracy got his exercise. In between, Dale told Tracy stories of the early days of 'nucler' power.

One particular time, an alarm went off during testing. Everyone froze in place and heard a high-pitched sound. This meant there was a pinhole leak in a super-heated steam pipe. The technicians carefully grabbed wooden broom handles, which were kept at the ready throughout the room. Then they gathered at the center walkway to exit behind Dale. They walked single file, one step at a time. Dale methodically waved his broom handle in front, up, down and to the side. Suddenly, the tip of Dale's broomstick flipped off four feet in front him, and ricocheted off the sidewall.

"That broomstick was seared clean-through instantaneously," and Dale laughed. "'I guess we better not go that gigaflickin' way,' I said to the boys, an' we about faced it to get the hell outa there, wavin' our broom handles, an' safe-steppin' the whole way," and Dale chortled, immensely pleased with himself.

"Yessiree," Dale said. "I never seen it happen thank God, but if a body didn't know no better, an' just ran out across that jet of steam their head would be cut clean off – no blood or nothin' – cauterized. The body would keep runnin', an' the head would just fall to the floor."

But the danger didn't stop Dale from having a little fun. When the pair went to Norfolk Naval Shipyard to do an on-site inspection, it was Tracy's first time there. The only thing Dale said was that they were going onboard for the inspection. As Dale and the newbie passed the aircraft carriers and battleships, Tracy wondered. Silent naval personnel led them to a long narrow slip of water, which was no more than seventy-five feet wide.

"Ok Tracy," Dale said. "Put the equipment down by the edge."

It was routine for Tracy to carry the equipment while Dale met their host. Tracy's job was to stay with the gear until they knew 'what was what', but it was almost dark.

"We'll be right back," Dale said. "We got to go to the bathroom," and in a flash, Dale and his cohorts vanished into a nearby boathouse and out of sight. It was peculiar, but Tracy stood alone in the huge vacant space.

Soon, bubbles appeared in the black water of the slip – first a few small ones, followed by large inverted gulps of air that churned the water. More came as two large cylinders rose from the middle, followed by a whale fluke that became a tower. The water sheeted off cleanly as the width of a townhouse elevated three stories a few feet from Tracy's face, which was followed by the surfacing of the whale-sized body.

But that's not what Tracy experienced. As soon as the inky murk began bubbling, Tracy reverted into his nine-year-old mind. His flashback of "Jaws" was complete with the bass-line soundtrack, and not being able to put his hands in soapy dishwater. As the tower rose, Tracy's stomach churned and he started to pass out. But Dale's laughter brought Tracy back in time, and the naval officers caught the lines to secure the submarine.

"You were a sight!" Dale screamed.

Tracy was still doubled over, but when he caught his breath Tracy was honest.

"Y'all almost lost yourself an employee for your playin'."

But Tracy recovered. He boarded the sub, and even within the small, contorted spaces, frequent travel and diplomatic shuttling, Tracy excelled. A year later, Saddam Hussein invaded Kuwait. Because of the company's expertise and his security clearance, Tracy had prior knowledge of Desert Storm. It was about that time Freddie called. There were rumors about the upcoming war. Freddie's tour was up, and the Army wanted him for the Reserves. Tracy urged his brother to get his discharge because there were so many unknowns. So Freddie returned to D.C., got a job, an apartment and a girlfriend. Then Freddie trained in computer science for his company, and things seemed good.

About a year later, Tracy had to travel for an outage near D.C. He swung by to check on Freddie, but Freddie still wasn't healed. It was difficult for him to come home without Vera there. That anchor had been ripped from him, and Freddie found it hard to adjust. To cheer things up, Tracy and Freddie went to a shooting range with David. After they dropped David off, "Work to Do" by the Isley Brothers came on the radio. Even though Freddie drove, it didn't stop him from singing the 'doot-da doot' bridge in Tracy's ear, like when the brothers were eight and nine. But when the song was done, the happiness from another time brought Freddie back too soon.

"I still miss Mom," Freddie said, "and it gets me into a funk I can't escape."

"Well," Tracy said, "maybe we should pay her a visit."

Freddie looked at Tracy, who had a weird expression.

"Come on, let's go together," Tracy said, and reached over to put his foot over Freddie's, and he accelerated the gas pedal.

"Cut it out! Cut it out!" Freddie yelled, and struggled to regain control of the car.

But Freddie remained depressed. That Christmas, Tracy stayed in Akron. Freddie went to West Virginia, and called Tracy from Granny's house low and dispirited.

"I miss you man," Freddie said. "I wish you were here."

As soon as Freddie hung up, Tracy packed a bag and drove the three hours to surprise his brother. They talked late into the night, but a year later, Freddie still had trouble. With so many emotions from the military, their mother's death and being on his own, Freddie still couldn't get his footing. One day, Freddie called out of the blue. Tracy was at the beginning of his lunch break, and Freddie was crying.

"How are you able to get through this so easily?" Freddie asked.

"God," Tracy said, but knew that didn't explain much.

"So, how do *I* do this?" Freddie asked. "It all happened so fast. I wasn't there for Mom, and then I had to get back to Germany. I still feel so lost."

"Well, I listen to a lot of TV evangelists," Tracy began but stopped. Freddie stayed silent as Tracy realized he wasn't the one for the job. "Freddie, can you stay on the line?" Tracy knew Lynn was also on her lunch break, and he dialed her for a three-way call. "Don't get upset, but do you remember Lynn? She was at Mom's funeral. Don't freak out, but I also call her Mom. I am dialing her now, and she'll know how to get you through this."

"Ok," Freddie said, and tried to pull himself together. When Lynn answered, she didn't miss a beat.

"Hey Mom," Tracy said. "I have my brother Freddie on the line. Do you remember him from when we buried our Mom?"

"Sure I do," Lynn said.

"He's still grieving," Tracy said, "and I don't know how to lead him, or well, break this down for him, but I thought you could."

"Ok," Lynn said. "Hi Freddie, are you there?"

Tracy listened as Lynn led Freddie in an effortless conversation. Like a surgeon with a blade, Lynn comforted Freddie with scripture, and her words turned the dark into mirth. Through the course of the conversation Freddie's soul was saved, and Tracy felt he witnessed a miracle. Freddie was going to be ok, Lynn became another Mom for his brother, and Tracy was reminded of a scripture himself:

Mark 10:
29 And Jesus answered and said, Verily I say unto you,
There is no man that hath left house,
or brethren, or sisters, or father, or mother, or wife,
or children, or lands, for my sake, and the gospel's,
30 But he shall receive an hundredfold now in this time,
houses, and brethren, and sisters, and mothers, and
children, and lands, with persecutions;
and in the world to come eternal life.

Chapter 22

- eddy current inspection

When Bill Clinton was elected president the nuclear industry was unsure what would happen. The first Gulf War was ending, and Babcock and Wilcox downsized with a series of layoffs. Tracy's job wasn't affected the first few rounds, and then Tracy called his father.

"Well son," Harry said. "I have never seen the Lord work so fast in getting you this job. He might have another one for you. Either way, we should stand on scripture."

So they did, along with Lynn. Whenever Tracy heard anyone say the word 'layoff', he quoted from Revelation 3:8 quietly to himself:

"I know thy works: behold, I have set before thee an open door, and no man can shut it: for thou hast a little strength, and hast kept my word, and hast not denied my name."

After several weeks there was to be one more round of layoffs. Friday morning, Allen, a co-worker, came by Tracy's office. He said Nate needed to see him. To review, Nate was the look-alike to the man voted sexiest alive, which Tracy met when he first saw the B&W logo at the hotel in Columbus.

"I'll be ready in a minute," Tracy said, and he dialed Marylyn Hickey's prayer line from memory.

Allen waited in the doorway to Tracy's robotics lab. He assumed Tracy was finishing up a test, which, in a way, he was. Tracy was standing on His word, but he wanted another faith-based person to agree as well.

"That's it exactly," Tracy said. "If this door is closing another will open, and we want the next door to be the one that He has for me," and Tracy listened. "Right. So, if this is getting ready to end, I am ready for the next to begin. Thank you so much, and I will keep you posted," and Tracy hung up the phone.

"You aren't concerned at all are you?" Allen asked, and Tracy looked at him. "No other employee has ever acted like this, and I've been doing this for weeks on end." When they went down the hall, Allen stopped outside the entrance to Amy's office.

"Amy isn't taking this well at all," Allen said. "But if all of this works out the way you just prayed – please pray for Amy. She's been taking these layoffs personally, especially yours. She pleaded with Dale and Nate not to let you go," which was true, because when Tracy walked into Amy's outer office she immediately broke into tears.

"I'm so sorry," Amy said. "None of us could do anything," and she began to sob. "You are like my son."

Nate came out of his office, and even his eyes were red. Then Tracy went in, and Nate announced news as obvious as it was old. But they were interrupted.

"Speed this up," He said. *"I have an important phone call for you as soon as you get home."*

Nate began with apologies, and how giving references would be a pleasure. Then he talked about the logistic procedures for ending Tracy's job - but He was insistent.

"Speed this up," He said again, and He meant it.

"Nate," Tracy said. "I hate to cut this short, and I'm very appreciative, but the Lord is telling me to speed this up."

Nate was stopped, but he was familiar with how Tracy came to Babcock and Wilcox in the first place.

"He's telling me I'll have a phone call when I get home," Tracy said.

"Oh," Nate said. "Did you send out your résumé?"

"No," Tracy said, and it was clear he hadn't thought about it. "But if we can wrap this up, I'll call before the end of the day and tell you what happened."

"Ok," Nate said, relieved. Amy overheard and was overjoyed.

"Well go!" Amy said after her final hug, and she was so excited.

Tracy rushed home, put his briefcase down, took off his coat, and sat in his living room that looked across the skyline of Akron. After about ten minutes, and Tracy was thinking about what to make for lunch, the phone rang. Before he answered Tracy got a pen and paper, sat down and answered professionally.

"This is Mr. Staples speaking," Tracy said, and the gentleman on the other end was equally professional, even though he had called Tracy's home phone number that wasn't listed.

"Mr. Staples, I am a recruiter for Siemens Nuclear Power in Chattanooga, Tennessee. We have an opening in the robotics department. We wondered if you were interested in coming down for an interview."

"As a matter of fact, I am highly interested," Tracy replied.

"Very good. How soon are you available?"

"I am available immediately," Tracy said. "In fact, I went through a layoff less than an hour ago."

"Very good. I mean, for us. Can I reach you at this number?"

"Yes."

"Good. I will call with a confirmation by the end of the day. By then, I hope to have a plane ticket for you to come see us Monday," and Tracy hung up the phone, thanked God, and called Amy.

"I have an interview with Siemens," Tracy reported, and Amy screamed and laughed at the same time. As they continued, Tracy heard the commotion he started in the office, and then he was curious.

"Amy, did you send them my information?" Tracy asked.

"No," Amy said. "That hadn't cross my mind, or I'd done it."

"I think I will be going Monday morning," Tracy said.

"Well, we have to do lunch," Amy decided, "with everyone! Oh I can't wait – they'll all be so relieved. It'll be a celebration!"

"Well, let's do it Wednesday," and Tracy laughed. "I should at least meet these folks."

"Oh yeah, of course," Amy said. "But who gets laid off, and gets an interview the same day?"

Over the weekend Tracy reviewed Lynn's trench-coat warfare for interviewing. He checked his cuticles. He rehearsed taking off his coat, sitting forward in his chair, and got his notebook ready.

On Monday, there was a foot of snow on the ground when Tracy drove from Akron to the Cleveland airport. When he arrived in Chattanooga he wore an overcoat, hat, scarf and gloves over a snappy wool suit, polished shoes and matching briefcase. When the Team Lead met Tracy at the airport, he was surprised. The people on the streets of Chattanooga wore shorts, sweatshirts and sandals, and the Team Lead was in casual Friday attire, even though it was Monday.

"My name is Chip," the Team Lead said. "An' you're not gonna need any of that stuff down here," referring to Tracy's layers of wool and formality.

Tracy had back-to-back interviews that were done by noon, and the team took him to lunch. Because their boss was paying, the team members ordered steaks and cocktails. Tracy ordered a salad so he could answer questions as prescribed by Lynn, but he noticed the different atmosphere. Granted, it was close to seventy degrees in February, and everything about the area was lax, but Tracy sensed something else that made his spirit uneasy. Chattanooga had a dark vibe, like his future associates who willfully took advantage when ordering lunch. Then, the team took Tracy back to the office before he was to fly back to Cleveland, and Chip took Tracy to an empty conference room.

"We're gonna discuss your interviews before you have to leave," Chip said. "Do you need anything while you wait?"

"Ask for a Yellow Pages," He said.

"How about a Yellow Pages?" Tracy asked.

"A Yellow Pages," Chip wondered. "Do you know someone here?"

"No sir," Tracy said. "It just seems things are moving fast, so I need to find an apartment quick."

Chip looked at Tracy, and cocked his head like a dog that heard a strange noise. When he returned with a phone book, he smiled as he handed it to Tracy.

"You're like a breath of fresh air," Chip said, and left to meet with the other managers.

Chip returned a half-hour later and took Tracy to the airport. On the way he pointed out Lookout Mountain, Missionary Ridge, and the many colleges in the area. At the airport they shook hands.

"You'll be hearing from us in two weeks," Chip said. "But I'm pretty sure you already know," and he looked at Tracy. "I don't know how you know," and he left it at that.

Back in Akron, it seemed all of Babcock and Wilcox attended Tracy's farewell lunch. Amy organized everything and coworkers arrived in two-hour shifts, which was more like a birthday party than a farewell lunch. As coworkers gave Tracy personalized gifts, he realized they needed the celebration more than he did. Tracy also recognized how God used him to touch the lives of those around him.

Two weeks later, Tracy received confirmation of his new job and starting salary. Then he was assigned a liaison, and she needed to contact the relocation team.

"When do you want to start?" she asked, and by now it was the end of February.

Tracy answered the first of April, which surprised her. Tracy wasn't thrilled about where God was sending him. He wasn't sure what it was, but Tracy detected a false veneer over something hidden. Something had also changed, or a page had been turned. When Tracy went to N.C. State, the magnolias were his marker. He remembered them from the picture book, and knew he was in the right place at the right time. Tracy also realized God had redirected him after leaving N.C. State for West Virginia, which wasn't God's plan.

Now, He wanted Tracy to go south, and it seemed Chattanooga was where He had flipped through the pages faster. Tracy got the feeling the upcoming scenes of his picture book were heavy with grief. He looked for other jobs, but every door was shut. As April loomed, Tracy tried to strike a bargain. Before he got into bed, Tracy got on his knees and wanted something settled.

"Ok," Tracy prayed. "If I have to go, show me how Mom died," and he went to sleep.

At 1 a.m., Tracy was wakened in the spirit. He stood in the hallway of a hospital. Everything shined white – the walls, the floor and ceiling. There was a single door in the middle of the hall on the left. The Tall Shiny Silver Figure stood by the entrance, but He didn't speak. Tracy knew it was the room where Vera had died. Then, the Tall Shiny Silver Figure pointed into the room like the "Ghost of Christmas Yet-To-Come", except He was the exact opposite of death and darkness.

When Tracy walked toward Him, the Tall Shiny Silver Figure disappeared. When Tracy looked into the hospital room, He stood at the foot of a gurney. He held His hand out palm up, and presented the form of a body under a white sheet. Once Tracy crossed the threshold, the Tall Shiny Silver Figure stood on the opposite side of Vera's gurney, which caused Tracy to seethe with anger as the sting of his mother's death welled up inside him.

"This is not what I asked you to show me," Tracy cried. "I wanted to see the events that led up to *how* she died, because I missed them."

Tracy wanted a reason - a cause. His flesh wanted something or someone to blame, but there was no room for that where he was. The Tall Shiny Silver Figure only allowed the emotion without pain, and, as Tracy's anguish flowed out, it was absorbed by the whiteness that surrounded them.

"You are showing me the wrong thing!" Tracy shouted.

But the Tall Shiny Silver Figure only raised His arm, and pointed behind Tracy at the door he had just passed through. When Tracy turned around, Vera passed by in a gown as pure white as everything else. She looked forward, and walked with a steady gate. Without stopping, she turned her head and looked at her son. Then, she motioned for Tracy to follow as she passed by the doorway. Tracy looked at his host.

"What am I supposed to do?" Tracy asked hoarsely, and the Tall Shiny Silver Figure gestured for Tracy to follow her. "You're not saying anything, which is very upsetting."

Instantly, Tracy was made to understand the teacher can not talk during the test.

"But I'm about tired of all these games," Tracy said, "when I know You can make it plain and simple."

Tracy was frustrated. He didn't want to listen to the promptings of the Tall Shiny Silver Figure. Tracy had said games, but really meant his mother's death, and the anger he harbored.

To the contrary, the Tall Shiny Silver Figure was pulling the irritation from him. Tracy wouldn't have to carry it any further once he left the room, and Tracy looked at his old friend. He still held up His arm, and gestured with a nod for Tracy to follow his mother down the hall. Tracy relented.

As he approached the door Tracy heard a party going on. Tracy crossed the threshold into a long brilliant corridor with a single door at the end, which Vera went through. A group of imps hung around outside the door, and they made a tremendous racket. They were dressed in black leather, had boom boxes on their shoulders, and played their music very loud. They yelled to Tracy and danced around each other. They invited Tracy to join their noise, and their dancing and taunting was a welcome distraction from Tracy's grief and frustration.

"Come on," the imps cajoled. "Let's party! You don't want to follow Him. You can come with us! Come on Tracy…" and the imps went through the doorway.

Tracy looked back at the Tall Shiny Silver Figure for guidance, who still gestured to go through the door his mother went through. So Tracy went down the hall, and the door opened to a landing. To Tracy's left was a floating staircase, which ascended sharply to another landing with a door on the left. At the top, Vera stood motionless facing her door. To Tracy's right, the stairs descended steeply to a landing with a door to the right. The imps were at the bottom with their clamor, enticing Tracy to join them.

As Tracy stood, the door behind him disappeared. Then, Tracy was alone on the landing between the two staircases, floating between glory and perdition. Tracy looked up at his mother in her white gown, who stood in front of her threshold and waited. The cacophony that came from the lowest landing was strikingly out of place. Then the imps ramped up their game to take Tracy's attention, but that was not his destiny, or what lived inside him.

As soon as Tracy took a step toward Vera, the noise ceased. The imps cowered as they looked toward Tracy, and they shook with terror in their eyes. When Tracy looked behind him, the Tall Shiny Silver Figure stood taller and larger than Tracy had ever seen him. His hands were crossed in front of His chest in absolute authority, and the command of His presence vaporized the imps. Their clamor was immediately replaced with peace, quiet, and a complete lack of confusion. As Tracy marveled at the change, the Tall Shiny Silver Figure pointed upward to Vera's landing. Tracy turned and looked. His mother's door opened from the other side to become a frame of light. Vera looked down at her son, just as she had when she passed Tracy in the hallway - expressionless but whole. Then she looked forward, and tilted her head at a forty-five degree angle toward the heavens.

When Vera did, a roll of white clouds descended at the same angle. Billows that moved like a fog of thick honey shimmered in the light behind the doorway, and cascaded from the top of the doorframe. A pair of hands came through the cloud and cradled Vera's head, the way a parent would hold an infant's face with love. Then, Vera was taken up quickly. Tracy gasped, and turned back to the Tall Shiny Silver Figure. His old friend nodded to indicate that it was done, and Tracy woke up.

Tracy's vision was so healing he called his Dad, and, even though it was two o'clock in the morning, Harry was fascinated. They spoke for a while, which was enough for Tracy to calm down, and from that point on Tracy had peace with his mother's death. But even though Tracy made the bargain, he still didn't want to go to Chattanooga. By the last week of March He broke His silence, and the Tall Shiny Silver Figure was His jovial self again - not the austere, silent, Dickensian personage of the last vision.

"Do I need to send a whale to Akron to get you to Chattanooga?" He asked.

He referred to when He sent the whale to redirect Jonah, when Jonah tried to go to Joppa instead of Nineveh. This made Tracy have a flashback of the submarine in Norfolk, and he wondered if the manmade whale was a portent or a joke. Tracy felt Him smile at that thought, but He was also serious, because childish things had to be put away for what was to come.

"Ok," Tracy answered, "because I don't want to see a whale on dry land. I can't even deal with "Jaws", let alone being in the belly of a whale."

Then, Tracy was reminded what Jesus had to do after He was filled with the Holy Spirit:

"And immediately the spirit of the Lord drove Him into the wilderness."

"But Lord," Tracy said. "I'm scared."

"Fine, go scared," He said. *"But this is what I want you to do."*

So Tracy knew he had to go through this. Somehow, Tracy also knew it would be over once he returned to Ohio. He just wasn't sure how long that would take, or worse, what he would have to face.

"Go scared," He said again with assurance, *"but go."*

"Alright," Tracy said, "but I'm gonna snot an' cry the whole way."

Later that week, four men and a large Amazonian woman arrived at Tracy's apartment. Tracy wasn't allowed to touch a thing, and they had his things packed within the hour. Tracy drove the rental car Siemens provided, but rather than follow the moving van, he went to West Virginia to check in with Granny and Moody.

To his surprise, as soon as Tracy crossed the state line the dread fell off. Like going through an invisible force field, once Tracy was out of Ohio he was jolted into happiness. He had made his first step, but Granny wasn't convinced.

"Are you sure 'bout goin' down there?" Granny asked.

"I have to," Tracy said, "but I was goin' kickin' an' screamin'."

"When did ya get ok with it?" Moody asked.

"Because I'm not," Granny added, "not to that part of the south."

"I wasn't excited," Tracy agreed. "But as soon as I drove over the border from Ohio, my joy came back. I looked inside for all the fear I had, but I couldn't find it. I also knew if I did a u-turn, I'd find it within twenty feet," but Granny still wasn't there. "And there was something else."

Tracy told Granny and Moody about the conversation about the whale. Then he described the vision he had of the hospital and his Mom. Granny and Moody were surprised, but reassured to hear about Vera's ascension. Then, overnight, Granny and Moody had their own epiphany about Tracy's vision and Vera's role in it. By the next day, they all knew it would be ok. Then Tracy left for his wilderness, which for him was Chattanooga, Tennessee.

Chapter 23

- chicken and waffles

Tramele Delmontei Staples-Wilson was born at sunrise on Easter Sunday, April 10, 1966. At that time, Vera had graduated high school and lived at home with Granny and Moody. They were at a party when Vera's water broke. Granny and Moody had planned to be home by eleven to be ready for Easter Service the next day, but rushed home to take Vera to the hospital. In the wee hours of the morning, Vera's doctor induced labor to speed up delivery to make it to church himself. The end result was little Tramele was brought into this world first thing Easter Sunday morning.

Twenty-seven years later, Tracy didn't want to spend Easter in Chattanooga. He had just moved, didn't know anyone, and Todd came to the rescue. He reminded Tracy that Darryl lived in Atlanta, which was a short hop down I-75. Tracy met Darryl during the frequent college disco trips to Chapel Hill from N.C. State. Darryl was as involved with the church as much as Tracy, and came with Sabrina to Vera's funeral where he led a prayer with Tracy's friends.

Darryl was a short, round fellow with a tight fade. He was bouncy, used conversational scripture, and continually lived in the future. After Tracy settled into his new apartment he contacted Darryl, who was pleasantly surprised to hear from his old friend.

"Where are you going on Palm Sunday?" Darryl asked.

"I hadn't planned on going anywhere," Tracy answered.

"Come down to Atlanta," Darryl offered. "There are some exciting midnight services I want to go to, and I think you'd like them. You can stay with me."

Tracy accepted, and on Saturday morning he drove to Atlanta to attend several services. The first was a vigil that started at eleven. There were several speakers, and it was well past midnight when they got there. Next, Darryl and Tracy went to a hotel with a service in a conference room. When Darryl opened the large door, the preacher looked past the crowd directly at Tracy. He was in the middle of his sermon, and because the congregation faced him, no one else saw Tracy and Darryl come in. They walked quietly to the side of the room to find a seat, but the preacher followed Tracy with his eyes.

'No one knows me in Atlanta,' Tracy thought, half asking, to see what He might say.

Tracy was sure they hadn't met, but the preacher looked familiar, which may have been because he looked like Moody with a baldhead. Then, Tracy wondered if he should remember the preacher from the picture book, but he didn't.

"You!" the preacher said suddenly, looking at Tracy.

By this time, Tracy and Darryl were half way up the wall aisle.

"You!" the preacher said again, and he pointed.

Tracy and Darryl scrunched down, but a seat couldn't be found.

"You hear me talkin' to you," the preacher demanded. "The Lord's got somethin' to say to you."

"He must be talkin' to you Darryl," Tracy whispered. "Don't nobody know me here in Atlanta."

The preacher got louder, and stated with thunderous authority.

"You hear me," the preacher said. "You just moved down from the north."

"Oh," Darryl confirmed, "he's talkin' to you Tracy."

Tracy jumped up like a jack-in-the box, and stared right back at the preacher.

"Didn't you just move down from the north?" the preacher asked.

"Yes sir," Tracy said.

The congregation turned to look at Tracy, which made a synchronized sound.

"The Lord's got a word for you," the preacher stated.

Exclamations came from the crowd, but not because the preacher interrupted his sermon. He had a word from God for the stranger, and everyone wanted to know what it was.

"As a matter of fact," the preacher said, "He has several of them, an' they're to let you know He's got your back."

The congregation became in awe and offered Darryl a seat. Tracy remained standing along the sidewall, and the preacher turned into a prophet. He walked back and forth across his platform, and reported what he heard.

"This will cover those dark periods you don't wanna go through in the book," the preacher said.

It wasn't exactly a surprise to Tracy the preacher knew of his picture book, or had seen it, but it seemed odd he knew to speak of it in front of the congregation.

"This will cover those dark pages," he clarified, "so they don't catch you off guard."

Then the preacher settled into himself. To Tracy, everyone except himself and the preacher disappeared into the room - almost like the great cloud of witnesses in the Highest. In the same way, this world's group watched, but they weren't involved.

"Number one," the preacher said. "You're not gonna have this job very long. Even now they are considerin' layin' you off, even though they just hired you. But don't be afraid – you are not to go back yet."

Then the preacher's eyes grew large at an unexpected thing, and he repeated what he heard:

"I see lots and lots of monies coming in and through your hands for the Kingdom of God, and how you come about this money many will say you are not a Christian. But you hold on. This is the persecution that comes with the hundredfold return."

Tracy was startled, because what the preacher said came from the same scripture when Lynn saved Freddie, from Mark 10:30, only now it referred to him:

"But he shall receive an hundredfold now in this time, houses, and brethren, and sisters, and mothers, and children, and lands, with persecutions; and in the world to come eternal life."

Then Tracy sensed the preacher saw his picture book again. The preacher was pained. When he came back to himself, he looked at Tracy with a warning.

"Now don't go jumpin' off into anythin' fast. God is tellin' me this is gonna take time. Don't be surprised if it takes ten years," and the preacher came out from the gloom and smiled. "This is to get you through the book's dark pages you don't wanna go through. But I have not seen that many lots of monies, and that's gonna be at the end."

Then the preacher was caught again, came back, and looked at Tracy in the present.

"I see you working with robots," the preacher asked. "Do you work with robots?"

"Yes sir, I do," Tracy said.

"Then, that's not what God has for you. That's just a layover to get you to your destiny. You're gonna be an entrepreneur, and God is telling me to tell you this: Whatever you have, or whatever He gives you, or whatever you invent as an entrepreneur, whatever price you put on it, people will pay it," and the preacher looked at Tracy and laughed, and nodded his head in agreement.

"Yes! God told me to tell you - whatever price you put on it, people will pay it!" and the preacher became serious. "He told me to tell you this because of the turmoil you're gonna go through. This will make it worth it, because it won't seem like it while you're goin' through it. But you hold on, because God is with you. He's tellin' me to tell you, that if you don't stop or quit," and the preacher had to take a breath and exhale from relief. "In the end, He'll make that turmoil like it never happened," and he paused. "An' I'm not talkin' about heaven Tracy," the preacher clarified.

Tracy looked at the preacher like the rest of the room, and the congregation murmured. Everyone knew the two had never met, and that the preacher had no earthly way to know Tracy's name. But the preacher remained unfazed, because His word was the only thing of importance.

"I'm talkin' about the latter end of your life," the preacher said. "You make it through these ten years or so, an' God will make you live in your dreams. You won't be able to stop Him blessing you, because He'll know that you know why He is doing it. It may not make any sense, but you are on assignment."

The congregation of witnesses stirred. As the preacher continued to speak, He told Tracy to give the preacher one of the two $100 bills in his pocket. Tracy had never sowed $100 into anyone's ministry, but He had never told Tracy to do this before either.

So Tracy put his hand in his pocket to separate one bill from the other. Then he took the folded bill out, and held it in his hand unseen.

"I don't know what that assignment is, just so you know," the preacher said.

Then the bald Moody-man preacher jumped off the platform with his microphone. He pointed at Tracy and stepped toward him, so Tracy came up the sidewall to meet him in front of the congregation.

"And just so you'll know a prophet of the Lord has spoken to you, within seven days, the Lord is gonna give you a gift only He can give you."

The two met in front of the platform. As he finished, the preacher laid hands on Tracy:

"And that gift will confirm everything, and your whole family shall be saved by what you do."

Then preacher's hands made Tracy feel a weight that made him buckle at the knees, and then, Tracy felt peace.

Once the preacher released Tracy, he stood up straight, shook the preacher's hand, and slipped him the $100 bill without anyone knowing. Then, Tracy went back to sit with Darryl, and the preacher returned to his platform to finish his sermon. This time, Tracy was offered a seat next to Darryl, but Tracy knew what just happened was the reason he was in Atlanta. The preacher's word was why they came, so they didn't need to stay.

After a few more minutes, they left before the service ended. The two managed to get to Darryl's apartment before the sun came up, and after a short nap, they went to Gladys Knight's place for chicken and waffles.

"So," Darryl said. "That was quite something earlier."

"It really was," Tracy said.

"What do you want to do for Easter?" and Darryl was excited.

"Whatever we do," Tracy decided, "it won't be here in Atlanta!"

Darryl laughed. "You scared?"

"Nope," Tracy said obstinately. "But God doesn't need my help doing whatever He's doing. So I'm stayin' away from Atlanta."

Darryl looked at Tracy and tried to read him.

"Look, if He's gonna do this in seven days, He can do it somewhere other than Atlanta," Tracy decided. "So find somewhere else for us to go for Easter."

"Ok," Darryl said. "I will."

After brunch, Tracy drove back to Chattanooga and wrote down everything the prophet said. Then he read it several times. Tracy was intrigued he wasn't supposed to have the job in Chattanooga for long, so he prayed.

"I know you opened up this door," Tracy said. "So, if you close this one, You are bound by Your word to open up another."

By midweek, Darryl's plan for Easter was to visit his family. Because Darryl didn't have a car, Tracy drove back to Atlanta to pick Darryl up. Then they had lunch before they drove to Charlotte, North Carolina. Darryl checked in with Tracy on the way.

"Did you receive your gift yet?" Darryl asked.

"Not yet," Tracy replied.

"Well, this is the sixth day. He's got one more."

"I know."

That night, they played cards with Darryl's family, and they went to bed early to attend a sunrise service. On Easter Sunday there was an overcast sky that was sure to rain. Tracy went with Darryl's family to a large brick church. The congregation wore grand Easter bonnets that were the course in Charlotte, although there were also dress jeans and pressed shirts without ties. The sermon was "The Power of Speaking in Tongues". It was delivered by a tall, slender, sharply dressed black pastor.

"Have you received the Holy Ghost?" the preacher eventually asked. "Now sure, many of you will say yes. You received the Holy Ghost when you were saved, and more importantly, the Holy Ghost received you! But since you've been saved, do you demonstrate His presence with the evidence of speaking in tongues?"

The congregation agreed with 'Amens' and 'Yes Lords'.

"Sure," the preacher said. "You all have fire insurance. Once you're saved, you're saved! But are you truly baptized by the Holy Spirit? Do you speak His language, the one prescribed by God, first made evident in the Upper Room with Jesus' and His disciples, before they were sent out into the world to preach His gospel?"

As he continued, Tracy was taken back to the little Pentecostal Church in Rand where he went with Aunt Z. But he was only twelve when he knelt at the altar, couldn't get up, and babbled for more than an hour. Tracy wondered if he really understood it, or if there was more. As soon as Tracy asked, he was reminded of Zechariah 4:6:

"So he answered and said to me: "This is the word of the Lord to Zerubbabel: 'Not by might nor by power, but by My Spirit,' Says the Lord of hosts."

"And here's the thing about the Holy Spirit," the preacher stated. "It's like riding a bike. You can get on that bike, or you can get off anytime you want. If you want to ride with the Holy Spirit, He's there for you! Amen! And if you get off and go it alone, that's fine. That bike is just sitting there waiting for you, whenever you want to get back on. It's your will that allows the Holy Spirit to speak through you or not."

The bike analogy was a revelation for Tracy. It was so easy, and he thought of Freddie and his 'runnin' cousins', and how they loved riding their bikes as kids. The preacher ended his sermon with an altar call. Before he finished asking, Tracy stood in front of the preacher face to face. Tracy didn't know how he got there, he stood alone, and the preacher blinked at seeing Tracy suddenly appear before him.

The preacher finished his sentence, and more souls came to the altar. Everyone received the baptism of the Holy Spirit with evidence of speaking in tongues. Afterward, the large group was led to a room with the Pastor. Assistant ministers took the group who had previously received the Holy Spirit, and, after a group prayer, Tracy left.

When Tracy emerged from the church, his eyes were fully opened. It was the most beautiful day he had ever seen. Every color was more vibrant, the way a colorblind person would see beyond black-and-white. The Carolina spring was the same, but the pigments danced because they were so much more numerous. Above, clouds puffed like cotton balls and marshmallows. But rather than gray, they glittered a silver Tracy could almost hear. Reds were all shades of ruby, blues were shallow clear to deep sapphire, and greens were a gamut of emerald to cream pastel.

Next, a fabric of rain wove the colors together. A tight silver sheen covered the earth that the Lord hath made, the way it looked before corruption, and Tracy was stopped. He stood on the steps of the church in awe, and knew his eyes were permanently opened. Tracy also understood that he would always see the world this way, and that was His gift.

This day that the Lord made was what would get Tracy through the oncoming days of darkness. Then, Tracy wondered if the morning he was experiencing was anything like the one when he was born, and Tracy immediately heard Him over his shoulder:

"*This **is** the morning,*" He said. "*Happy Easter Tracy, and happy New Birth in the Spirit,*" and with those words, Tracy recognized he had ammo, and that his training had begun.

Just as Jesus was baptized and driven into the wilderness by the Holy Spirit, Tracy was now equipped with the very same. He would be able to face his demons. He also knew that when he came out at the other end, Tracy understood he would stand against the devil and win – not by might, not by power, but by His Spirit.

Chapter 24

- the archangel Uriel

When Tracy returned to Chattanooga he had another vision, but it was nothing like when the Tall Shiny Silver Figure spoke to him. At those times He was with Tracy, and the Tall Shiny Silver Figure's interaction was in the present - in physical time. Now, in the spiritual wilderness of Chattanooga, Tracy's visions were like dreams, except he felt awake and that they were lessons. Sometimes, Tracy interacted within the vision and he saw, felt and experienced what was happening. On occasion, Tracy watched himself within the action simultaneously.

The first vision Tracy received in Chattanooga was on a huge playground. The children were about two feet high, but in their adult bodies. Monkey bars stretched the length of houses, and the roundabouts held hundreds. The slicky-slides were as tall as a rollercoaster with as many twists and turns. Tracy was made to understand the equipment was on a grand scale because it was in abundance. Tracy knew his playmates were the world's children, and they were small because their souls were small. The adult children scampered, climbed, slid, and yelled with joy as at any spring recess. With them were animals of every sort - dogs, cats, birds, rabbits, wolves and lambs, calves and lions. They frolicked and played with the children as at Easter, or as on His holy mountain, as written about in Isaiah 11.

Then the imps appeared. Like Tracy's vision of Vera in her hospital room they wore black leather, but they weren't partying with boom boxes. Instead, the imps carried whips and chains. Next, Tracy heard chainsaws carried by more of them, and they kept coming. Tracy's only thought was that he didn't have weapons. From his Kung Fu training, he wanted a sword, nunchucks, butterfly knives or a staff but they weren't present.

Suddenly, the children ran to a bus stop, which was on the scale of the giant playground equipment. It was many rows deep, and had the usual clear glass on three sides. Tracy looked into the enclosure. The children were huddled in the far left corner, but now they were old. Fear had made them aged and infirm, and they were crying. Tracy turned and stood in front of the bus stop, so he could protect them as the imps closed in.

"What should I do Lord?" Tracy asked.

"Pray in the Holy Ghost," He replied.

Tracy knelt with his back to the bus stop and faced the oncoming army. He bowed his head, and prayed in the Holy Ghost. Then the noise of the chainsaws, the snap of the whips, and the clang of chains stopped. Tracy kept praying with his head down, and the crying of the children stopped. It was replaced by audible sighs of relief, and Tracy heard a tiny giggle.

When Tracy looked up, the imps were gone. Tracy turned and looked at the children. Some emitted spurts of laughter, while others were in a state of amazement, but they all looked at Tracy and pointed behind them. The enclosure was glass, but for some reason, Tracy couldn't see what the adult children saw. Whatever it was made them ecstatic, and all fear had left them. Tracy was curious, so he got up and went to the edge of the bus stop.

When Tracy went around its corner he became small – about one foot high. Behind the enclosure were five angels that stood as a regiment, who were turned and faced Tracy's left. They were tall, and each held a sword or spear at the ready. The far left angel had a trumpet, which he blew at a forty-five degree angle toward the heavens. Once Tracy had fully turned the corner the trumpet was the only thing heard, because it was an all-encompassing sound.

The five angels were bright because they were made of light, although Tracy could see they wore sandals laced to the top of their calf. They wore a biblical warrior's garb that included a remarkable golden breastplate, which was jeweled with each angel's name etched on it. The names were in a foreign language, but Tracy understood each angel had a specific duty. The most obvious was the trumpet, which still sounded.

When Tracy took a step toward them, he grew to half his normal size. The five angels turned to look at Tracy over their left shoulder, and their expression said everything. They were so grateful to have been summoned. Their gaze impressed upon Tracy they were not used nearly as much as their purpose, and how long they had been waiting. Now, finally they were called, and the vision was done, and Tracy woke up.

Selah.

The second vision Tracy had was more hands-on.

"Wake up!" the angel commanded. He was one of the five angels from Tracy's previous vision. He was dazzlingly white, especially since Tracy was half asleep.

"It is time for your test," the angel said rapidly.

"What is this?" Tracy said, and he rubbed his eyes.

"You have got to pass the test," the angel explained, and thought that fact was obvious.

The angel was to the point and seemed annoyed. His large sword was now in its sheath, and hung from his gold waistband. His breastplate's jewels and ornaments were more intricate because he stood so close to Tracy. Most strikingly, the angel held a legal-sized clipboard in his left arm. By his stance and businesslike manner, Tracy knew this was no time for jokes.

"Did you not recently receive the gift of the Holy Ghost with evidence of speaking in tongues?" the angel asked officially.

"Yes," Tracy answered.

"Time to learn how to use it," the angel said. "And remember, I can not talk during the test."

Tracy sat up in his bed. "What?"

"You are not getting it," the angel stated. "Time is of the essence," and his disdain was not hidden.

Suddenly, Tracy stood on a street corner and was dressed. Each street led somewhere specific, and Tracy faced the middle of the intersection. It was dark, except for the light that came from the angel standing next to him. Then, the angel held a pen up to his clipboard, which clicked like a ballpoint retractable pen only louder.

"The test begins...now!" and the angel double clicked his pen, and touched the pen to his clipboard.

As the angel watched Tracy, the pen wrote everything down. The angel wasn't writing, quite the opposite - the pen had a direct download from the angel's eyes, which recorded a physical record of what he saw. The angel simply stared at Tracy and noted his every nuance, which, at the moment, marveled at the pen that wrote the angel's observations by itself.

Then an imp came around a far corner. As he ran for Tracy, the creature grew from an imp to the size of a demon, slightly larger than Tracy. The demon still wore black leather, but screamed and wielded a knife to stab him. Tracy faced him and took his Kung Fu fighting stance. But the demon overpowered him in an instant, and stabbed Tracy repeatedly. Tracy didn't feel any pain, but he was quickly defeated.

'Oh this is stupid!' Tracy thought. 'I could have blocked that blow, I should have skirted that jab...'

The angel double clicked his pen. "Time is up!"

The demon was gone. Tracy felt for his wounds, but they had disappeared. Then Tracy got another man like in a video game, except the new man ready for play was himself. Another Tracy stood beside Tracy, like a reset. The actual Tracy looked at the angel.

"What was that!?!" Tracy cried.

"No talking during the test," the angel said brusquely. "Start over," and the angel held his clipboard out to his left side, and held up his pen to signal the start.

"You mean I didn't fail?" Tracy asked.

"No failing", the angel said curtly. "Keep going until the light comes."

At those words, Tracy understood the light was the revelation of the vision's purpose. The light would come once he understood the lesson. Tracy also knew he just needed to keep going until that happened. He would never run out of men, and the test was a loop until he figured it out.

"Reset!" the angel said.

Tracy was back on the street corner and looked down the roads. There were many to choose from, and he knew a decision had to be made. As Tracy stood there, the demon came from around a building hell-bent for him. This time, Tracy ran to a gun store. The angel followed and hovered around Tracy to observe his every action. Simultaneously, everything was recorded onto the clipboard by the pen. Sometimes the angel sat, or, if the action got more complicated he stood, or leaned to see everything Tracy did. But the angel was never in Tracy's way or interfered.

When Tracy got to the gun store, he broke down the door and grabbed a large gun and ammo. Then he ran out, and got far enough from the demon to stop and load his weapon. As the demon charged, Tracy faced him.

"Halt, or I'll shoot!" Tracy yelled.

The demon continued his charge, and Tracy emptied his clip. As the bullets sprayed the demon's body flinched and jerked, and he was arrested. But when Tracy was out of bullets, the demon came for Tracy wielding his knife just as before. Then Tracy heard the double click before he would have been stabbed.

"Time is up!" the angel said sharply. Tracy looked at the angel who had a rather bored expression, and Tracy was unimpressed.

All his interactions with the Tall Shiny Silver Figure were wonderful. Sure, sometimes He was annoying - God definitely got His way, but He always helped Tracy. The Tall Shiny Silver Figure was more like a brother, and Tracy always knew how much He loved him. The angel, on the other hand, as magnificent as he was within his stature of light and exquisite garb, was a little snarky. He wasn't interested in helping Tracy at all. The angel simply held out his clipboard, and raised his pen to start the next trial.

Tracy quickly got ready, and this time he thought he would run. As soon as his mind was purposed, Tracy was dressed in loose fitting pants, a T-shirt and sneakers.

"Reset," the angel said, double clicked, and Tracy started running.

He ran and ran, but soon Tracy realized his running would be eternal. Like a mirror that faced a mirror, Tracy ran in-between. His first steps running never ended. Tracy saw hours, days, weeks, months, years, decades, centuries and millennia pass the same as the present. The sun came up, and the sun went down. The moon waxed and waned over a landscape that was meaningless. Oddly, Tracy didn't need food or water, even though he ran through time. The only difference was that Tracy got tired and increasingly out of breath, but he thought he could run until six a.m. Tracy's plan was to run until his alarm went off, and he could wake up from this awful vision. But the angel stayed with him, and hovered while his pen took notes as the demon ran behind. Then Tracy looked at the angel.

"Why aren't you helping me?" Tracy panted.

The angel didn't answer and kept doing his job, and Tracy finally yielded.

"Ok I quit," Tracy said and stopped, turned, and got stabbed by the demon.

Because Tracy used time in this trial the angel couldn't say, 'Time is up', so he just stopped. Then they were back at the intersection. Tracy turned to the angel.

"Obviously there's somethin' I'm not gettin' here," Tracy said.

The angel rolled his eyes as if to say 'ya think?' Then he changed. The angel removed the pen from the surface of the clipboard, and the angel thought doing this was extremely unusual. The angel turned to Tracy as a teacher, not the administrator of a test, and his mood had significantly softened.

"The words that I speak come from Him," the angel said. "When I do something, I do it because He tells me to. When I tell you something, it is because He tells me to. I was sent to you for a purpose. In the beginning, what did I announce my purpose was?" and the angel put his pen back up to the clipboard so it would be ready to write.

"Reset," the angel said, and touched his pen to the clipboard.

Immediately, they were back at the intersection. The creature came around a corner and Tracy ran. The angel followed, but held back a little as Tracy racked his brain.

"What did he tell me?" Tracy panted. "What was the purpose?"

The creature caught up to Tracy, and he had to turn to fight. As he ducked his blows and dodged the demon's knife, Tracy kept thinking.

"What is the reason?" Tracy asked, and then he yelled, "I don't remember!"

Suddenly, Tracy heard His voice: *"He brought back to remembrance."*

At once the vision was paused. The demon was about to stab Tracy in the leg, but the demon was frozen. Tracy could move out from under the attack, because the demon was immovable, even though he was conscious. The creature's eyes darted between looking at Tracy and the angel, and wondered how he was stopped. The angel also stopped his scribing. Then he turned in the direction of the Tall Shiny Silver Figure, who was revealed from the sidelines. His light was unmasked, and He was much taller than the angel.

Tracy watched the Tall Shiny Silver Figure converse with the angel without words, using only His eyes and facial expression. Tracy was made to understand, and it went like this:

The angel was surprised when the Tall Shiny Silver Figure interrupted the vision, because it was not lawful to interrupt the test. Then the angel was reminded of the scripture:

"What is man that You are mindful of him?"

Five was the number of Grace, He explained, hence the five words: *'He brought back to remembrance.'* The Tall Shiny Silver Figure did so, because He had already paid for the test to be conducted. Then, the Tall Shiny Silver Figure looked at Tracy and spoke.

"Angels long to look into these things," He explained. *"They long to know and understand Grace, and why it is toward you."*

So the four stood there - the Tall Shiny Silver Figure, the angel, Tracy, and the demon frozen in his murderous attack. The angel pondered Man and Grace as he watched Tracy and the Tall Shiny Silver Figure continue. This also explained the angel's attitude toward Tracy - continually wondering what it was that God saw in Man that was the least bit interesting. Meanwhile, the demon wondered how he was still in the presence of the Tall Shiny Silver Figure, and realized it wouldn't go well for him.

"In the beginning of this vision," the Tall Shiny Silver Figure said, *"what did the angel say was his purpose in coming?"*

Tracy could think, because it was peaceful now.

"The angel told me he wanted me to learn how to use the gift You just gave me," Tracy said.

Tracy's friend was pleased. *"Very well. Use the gift."*

Then He looked at the angel, and it was understood to resume the test. Without turning, the Tall Shiny Silver Figure slowly backed away. Then He sat, and His chair continued as if on a trolley being removed from a movie set. Next, the Tall Shiny Silver Figure was obscured as with a curtain, although Tracy knew He watched, and Tracy was brought to remembrance. The demon looked at Tracy as if to say, 'Uh-oh', and Tracy took his position before the 'pause' happened. Then, in slow motion, the angel clicked once, and the action sped up to the second click. When the angel's pen moved faster and touched the clipboard, time resumed.

Tracy dodged the demon's swipe at his leg. They fought more until Tracy could back away from the creature enough to stand up. Tracy fixed his stance, pointed at the demon, and spoke in his prayer language. The demon froze instantly. Tracy stood and looked at his hand, which was just his hand, and he felt the words that had left his mouth as the weapon.

Tracy realized he now had possession of the demon as with a remote control, and that he had pressed the pause button through the power of his tongue. With the demon under Tracy's power, he had time to think what to do. For the moment, Tracy stood firm and pointed at the demon's hand that held the knife. Then, with the words of his prayer language, Tracy concentrated. Straight away, there was a spark that grew into a small firework, and the knife exploded in the demon's hand along with his upper arm. Now, the demon was not only held in captivity, he was literally disarmed. This made Tracy laugh as he thought, 'and I was afraid of you?' But rather than destroy the demon piece-by-piece, Tracy wanted to understand. So he walked around the demon to observe his impotence.

"I oughta kick your ass," Tracy said, but he wanted to stay in the vision. Tracy realized there was more to this because he hadn't woken up.

At that revelation, the angel's eyes grew large. He sat perched on the edge of his seat, keenly intent on Tracy, and his pen scribed at a furious rate. Tracy walked around the demon a second time, and he received revelation after revelation. Tracy began to understand the dragon as a worm, and his place in this world as God had ordained:

Psalm 8:
O Lord, our Lord, how excellent is thy name in all the earth!
who hast set thy glory above the heavens.
2 Out of the mouth of babes and sucklings
hast thou ordained strength because of thine enemies,
that thou mightest still the enemy and the avenger.
3 When I consider thy heavens, the work of thy fingers,
the moon and the stars, which thou hast ordained;
4 What is man, that thou art mindful of him?
and the son of man, that thou visitest him?
5 For thou hast made him a little lower than the angels,
and hast crowned him with glory and honour.
6 Thou madest him to have dominion
over the works of thy hands;
thou hast put all things under his feet:
7 All sheep and oxen, yea, and the beasts of the field;
8 The fowl of the air, and the fish of the sea,
and whatsoever passeth through the paths of the seas.
9 O Lord our Lord, how excellent is thy name in all the earth!

The angel's eyes were all wonder and curiosity to see if Tracy would figure it out. He had never seen this before, and, as Tracy's understanding grew, the cloud of witnesses gathered. The curtain was withdrawn, and Tracy, the angel, and the demon were on a small stage of a theater in the round. The great circular audience watched with incredible excitement, and they chattered among themselves: 'Is he going to get it?'

"A little lower than the angels," Tracy said aloud. "Crowned with glory. Yet He made *him* to have dominion over the works of His hands… and God made the angels."

There was a gasp from the cloud of witnesses, and the angel stood. Tracy stopped pacing around the demon and faced him head on. Then, Tracy stood back to raise both arms out to his side with his palms open. With absolute command Tracy spoke in tongues, unknown even to him, and used the gift of the Holy Spirit to speak over the demon. As he did, the angel's incandescence grew. Because he was summoned, the angel faced Tracy. He unfurled his enormous wings, even while he held his clipboard in his left arm as the pen scribed, and the angel's two pinions of feathered radiance lit the faces of the great cloud of witnesses.

Then, the height of the angel combined with the breadth of his wings formed an illuminated cross. Tracy stood with his hands outstretched and palms open, which formed a shorter human cross. Tracy continued speaking in tongues, and the two faced each other with the demon between. Then, because the angel was light, at the speed of light, the angel's terrible sword was unsheathed and cut the demon asunder. The intensity made a flash like lightning, and above the boisterous approval of the cloud of witnesses, the angel looked at Tracy in absolute awe.

'Wow, you did it!' the angel thought as he looked directly into Tracy's eyes and smiled.

Then, Tracy heard the Tall Shiny Silver Figure's loud approving voice quote Isaiah 45:11:

*"Ask Me of things to come concerning My sons, and concerning the work of My hands **command ye Me**."*

Selah.

- Freddie

Chapter 25

There are many kinds of deserts. Scorching hot sand, miles of glassy sea, or frozen tundra are the idyllic scenes. But they can be found in everyday cities just the same. By any definition, a desert's moniker is desolation. The calling card is emptiness and death, even if masked within nights of carnal abyss. But whether deserts team with unfettered life, or have an unrecognized beauty in their loneliness, the underlying association is with endurance, tediousness and long-suffering, whether admitted or not.

When Tracy was driven out of Ohio, his first desert was Chattanooga. As prophesied, Tracy was soon laid off from Siemen's Nuclear Power. Tracy decided to finish his associate's degree in order to have a piece of paper to prove his experience. He went to Chattanooga State, and only made a few friends with the local Kung Fu family there.

Tracy did make associations at the pizza place where he worked part-time so he could eat. Munchies Pizza was a family business. Tracy wasn't Italian, but it didn't matter because the family was German. Helga, the grandmother, made a mean pizza crust, her son made an awesome sauce, and they took Tracy on as their own. Tracy's other part-time job was at Nation's Bank, soon to be Bank of America, which was not a family-oriented business. It was 1993, and Internet Banking was coming over the horizon. Computer engineers were needed, so Tracy took classes. The sun came up and set, moons waxed and waned, and Tracy kept walking.

In September, Tracy had his third vision in Chattanooga. It was more of a message than a visual vision, and he had it while he slept.

"In three days," He said, *"you are going to lose a member of your family. But do not worry. It is just fine. They will only be asleep,"* and Tracy understood that 'asleep' meant the person was saved.

"Can you tell me who it is?" Tracy asked.

"I am not allowed to reveal that," He said. *"But when you get the news, I urge you to begin a three day water fast."*

Then Tracy woke up, and at first he didn't understand. Tracy loved to eat, and never considered a fast, especially of just water. The water fast also made the information of someone's death more ominous.

The next day, Tracy reached out to every last person of his family. As Tracy checked off his list, he realized the time given him was to close any gaps, or resolve any issues. Tracy also recognized he was being emptied out before it happened. Most of Tracy's family didn't know why he called out of the blue, but he told a few. Granny was particularly intrigued and got prepared. Tracy also told his Kung Fu buddy Bill. Tracy met Bill working out at a Martial Arts studio in Chattanooga. They were compatible because Bill loved Munchies pizza and movies, which were the only prerequisites.

By this time, Bill was also one of the few Chattanoogans familiar with Tracy's relationship with God. So Bill was not surprised when Tracy told him someone in his family was about to die. Bill also didn't know what to do with that information.

"It will be just fine," Tracy said. "I'll let you know."

Three days passed. After working out, Bill came into Tracy's apartment to borrow one of Tracy's Kung Fu movies. When the phone rang, Tracy looked at Bill. It was like when Tracy was little, and he told his Mom the phone was about to ring, and Granny was going to ask to borrow a cup of salt.

"You remember the vision I told you about?" Tracy asked.

"Yeah," Bill said cautiously.

"I think this is that phone call," and Tracy answered. "Hey Granny," and he looked at his watch, because it was an unusual time for her to call.

"Is someone with you?" Granny asked.

"Yes," Tracy said. "Who was it?"

"Put 'em on the phone," Granny said.

"It's for you," Tracy said to Bill, who became alarmed. Tracy handed Bill the phone, and he spoke with Granny soft enough Tracy couldn't hear.

Bill had met Granny on a trip to workout with Ron in Charleston, so they weren't strangers. After a while, Bill held the phone to his chest.

"Granny asked me to stay with you for as long as you needed," Bill said, "and I told her I would. I also told her you told me about the vision, and you were prepared for this news," and Bill handed Tracy the phone.

"Are ya sittin' down?" Granny asked.

"No," Tracy said. "I'm standin', but I'm leaning on this doorframe so go ahead."

"It was Freddie."

"What happened?"

"He was shot by a security guard."

Tracy was ready, but the desolation of losing his brother who was eleven months and five days younger was more than he expected. In many ways, Freddie was the embodiment of youth, laughter and pure happiness for Tracy, and having his closeness taken away by the heat of bullets burned a hole in Tracy's heart immediately.

Bill stayed with Tracy for a while, and then Tracy started his water-fast to extinguish his anger. The next day, Tracy traveled to West Virginia to join the family, and they went to D.C. for the funeral. All of it was unbelievably unfair, and Tracy's desert expanded in a way he hadn't considered. The embers of death's all-consuming fire fell about him, and everyone was in shock. But Tracy was ok, at least with the fact that it happened. Why it happened, from an earthly perspective, was totally unacceptable.

An Army buddy came to visit Freddie. They played video games until Freddie's girlfriend reminded Freddie he had to go to work in the morning. She said Freddie should either take his friend back to his hotel, or he should crash with them in their apartment. It was a warm night and the hotel wasn't far. So Freddie kept his shorts on, put on flip-flops, and didn't bother to put on a T-shirt because he didn't plan to get out of the car. Then Freddie drove his buddy to the hotel and dropped him off. As soon as Freddie's friend went through the front door, the security guard ran out.

"Stop!" the security guard shouted. "Police!" and he ran to the back of Freddie's car.

Freddie assumed the security guard was shouting at someone else, because he still sat in his car. From his Army training, Freddie looked into his rear view mirror to see who might be out there. Without another word, the security guard fired three shots through the rear window. Freddie sped off unaware of what was going on, but the shots hit the back of Freddie's seat and went through.

Then, Freddie realized he was hit in the abdomen. He managed to get back onto the highway and went down the hill to the light. Freddie had to turn left to get to the hospital, which was just at the top of the hill. But Freddie bled out before he reached the intersection, and his car simply veered off the road. Freddie was found in his car, and there wasn't much investigation. The security guard said he thought the hotel was being robbed because the safe was open. But Freddie never got out of his car, and his Army buddy walked in as the security guard ran out. But that was all there was to it, and Freddie was dead at the age of twenty-six.

Selah.

The water fast helped Tracy stay calm at the funeral. Granny, Moody, Jinny, Alvin, and Tracy's cousins were there. It was odd that Vera was absent, and more unusual it had only been four years since she had passed. Because she was gone, the circumstance of Big Freddie attending his son's funeral with Bobby was awkward at best. Even though they were cousins, Vera's two husbands fought the entire time, considering whether to engage another cousin who was an attorney. They argued whether to sue the hotel, the guard, or the security company that allowed the guard to carry a weapon, or all of them. But their misplaced anger just stoked the fires, and Tracy drank water to drown out their confusion.

"It's too bad you couldn't show this much energy for Freddie's wellbein' when he was alive," Jinny pointed out.

Over the years, the tough talk unraveled to nothing. But everyone was rattled by Freddie's passing, especially the cousins that grew up with Freddie in Jinny and Alvin's house. The three musketeers were down by one, and they hadn't reached thirty. Tracy's unruffled demeanor and water fast also irked his 'sister cousins', because they didn't understand.

"You better eat before you pass out," Mia said at the restaurant. "You look odd, sittin' there just drinkin' water.

"God ain't never told me to go on a fast," Demi said. "You're just actin' weird again, 'cause you was the favorite."

Marie kept quiet as usual, even though she was just as seared on the inside. Granny shot a look at Jinny's girls that was enough for them to leave it alone, although, Granny had never seen Tracy drink so much water in his life. As for Tracy, the more he drank, the lighter he was. With Freddie gone, Tracy realized he was the last of Vera's side of the family. He was the last male and last Staples, which was the end of Granny's line. The water helped carry that weight away, and Tracy kept breathing.

The next day, Freddie's funeral had a small military guard. It rained heavily, which was peculiar for September. Freddie's relatives lined up along the edge of his grave, stunned at who was going in the ground. Across the expansive cemetery, acres of headstones stretched over a low sloping hill. Most were flush to the ground with uneven corners popped up. The lawn was scorched from August, so the rain slid off the dead grass, unable to penetrate the hardened soil. Freddie died a Private First Class, and his girlfriend was given Freddie's flag.

At the end of the ceremony, Bobby unexpectedly began to cry about Vera, but Momma Ro wasn't having that.

"Hush up Bobby," Ro said quietly. "This ain't the time nor place to be makin' this all about you. You already did that, and now they're gone."

After the funeral, Momma Ro took Tracy aside after the others left. They stood under the cemetery tent, and her words were punctuated by the sound of raindrops.

"Trace," she said. "I know you don't have a reason to come back here anymore. But don't you forget about your Momma Ro. You're my son now, just like I promised your Mom. Even with Freddie gone, I'm still your Momma Ro," and the rain poured itself out as they hugged, and Tracy was awash with water inside and out.

Like cleaning an open wound, the water rinsed his soul. Another thing also calmed Tracy. The preacher's eulogy had been pleasant. He knew Freddie well enough to be invited to dinner by Freddie and his girlfriend. Everyone was sure they would have married, given a little more time. But with his last remark, the preacher confirmed what He had told Tracy three days earlier.

"Goodnight Freddie," the preacher said. "We'll see you in the morning."

Tracy knew that Freddie was only asleep, and that he would see him again. What Tracy didn't know was how soon that would be, although, it was just like his annoying little brother to surprise him when he least expected it.

About a year after Freddie died, Tracy woke up in a room that was all white. The bed was large and comfy. Tracy looked to see if there was an angel or demon lurking, but it just was a normal, comfortable house, and Tracy felt at home. The doors and windows were outlined in white. The bedroom had a high, oddly vaulted ceiling, and a large bathroom was through the door on the left. Tracy went to the hall where there was a small bath to his right, and a staircase went down to his left. The angles of the house caught his attention, and everything was bright and clean. Tracy went to the bedroom at the end of the hall and looked in.

"Tracy," Freddie said easily. "What are ya doin?"

Freddie was stretched out on the neatly made bed, wearing sweatpants and a sweatshirt that were white. His long legs were crossed, and his hands were behind his head resting on pillows. But Freddie didn't get up, which Tracy realized had significance. When Tracy went to hug his brother, Freddie didn't move because he had to stay in repose. As much as Tracy missed him, Tracy knew this vision was one where emotions weren't relevant, but was packed with information if he observed and remembered.

"Do you like your house?" Freddie asked. Tracy didn't recognize it at the time, but that was five words. Tracy did understand the house was his if he said yes.

"Yes," Tracy confirmed quickly. "This is great. But what are you doin' here?"

Freddie didn't answer. Instead, he relaxed, unconditionally happy and full of joy, and smiled a big Freddie-sized grin.

"The phone is for you," Freddie said, (another five words).

Like when he was a child, or got the call Freddie had died, Tracy knew the phone was about to ring. He also knew Freddie wasn't going to say anything else, so Tracy smiled back. The two brothers enjoyed the moment, because Tracy knew Freddie would be gone again.

Then the phone rang, and Tracy had to go. He went downstairs, which ended at a wall to the small bath by the front door. To the right was a townhouse-sized open dining room. A breakfast bar divided the kitchen behind. Granny stood next to the kitty-corner sink and spoke on the phone. Tracy went through the dining room to the kitchen. Past the refrigerator was an opening to the living room. There, Granny Berger sat on an overstuffed burgundy couch. She smiled at Tracy, so he went past Granny to see her.

"Granny Berger!" Tracy exclaimed. "What are you doin' in my dream? I haven't seen you since…"

Then Tracy realized Granny Berger and Freddie were both dead. Freddie was reclined, and Granny Berger sat on the couch and smiled, but didn't speak. Granny was the only one who stood, and was the only one still alive in this world. This revelation made Tracy wonder who was on the phone. The voice that came through the speaker sounded like Vera, but it wasn't exact, although it was familiar and nurturing. Then Tracy puzzled why his Mom would be on the phone, and why she would be calling.

"Here, this is for you," Granny said, (five words), and she handed the phone to Tracy.

"Hello?" Tracy asked.

"Trace," Vera said. "I'll be talkin' to you," and at the sound of her voice, Tracy woke up.

Tracy stayed in bed and meditated on what he had experienced. Then he received understanding:

Tracy knew Granny's death would be the last death, and he wouldn't grieve as much. Tracy also understood that when Granny handed him the phone, something was activated. When Granny died, Tracy would have a line – a connection to get unknown information known. When that happened, Tracy could connect with anyone on the other end.

But that was what was to come. For now, Tracy kept walking. As the years went by, Tracy wasn't released from his desert. Instead, Tracy's proving ground changed to various workplaces in Atlanta, and his tests became merged in real time.

Chapter 26

Tracy had been in Chattanooga for five years, finished school, and was enrolled in a Management Training Class for Bank of America. When he finished, the bank paid for Tracy's move to Atlanta and set him up in an apartment. Tracy didn't like the masked cutthroat politics of banking, but at least it got him out of Tennessee. It was 1997, and the only thing left was to find a church home. From his recent experiences, Tracy knew he needed more scriptural knowledge, and how to use it. His visions fighting demons had gotten him started, but Tracy was led to Proverbs 4:7:

> *"Wisdom is the principal thing; therefore get wisdom:*
> *and with all thy getting get understanding."*

Tracy turned to World Changers Church founded and pastored by Creflo Dollar. Like his father's church, it was non-denominational and charismatic, and based solely on studying the Word of God. As a mega-church it had a fairly anonymous congregation, and was ten minutes from Tracy's job. When he got paid at the end of his first month, Tracy was led to pay his tithes, and ran down to the church on his lunch break. On the way back, Tracy was at a stoplight when He spoke.

"Do you believe I gave you the inspiration to pay your tithes at lunchtime, and that this is about more than paying your tithes?"

"Yeah," Tracy answered, because 'yes' was usually the right answer.

"Good," He said. *"You need a new car. How about that red Jeep to your left?"*

Tracy looked. Sure enough, there was a used car dealership to his left. Next to the entrance was a Jeep Cherokee on a display rack that was fire-engine red.

"Ok, cool," Tracy said, and turned into the lot crowded with high-end luxury cars. Tracy knew his credit hadn't been very good, but he hadn't checked in a while. He was headed for the Jeep when a salesman came over dressed in a tuxedo.

"Good afternoon," the salesman said. "Is there something I can help you with?"

"I guess so," Tracy said. "I think I'm here to buy this Jeep." Tracy had never bought anything with the Lord before, so he wasn't sure how it worked.

"I can run a credit report if you like," the salesman said. "Do you have time?"

"Well," Tracy said. "I'm on my lunch break, so I don't have too much time. I'm only here because He told me to come in here," which made the salesman look around to see if someone was with Tracy.

"Ok," the salesman said. "I'll run your credit. In the meantime, take a look around."

"Sure," Tracy said.

Tracy gave the salesman his information and looked over the previously leased luxury cars. But the Jeep was for Tracy. It was a two-door, four-cylinder base model, big enough to haul his Kung Fu buddies back and forth to North Carolina for classes.

It was also a five-speed stick shift, Tracy thought. Freddie always said if you get a stick, carjackers were less likely to steal it. It also didn't have a high-end stereo, which was one less thing to worry about.

"And it's red," Tracy said aloud. "I like red."

"I know," He said.

The salesman came back, and put his tuxedoed self between Tracy and the Jeep.

"We just ran your credit Mr. Staples," the salesman said. "You can get anything on the lot," and he spread his arms wide toward the luxury cars, but Tracy looked behind the salesman at the Jeep. "Do you want something to impress?" the salesman said with a smile.

"I like the Jeep," Tracy said, and the salesman's feathers went down.

"Well, you could go for basic and functional. We just put this up on the rack because someone traded up for one of our nicer cars."

Tracy wasn't the least bit interested in the salesman's pitch.

"But I can get the mechanics over here," the salesman said, "and they can get the Jeep down so you can do a quick test drive."

"That sounds good," Tracy said.

Tracy drove his new Jeep around the block to go through the motions, but ultimately, Tracy knew the deal was done when He asked Tracy about his tithe at the stoplight.

"How soon do you want it?" the salesman asked. "We can have the paperwork done by this afternoon. If you can get the insurance for it by then, you can drive it off the lot when you get off work," and that's what happened. Tracy drove home that evening and named his Jeep, Bruce.

The next day, Tracy drove to work in Bruce. The Director of the Management Training Program, Sally, happened to look out her window as Tracy parked his shiny red car. She was a racist white woman, and by the time Tracy reached the office, Bruce was the sole topic of discussion.

"You bought a brand-new Jeep?" Sally exclaimed.

"It's just a two door base model," Tracy replied but thought, 'the only thing shiny on it is the color. It's a year old, and has 10,000 miles on it.'

"It is about the car," He said. *"It has always been about the car. Remember the Impulse? This is the same thing, but instead of Granny's pride, this is about Sally's. But I think you are ready for this fight now. You are ready to pass the test, just follow My lead."*

'What should I do?' Tracy thought.

Immediately, Tracy was brought to remembrance. He knew all he had experienced in his visions and the lessons they taught, so Tracy quietly prayed under his breath in his prayer language. Then Tracy's peers in the Management Training Program gathered for the day, and Sally was everyone's boss.

"We must be paying you too much," Sally said to Tracy with disdain, and Tracy continued praying softly with the weapon of his tongue.

"Watch Me turn that weapon against her," He said.

'I don't understand,' Tracy thought.

"That tongue," He said, as if it was the nastiest thing in His presence. *"I am going to make her reveal the dark secrets only she and her husband talk about in the privacy of their bedroom. This is going to be funny Tracy."*

'Ok,' Tracy thought, and knew not to laugh as he kept praying.

"I think I'm going to have to review all of your salaries," Sally went on. "Because for six months, I've been talkin' to my husband about gettin' me a red Jeep for Valentine's Day. All I wanted was a red Cherokee…"

'That's funny Lord,' Tracy thought. 'She looked at my little base model and saw a Jeep Grand Cherokee - all to reveal her jealousy.'

"...He says our mortgage is too high," Sally blathered on. "He's always goin' on about our mortgage, and how we shouldn't have gotten our house in the first place, just to impress all these fake associates of mine who don't give a damn..."

'And she works in a bank,' Tracy thought, 'training *me* on fiscal responsibility?'

"...My husband says, 'You wanted the house'..." Sally said.

By this time, the shorthaired lesbian H.R. Director came out of her office to see what the commotion was about. It wasn't cool for her and her partner to be out in the workplace yet. However, that didn't stop her from staring at Sally as if to say, 'WTF? Take your pill and teach your class girl!' and her look was enough for Sally to come back to herself.

Sally's rant ended, and the new trainees filed awkwardly into the boardroom. But there was nothing Tracy could do. He was the vehicle, or rather, his new Jeep was. Tracy was actually not responsible for the situation, which made the scene so much sweeter. As if to prove this, a fellow trainee who was a female of color hit Tracy's arm as he entered the boardroom.

"Nice Jeep Tracy," she said with satisfaction, and Tracy knew he had passed the test.

But the rivalry didn't stop, and Tracy knew his days at the bank were numbered. He also knew he was only there for the managerial training. Tracy sent out his résumé at the beginning of August. At the end of the month, Tracy's training ended on a Friday, and He gave Tracy the heads-up.

On Monday morning, the day after Princess Diana died, Bank of America planned to fire Tracy. Before they had a chance, Tracy announced he quit. By midmorning, Tracy drove Bruce home to pack, in order to move into a cheaper apartment until he got a new job. As he did, the phone rang.

"Trahhmayehl?" the voice said. "Is this Mister Trahhmayehl Stayyplz?"

"Yes," Tracy said.

"Mah nayem is Thereeesah," the woman continued. "But yeeoo cayen cahhl mee Laydee Teeeee. Ahhh work for TahVah Technahlojees. Would yeeoo bee iynterested iyn comin' on ouver heyre for an interveyoo?"

The voice on the other end of the phone produced vowels longer and wider than seemed humanly possible. What made the accent harder to comprehend was that it needed no breath. Because of the time the middle of each syllable absorbed, the bent distortions made it impossible for Tracy to fit any part of a word in edgewise, particularly given the time needed to decipher the phrase. The following conversation is amended to save paper:

"Uh," Tracy tried.

"Greg was wondering if you could come in today," Lady T drawled.

"Actually, I'm in the middle of packing."

"Well, I don't say this to too many people, but Greg is really interested in talking to you, so you could probably stop packing right now and come over here, and then you wouldn't have to pack at all."

"I would have to get my suit out, and it's not…"

"Do you have a tie and slacks?"

"Yes Ma'am."

"Well, that's overdressed around here, so why don't you just come on in."

Tracy was bewildered by what was happening, and too befuddled to check in with Him. However, the silence was enough for Tracy's attacker to yield a tiny bit.

"Ok," the woman decided. "How about tomorrow?"

"What's your earliest convenience?" Tracy managed.

"Let's see. Greg's usually not around till seven a.m. to open up the shop, and then the team gets here around eight to eight-thirty, so how about you come on in at nine-o'clock or so?"

"Sounds great."

"Alrighty then, I'll let Greg know to see you at nine," and she hung up the phone. Tracy listened to the dial tone for a moment, and wondered why she had finished talking. As soon as Tracy hung up the phone rang.

"I guess it would help if I gave you directions," the woman said, and she did.

The next day, Tracy found the building and the office. It was a large space with a single reception desk at the end. Behind it was jet-black hair with a bun held in place with hair sticks. Because the woman underneath was so short, that was all that was visible. When Tracy entered, the tiny Japanese woman stood and came from behind her desk. Tracy looked around for someone else, but they were the only ones in the room.

"Good morning," Tracy said. "My name is Mr. Staples, and I'm here for a…"

"Well of course I know that," Lady T drawled.

Tracy was appropriately shocked that the four-foot seven, very Asian woman that came over to shake his hand also owned the voice from their phone conversation.

"Hello Trahhmayehl," she said with her bent vowels. "I know, I don't speak a lick of Japanese, and I know what you're thinking, but I like the shock treatment when folks come through the door, so I always give them a long visual first." Tracy was speechless as they shook hands.

"Of course I'm Theresa, but you can call me Lady T because everybody does. Now, can I take your jacket and your hat? Do you want something to drink? I bet you like coffee. I'll go on and get you some," and Lady T went to a corner of the huge room that had a small table, tiny fridge and coffee maker, yet she didn't stop talking. "How was your drive in? I can't believe I didn't give you directions at first…"

There was no question about it – Lady T was everything. As the staff arrived for work, it was evident that she knew everyone's birthday or anniversary, and what child or spouse had what issue. So, Tracy knew who to ask. He had looked up the company the night before, but wasn't exactly sure what they did, or why they were interested in him. As Lady T handed him his coffee, he asked.

"So," Tracy said, and pulled out his kinfolk accent. "What is it exactly that y'all do around here?"

Lady T laughed. "Y'all are so silly. You'll be perfect. We work with IT automation, and Greg already loves you. I told him so myself."

Then, as Tracy waited for Greg to come from the warehouse, he sat in Greg's office and prayed.

'Lord, I don't know how I fit in with this company. My background is in programming and robotics. What do I know about any of this stuff?'

"This is your next step," He said, which was all Tracy needed to hear.

Tracy was hired on the spot. The next day he was thrown into Year 2000 Compliance. Then, in a whirlwind, Tracy was shown the world, and his coworkers were shown the Lord.

Chapter 27

- a zoetrope

It was 1999, and the 'millennium bug' needed to be solved and tested before the year ended. Y2K compliance was a scramble, and Tracy was dispatched to test all manner of electronic equipment. The team traveled at a manic pace, and sometimes the tasks were downright dangerous.

One time, Tracy's team was sent to Canada for a job in a warehouse. The equipment to be tested was fixed to the ceiling a hundred feet above the floor - at least in Tracy's mind. Because he was the lightest and tallest, Tracy was chosen to go up in the cherry picker for the test. Once they were buckled into their harnesses, the operator ran the controls and pushed them slowly to the top of the ceiling. When they got there, Tracy wasn't close enough to read the instrument.

"Don't worry," the operator said. "We can inch forward."

This didn't seem like a good idea to Tracy. But it took a good five minutes to get up there, which would mean ten minutes down and back up. Because of the height, Tracy was barely able to stay in the basket as it was. So the operator inched the picker forward, and nothing happened. Then he inched the picker forward again.

"Now wait," the operator said.

In a few seconds the basket moved what seemed ten feet one way, and then ten feet the other. Tracy felt he was in the final scene from "It's a Mad, Mad, Mad, Mad, World," swinging off the end of the fire-truck ladder like a rag doll. The other warehouse guys had their feet safely on the ground. So, when they laughed at Tracy, he gave them his lunch.

But for the most part, unlike the desert that was Chattanooga, Tracy came into a season of harvest in Atlanta. The time of dark trials and sadness had passed, and Tracy grabbed everything the Lord had for him. He made good friends at TAVA Technologies, the first of which was Lady T. She knew everything, including that Tracy was looking to downsize to a cheaper apartment. After his first travel was finished, she handed Tracy a list.

"Here you go honey," Lady T said. "I found these in your price range," and she ducked out of Tracy's office.

But no matter how far away Lady T was, or should have been, she was always within earshot, and could appear at whim. Regardless, Tracy began his calls and used his speakerphone. The first on his list was a small bungalow. The woman answered right away.

"Yes, this is Mr. Staples," Tracy said. "I am interested in the bungalow for rent."

"Oh yes," the woman said, with an antebellum accent most becoming. "It is a charming unit, behind a large old home on a lovely tree-lined street."

"That sounds nice," Tracy said.

"Oh my, it most certainly is," she said enthusiastically, "and by the sound of your voice, I can tell you would fit perfectly here. All the houses in the neighborhood are white."

"That's ok," Tracy said. "I don't mind painting."

Lady T's head peaked around, exactly in the middle of the office doorframe. "Trahhmayehl!" she hissed. "Hang up the phone!"

"And how much did you say it was?" Tracy asked.

"Hang up the phone right now!" Lady T said louder.

"That sounds good," Tracy said to the woman.

"Hang up!" Lady T ordered with a growl, and started for him. The hair sticks in her jet-black bun seemed to glow with anger.

"But I have to go right now," Tracy said, "a colleague needs me," and he hung up the phone. "What's wrong with you?"

Lady T immediately changed her stride, donned a 'bless his heart' look, and came over to put her tiny hand on Tracy's shoulder for comfort.

"Honey," Lady T drawled. "When that woman said, 'all the houses in her neighborhood were white', she wasn't talkin' about the paint color." Lady T nodded her head. "She's racist sweetie, and I don't want to see you in that environment."

Lady T had Tracy's back, and more followed. Tracy worked with different teams, but after a while the 'Trifecta' became the norm. Christopher was a nerdy genius, who at eighteen earned his bachelor's in engineering from Georgia Tech. He also spoke several languages, which was why he had recently returned from Japan. The team lead was Vince - a large, black, retired Navy guy who talked to the client too much. Different fourths joined the three on trips to record data and provide the laugh track, but Lady T made sure Greg kept the Trifecta of Christopher, Vince and Tracy together.

Tracy found this fact out on one of their breaks. Lady T went outside to smoke, and Tracy ate his banana. In return for Lady T's watchful eye with scheduling, Tracy made runs for Happy Meals because Lady T was addicted to collecting Beanie Babies. Tracy eventually had to stage an intervention, which happened on Thursday, February 23, 1999, when Lady T had her radio on in her office.

"And now for traffic," the announcer said. "There's been an accident on 285, and get this, Beanie Babies are scattered across all four lanes! Motorists are stopping to risk life and limb to grab as many as they can, ignoring police direction, and practically shutting down both sides of the interstate."

"Trahhmayehl," Lady T screamed, and bolted out of her office pulling on her coat. Tracy met her in the hall, and looked to see who else needed to escape the fire.

"Come on," Lady T panted. "We got to take an early lunch sweetie. There's piles of defenseless Beanie Babies on 285, and they're in desperate need of rescuin'!"

When Tracy heard Beanie Babies, he grabbed Lady T's arm and arrested her. She tried to explain the urgency, but Tracy wouldn't let go. Eventually, Tracy managed to calm her with some cookies, and soon, the great Lady T was back in control of her office.

With that crisis averted, Atlanta was soon fixed electronically, and the Trifecta headed up the east coast. When the team went to Waltham, Massachusetts, they had a weeklong stint, and Tracy had another encounter with the angel. As the team came back from lunch, Tracy drove the rental car. Christopher was copilot, and Vince and the fourth guy were in the back. When they approached a red light, Tracy stopped.

"Come here," the angel said. "I want to talk to you about some things."

Tracy was pulled out of his body, and taken to an open room with white walls. It was the same angel with the clipboard and scribing pen. Tracy knew he was sent by His instruction, but it was odd to happen while he was driving. Nonetheless, the angel turned to Tracy in the pure whiteness.

"He has big plans set out for you," the angel said. "See if you agree."

Tracy thought this was mostly a rhetorical statement, but God gave Man free will, so Tracy had the right of first refusal.

"I have been sent to talk to you about them," the angel said.

From experience, Tracy knew this would be less talking and more showing. He hoped he wasn't about to be hunted by more demons, or like visceral lessons, but the room was peacefully white. The angel wasn't snarky and actually pleasant to Tracy, perhaps from their last encounter with the demon. They also seemed to have all the time in the world.

"Show me what?" Tracy asked.

Since Tracy asked, the angel produced a small object from his pocket, which resembled a thick, oversized playing card. The angel held it with his left palm facing upward. When he rubbed his right index finger across the top, it flicked an image onto the wall as a projection.

The first scene was of canals that ran by warm brick houses next to green lawns. Smooth plastered homes sat next to a low bridge. This led to a large square, where official white buildings had affixed gilded ornaments. Every building was lived-in, well cared for, and had earned its place. The canal water was clear, and smelled sweet from the linden trees that shaded them.

Then, the angel waved another scene onto the wall, and the first image shifted to the left. The second image was a field of green wheat. In the center, a great pyramid of grass had a bronze lion on top. The mound was incredibly steep and full of rabbit holes, and long ears randomly popped up, followed by eyes to see who was on their roof.

"This is like the picture book," Tracy said, "only on a much grander scale."

"He said you catch on fast," the angel said, and his eyes lit up. "Let us see how fast."

The angel flipped more pictures onto the wall. As he did, the previous image went to the left, and bent in an arc behind Tracy. As more wonderful images flew onto the wall, they were whisked out of the way for the next, and soon, Tracy was inside the drum of a life-sized zoetrope.

"These are the things I have been sent to show you," the angel said.

The angel waved his hand counterclockwise, and the pictures flew around with Tracy as their axis and gained momentum. Faster and faster, the pictures formed a whirlwind of things to come. Amid the tumult of sights, sounds and smells, the angel turned to Tracy.

"Do you take on this mission?" he asked.

Tracy was busy absorbing the wonder and diversity of all he was shown, but he smiled and nodded. With that, the angel stopped the visual tornado. The pictures flew back into the card on the angel's palm, and the walls went white.

"Do you have all that?" the angel asked.

Tracy knew the answer was yes, even with as many questions he had about what he was shown. Tracy also knew He would bring it back to remembrance, which was Grace, so Tracy nodded again.

"Good," the angel said, and Tracy was immediately put back into his body.

Tracy's foot was on the brake of the rental car, and he and his three companions sat at the red light. Tracy was rightly disoriented, and now terrified he was driving.

"How long have we been at this light?" Tracy asked carefully. The team was puzzled by the question, but Christopher answered.

"We just pulled up to it."

"You mean we didn't just sit through a cycle of lights?"

"No," Christopher said. "You just stopped the car Tracy."

To Tracy's mind, he had to have been gone at least five minutes with the angel. It was difficult to comprehend that the vision was out of time, even though he felt time pass.

"That's weird," Tracy said.

"No Tracy," the Tall Shiny Silver Figure said. *"It is not weird, this is real. And to prove to you this is real, turn on the radio."*

Tracy abruptly turned on the radio. On cue, the trumpets blasted in perfect synchronicity. The bass drum's hit followed, and the horns finished the famous riff. Then, the signature bass line of "Got to Be Real" by Cheryl Lynn serenaded Tracy and the team. The lyrics were even more extraordinary, particularly as Tracy realized how much the definition of love transcended flesh, and how His love *is* your love, and our love *is* His love, and all of love *is* here to stay...

"That was real!" Tracy screamed.

This was Tracy's second musical gift, and he was nearly out of his mind. He danced in his seat like when he came home from the hospital as a toddler, or stood in front of his Pawpaw's stereo console singing "Oh Happy Day" at the top of his lungs, except now, it was real.

But Christopher wanted to know. "What was real?"

"You have no idea what just happened to me," Tracy yelled and laughed at the same time, and the light turned green. Tracy took off through the intersection, and his team feared for their life, wondering about the madman behind the wheel.

As time went by, Tracy's co-workers were intrigued. Because Christopher, Vince and Tracy traveled together so often, Tracy felt comfortable enough to share his encounters. As more time passed, his associates saw more things revealed to Tracy, and they believed. Then, from experience, they knew whatever problem came up - if Tracy was involved it would be a success. Then the team went to Europe and stayed abroad for two weeks. There, the scenes Tracy previewed with the angel turned into déjà vu moments from the picture book.

Then, Tracy felt Him beside him as his guide, and the Tall Shiny Silver Figure's presence drew Tracy's attention to things that were important. In Belgium, it was the dew on the crisp green grass, and He pointed out the scent of the outlying vineyards. As Tracy gazed at the intricate Flemish architecture of the college of Louvain-la-Neuve, Tracy felt the centuries of struggle. He appreciated the winemaking that built the campus, and the victory of each building's survival through World War II.

From there, Tracy was soothed by the old-world comfort and heaped chocolates of Bruges. Like the Easter he experienced in Charlotte, Tracy's eyes were opened to a sharpened vibrancy of color. He felt the textures of the building materials reflected in the bends of the circular canals. Everything was familiar, and the Tall Shiny Silver Figure delighted in showing Tracy the gem sites planned for him so long ago on His lap.

At Waterloo the team arrived too late to enter the grounds legally, but it was an easy jump over a fence to cross the field of midsummer wheat. The sun glowed over the trench mounds and enormous field. Tracy crossed the wide expanse, and rabbit holes and eyes were everywhere. At dusk, the two scaled the back of the pyramid to remain undetected, and encountered the massive bronze lion atop his granite perch. There, silence held pall over the enormity of war that stretched from 1815, to the beautiful peace of the evening rolling out before them.

Tracy's travels were also interesting. The new pill for sexual enhancement was noteworthy. During that testing, Tracy was placed in a small kitchen-sized room. In the center was a machine with mechanical arms in every direction that made the tablets. There was a fine white dust everywhere, and Tracy wore a clean suit. Because of secrecy, thirty-six cameras watched his every move.

The first time Tracy was introduced to this type of equipment was in the states. Now, he was in Sandwich England. Surprisingly, it was when the team ordered a bucket of extra crispy chicken that they met a man familiar with the process. The team's server was in his late-twenties. He had a pale, attractive face that matched his British accent, which intrigued Tracy.

"So, what are you blokes doin' in town?" he asked.

"We're doing an inspection at one of the local plants," Tracy said.

"Oh yeah?" he said. "I used to work there," he said with a twinkle.

"Please don't ask," Christopher said quietly.

Tracy smiled. "What did you do there?"

"Well," the young man said. "I musta been a test subject for the little blue pill then, mustn't I?"

Then the chicken was ready, so the man left to put their meal together. Christopher moved closer to Tracy, and spoke to the side.

"Please," Christopher said. "He is using his hands to get our chicken, and I don't want to know anything about this right now," and the attractive server returned.

"So, how did you know it worked?" Tracy asked.

"You know," the Englishman said, "the normal reaction expected."

"He's handling our meat Tracy," Christopher said, and realized what he said. "Please don't go any further with this."

"How did you make it home?" Tracy pressed, and the handsome server handed the team their bucket of food.

"It took a few shots," and he winked at Tracy, "but I got there eventually."

Then it was time to return stateside. They nearly missed their flight because Vince thought someone stole the steering wheel. He had a harder time driving on the left-hand side of the road to the airport. The team was forced to zoom by the white cliffs of Dover without stopping, but Tracy vowed he would return. Back home, the Trifecta was summoned to the office in Atlanta. As the millennium approached more markets opened up. From their success abroad, the team was offered the trip of a lifetime. Australia was the most remote place Tracy ever thought of going, although for the company, it was the gateway to the islands in the Pacific. So when Tracy's team was offered the opportunity, they jumped on it. Tracy also thought He was up to something, so that night, he prayed.

"What's up with this trip Lord?" Tracy asked.

"This will be the last one," He said. *"I had to make it different for you, so you would be ready to move on,"* and Tracy did become weary of travel, as he flew economy the two days it took to arrive.

In Sydney, the vibe of being at the bottom of the other side of the world was immediate. To Tracy, the continent seemed the beginning of time itself. Australia was crisp, alive and invigorating, with a distinct citrus aroma. Then, Tracy realized the 'joie de vivre' he experienced was because the continent's creatures, great or small, were trying to kill his ass. Life was cherished, because everything Aussie was poisonous. Nothing had time to be sluggish, and had to enjoy every single minute they had left. Brown snakes the size of earthworms packed more venom than a cobra. Bottle jellyfish strewn across the pristine beaches looked like used condoms, but were a death trap. The parrots of Sydney were like colorful pigeons, except their beaks had the tensile strength of a vise, and they could swarm with Hitchcockian accuracy if a sandwich was desired.

But for Tracy, the most ominous creature seemed related to the imps from his visions. In a park behind the skyline of Sydney, weirdly caped balls of fur the size of second graders drooped from eucalyptus branches. When evening came, their beady eyes lit up. Then, of one accord, an army of flying foxes took to the air. The huge bats screeched across the dying light to hunt, just like the bloodthirsty monsters in the Dracula movies Tracy had watched as a boy. It was then that Tracy realized he was ready for the next thing. He knew that he wanted to go home, and that he wanted to stay there.

Chapter 28

- a flying fox

Fixing Sydney for Y2K was a lot to do in two weeks, especially after Tracy had two years of dynamic travel with his job. On the tedious flight home across the globe, Tracy decided he was done. Little did he know, over the next three years Tracy would experience three jobs in rapid succession, which would prepare him to become independent from this world's system. So, even though what God prepared for him looked like setbacks, they actually set Tracy up to catapult him to the next level. As He planned, the first steppingstone was with TAVA Technologies itself, even though Tracy had decided to quit.

As soon as he got off the plane, Tracy went into the office. He filled out his time sheet and expense report, and updated his résumé. Tracy hit 'enter' to print five copies, and went to the copy room to get them before anyone else saw them. As Tracy waited for his résumés to collate, Lady T appeared. She went over to the fax machine and glanced over Tracy's shoulder.

"Trahhmayehl," the Southern Ninja Belle said. "I don't need that many copies of your expense report."

"I know," Tracy said, still jet-lagged. "I already handed them in."

"Oh," Lady T said, and she abruptly walked out of the copy room with her un-faxed papers. She went to her desk, saw Tracy's report in her inbox, calculated, and returned to the copy room. She arrived as Tracy pulled his résumés off the printer tray.

214

"By the way," Lady T said. "Greg wants to see you in his office," and Tracy looked at her, caught with the evidence. "And you can probably get rid of those. The shredder is right over there," although she thought better of it. "But give me one to put in your file," and Greg was ready to see Tracy by ten a.m.

"Tracy," Greg said. "I'd like you to have a seat."

Tracy thought he was in trouble - creatures, Australian or not, were not the only things that could be poisonous. Then, the Accounting Manager joined them. As Greg continued looking through one of Tracy's newly minted résumés, Tracy recognized Lady T's handiwork.

"I see you've had some banking experience," Greg said.

"Yes sir, I do," Tracy said.

"So you know a little bit about financials and business."

"That's not what my degree is in, but yes."

"Not a problem. And you have some programming in your past?"

"Yes," Tracy said, and he silently checked in. 'Where is this going Lord?'

"You passed the test," He said. *"This is your promotion."*

Without warning, Greg slapped his hand on his desk as if he had a eureka moment.

"Good," Greg said. "Because you're going to head up our new department."

"What?" Tracy asked, and Lady T's head appeared around the doorframe.

"Shut the door T," Greg said, "and we don't want to be disturbed."

For the next forty-five minutes, Greg, and Lisa from Accounting explained how they wanted Tracy to become the Systems Administrator for TAVA Technologies. Oracle Financials was coming to the forefront for accounting, and they wanted Tracy to make that happen. Their plan was to have him learn the present system, train in Tempe Arizona with an Oracle consultant, and come back to start implementation.

"In order to do this," Greg explained, "we have to make you an officer. Of course this would come with a 10K raise, and we have a corner office for you. It doesn't have windows or furniture yet, but we're going to be moving locations soon, which, by the way, won't be announced until next week, so please keep that quiet."

Tracy was blindsided, but realized the importance of what was happening.

"Who would I answer to?" Tracy asked.

"Us," Greg said, and Tracy realized the other two people in the room were officers of the company. "But before we can go any further, we need to know if you accept."

"What if this doesn't go as planned?" Tracy asked.

"Then I made a mistake," Greg said. "You will be heading up your own department, and we will be looking to you for the best way to do that."

Immediately, Tracy was shown Joseph from the Bible – the one with the amazing coat of many colors. This was the same thing - he had all of the authority, but none of the responsibility.

"We have to know if you agree," Greg continued, "because we need to swear you in as an officer before we can discuss anything further."

Because He had said, 'This is your promotion', Tracy said, "Yes," out loud.

"Good," Greg said, and opened the door to tell Lady T to print the documents.

"It's already done Greg," Lady T hollered from down the hall.

"She was listening?" Greg stammered, and Tracy couldn't help himself.

"How do you think she knows what to get your wife for her birthday?"

"Oh," Greg said, which confirmed Tracy was the right man for the job. When Lady T came back with the papers, Tracy was sworn in. Afterward, Greg stood to shake Tracy's hand. Then he reached into the big drawer of his desk to hand him a thick book.

"Pick out furniture for your new office over the weekend," Greg said. "Here's the catalogue."

Tracy's new job started Monday. He spent the weekend meditating over the fact he was now an officer of a company, and how good God was. He also wondered if Corinthian leather was actually made by Corinthians, and if they would deliver his office chair in short leather tunics. Then, for two weeks, Tracy went over everything with Lisa in accounting. The two weeks following, Tracy went to Tempe Arizona for his first training seminar in Oracle Financials, and he was hooked.

Once he was back in Atlanta, Tracy sought out every class offered and took it. He started his department, and soon there was a company merger that used Tracy's new accounting structure. Similar to when he studied electrical engineering, learning Oracle Financial Systems was like breathing. Tracy had the desire, and the walk was easy. Tracy loved his job, and was surprised how much he liked to lead. He was also his own boss, and had a nine-to-five. He had no travel, no overtime, and could have a banana break with Lady T anytime he wished.

God also used Tracy to minister in the office. Rumors of his experiences in the field came home to roost, and Tracy's advice was sought out as the end of the twentieth century loomed. Y2K compliance would soon be obsolete, so TAVA Technologies downsized as projects dwindled. Because he was the company's computer guru, Tracy helped employees run search engines for new jobs. As colleagues were laid off, just as many found new, better paying jobs with Tracy's help. Word spread, and praise reports came back.

"Prayer works dude," a tech assistant said.

By the end of November, TAVA Technologies was pretty thin, but Tracy was still grateful. He had seen much of the world, and the company instigated and paid for his training in Oracle Financials. This was a pivotal step on his path, and would eventually lead Tracy to the rendezvous page in the picture book. But now, it was time to move on. Late one Sunday afternoon, the Tall Shiny Silver Figure gave Tracy a directive.

"Look on the computer to see what Oracle jobs are paying," He said.

"But I love my job, and they are so good to me."

"Just see what other companies are paying for your experience level in Oracle," He said.

"Ok, if you insist."

"I do."

So, Tracy ran a search engine the same way he helped so many of his fellow employees. Job after job popped up, and many were local. Each job also paid a minimum of twenty-five thousand more than Tracy's current salary.

"The devil is a liar!" Tracy yelled, but was conflicted. "Although, I'm still grateful for the job you gave me Lord. This is the brook that is feeding me, so I will stay here until I am told to go elsewhere."

There was no answer until the next day.

On Monday, Lisa called the project managers in for a meeting. The ones leaving were briefed on their exit interviews and paperwork. After the meeting, Tracy received a praise report in the hallway when a colleague told Tracy he had gotten a fifteen thousand dollar raise and had become a manager.

That afternoon, when Tracy sent in his follow-up paperwork to Lisa, he got a return email to see her in her office. When Tracy arrived, Travis stood behind Lisa's desk. He was a tall, broad-shouldered white man, who easily weighed three hundred pounds. Originally, he was a Georgia chicken farmer and he preached at a small church on Sundays. Travis had heard about Tracy's insights. He was puzzled, because Travis couldn't understand how a gay black man from West Virginia could possibly know so much about God.

"I'm afraid we have some sad news," Lisa said.

"What happened?" Tracy asked. "Is it something we can pray about?"

Lisa's eyes swelled with tears. She had become close working so directly with Tracy over the past two years, and this situation was difficult for her.

"Travis is here because we have to lay you off," Lisa admitted.

"Are you serious?" Tracy asked.

"Yes," Lisa said meekly.

"Hallelujah!" Tracy yelled, and began praising God. Then he looked at Travis and was stopped. "But you think you're in here for Lisa," and Tracy laughed, "but you're actually here to be a witness!"

At first, Lisa and Travis weren't sure if Tracy was having a nervous breakdown.

"Last night," Tracy explained, "He pushed me. God told me to look online, and do you know what I found?" and Lisa and Travis stayed wary. "The lowest salary listed for my competency level in Oracle Financials was twenty-five thousand more than I make now, and there are a lot of jobs out there."

Travis smiled, slowly able to see past the physical roadblocks of this world, and see the spiritual events unfolding.

"Now, I'm gonna miss you guys, but God's giving me a promotion," and Tracy pointed at Travis and smiled. "And you're here to see it. I didn't see it coming either. I would have stayed here another five years if you wanted me to," and Travis understood. Lisa was still confused, but was relieved as she began to understand how little she had to do with what was happening.

"But you are releasing me," Tracy said, "and I am so grateful."

"I've never seen anything like this," Travis said under his breath.

"Isn't God good?" Tracy asked, and danced again as he headed out of Lisa's office. "Hallelujah!" Tracy yelled from the hall. "God's got promotion on His mind!" and he clicked his heels.

"Hallelujah," Travis repeated quietly, and marveled at such circumstance. So, Tracy left TAVA technologies and looked for a job. Unlike the colleagues he helped, Tracy didn't find one.

Over the next weeks he was offered a few, but Tracy recognized them as distractions, and he sensed confusion. Either the job wasn't a good match, or not the salary God showed him. Because he had time, Tracy took more training courses in Oracle Financials. This prepared him for the last whirlwind of tests God planned before Tracy would return to Ohio. However, at the moment, money was drying up, so that night Tracy got on his knees.

"It's getting close to the end of my savings Lord. I need you to open up a door fast, because I didn't cause that last door to shut."

His answer was immediate: *"Go downstairs, retrieve your old waterbed, clean it up and set it up tomorrow."*

"I asked You about a job, and You tell me to put together a waterbed?"

"Do you believe I heard you, and that My answer is to put your waterbed together?"

"Yeah."

"Good. Do the simple thing, and I will do the impossible. After you get the waterbed together, it will take the whole day to heat up so you can get a good night's sleep. Because the day after tomorrow, you will need to be up early to receive a phone call."

"How early will that phone call be Lord?"

"Early, so get a good night's sleep."

The next day, Tracy put his waterbed together, heated it and slept well. The following day he got up at five, got his coffee, ate his cereal, and did his praise and worship. Then, Tracy felt a nudge to shave, shower, and get dressed for work. By seven, Tracy was in a suit and tie waiting for what was to come. The recruiter called at eight-fifteen.

"How soon can you meet with the client?" she asked.

"I'm ready to go out the door right now," Tracy said.

When the recruiter told Tracy where the interview was he recognized the address. Tracy had met with this client, but the position was not a match. However, that was before, and this could be different. Tracy arrived at nine, and Teddy met with him immediately.

Teddy looked like a panda, but spoke like an Acadian from New Orleans, so the two liked each other immediately.

"You got here fast," Teddy said. "I just talked to the recruiter forty minutes ago."

"By faith," Tracy said, "I am ready to go."

"I like your spirit," Teddy said. "When can you start?"

"I'm ready now," Tracy said, and Teddy laughed.

"Well H.R. isn't. We just developed this position an hour ago. But I tell you what, let's meet with the team, an' you can start tomorrow," and Teddy lumbered out of his office. "I still can't believe you got here so fast," Teddy said again softly. Then they went to meet the team that was to develop the new Oracle department for WebMD, and Tracy smiled.

He knew this was what God meant when he left TAVA Technologies. But to say God had promotion on His mind was an understatement. As the millennium dawned, Tracy was swept into the tech revolution. The dot-com industry swelled, Atlanta got WebMD, and Tracy's expertise in Oracle and merging tech companies put him in the forefront. Tracy developed the Help Desk, and became head honcho of System Administration. Behind the scenes, God gave Tracy insights on how the system worked from His perspective. The result was that Tracy was able to solve every problem.

Soon, Tracy was on call 24/7, and he carried a pager to keep every techie and medical merger in Atlanta on track. Tracy rode the wave as companies started, boomed and merged, which created a sea of thirty-somethings with way too much money in their expense accounts. Teddy began building a plane in his three-car garage and tried to talk Tracy into skydiving, but Tracy talked him into studying Eagle Claw Kung Fu instead. Another director drove a different color motorcycle for each day of the week.

To throw fuel on the fire, Atlanta hosted the Super Bowl in 2000. As a high-ranked employee, Tracy was invited to the dinner before WebMD's private concert with Elton John at the Fox Theater. There, Tracy experienced what it was to be swanky. Dress was black tie, although Elton inspired hyped couture that translated to diamond studded fishnet stockings, lace on top hats and feather boas, and almost everything was spattered with sequins.

After the concert, everyone went to the clubs where things went from crazy to insane. The chant was: 'Ain't no party like a WebMD party, 'cause a WebMD party don't stop! Say what!?!', and repeat. The best part was – that was what actually happened. In the small hours of the morning, Atlanta was socked with an ice storm. So, wherever revelers were, that's where they stayed until midweek. Then, like a strange spring, the carnival of party animals was finally able to call it quits. Flattened hairdos from days spent in a car crawled to gas stations and diners, and then deflated furs, wrinkled tuxedoes, and exhausted stilettos finally went home.

Then it was back to work, and everything was great for a year. Then, just as quickly, there was envy and strife, and confusion was followed by every evil work. Because WebMD's star rose so quickly, there was a hostile takeover. Its founder was ousted, and the company planned to move to Nashville. Tracy not only didn't want to go back to Tennessee, the culture of the company had changed drastically. Teddy was fired, and then Tracy's friendly outgoing nature was misinterpreted by his replacement.

Tracy had no previous experience working a Help Desk, and because Oracle was so new, few knew how to run an Oracle Help Desk either. But this seemed to be God's point, and His light made Tracy's expertise shine like a lighthouse. The office at WebMD had a row of private offices on the side, and an open room with cubicles where Tracy sat front and center. Tracy frequently went to co-worker's desks to solve issues on their computers, where he was also overheard.

In addition, the Tall Shiny Silver Figure was more eager and noisier. He began first thing in the morning. As Tracy got ready for work, He talked a blue streak about what they were about to do that day. By the time Tracy reached his desk, He literally ran circles around him. He spoke to Tracy in the past, present, and future tense as He whirled around him. As He did so, Tracy saw parts of His face, or sometimes His arm or leg went by in a swish of light and colors. A little like the zoetrope, He swirled around Tracy in a tight 360-degree circle, and Tracy saw hues and flashes of silver as He spoke of many things at once:

"Get this phone call... We healed that last year... In two years we are going to..." the Tall Shiny Silver Figure said at once, in a dizzying funnel around Tracy's face.

Then He repeated His statements as a mantra, which created a driving rhythm of what had happened, was happening, and would happen. When Tracy went to someone's desk, he saw pictures of his co-worker's families. Tracy learned who was in the hospital, or whose birthday it was, just like Lady T had. As he did, the Tall Shiny Silver Figure gave Tracy wisdom concerning his co-workers lives.

Therefore, Tracy fixed the Help Desk ticket and the personal problem at the same time, and the two were on fire. Tracy called the phenomenon 'Swirl Sutra' from the way His words and the rhythm of colors and light spun around Tracy's head. Because Tracy *was* the Help Desk, and his cubicle was front and center, the hype of 'Swirl Sutra' became a beacon.

The upshot was that when Tracy simultaneously solved Help Desk issues and his co-workers issues, Dick, his new supervisor, misinterpreted Tracy's time spent on the phone as 'personal phone calls'. Back when Teddy managed the office, this comradery was encouraged. But Dick was the opposite of the amiable panda. He was a tall, skinny white boy, whose dislike for Tracy may have stemmed from his racism, or perhaps from him being a closeted gay man.

Whatever the reason, Dick spent thirty days gathering information by listening to Tracy's calls, and recording what was said. What Dick didn't realize was that Tracy kept stacks of black composition notebooks. In them, Tracy also recorded everything he said or did, which was an invaluable resource in solving Oracle issues. The notebooks also kept track of everyone's birthday, concerns about their family, and what the Tall Shiny Silver Figure had said. That way, Tracy could check back with his co-workers for a praise report. The standoff occurred at the end of the month, when Dick set up a bogus problem for Tracy to solve with a time limit.

Shortly before 4:30 p.m. on a Friday, an innocent IT guy called the Help Desk. He said he needed Tracy to fix his MICR printer. Tracy thought this was odd, because MICR printers were only used to print checks, which was done in the Accounting Department.

But according to the IT guy, the printer was supposed to be online and working by 5 p.m. So Tracy collected his black notebooks and left the Help Desk. On the way, he passed three of Dick's stooges, one who was the new IT Director. It was more than suspicious they hung around the water cooler by the MICR printer, and Tracy recognized the test when the 'Naysayers' sneered as he passed.

"So," one of the Naysayers said. "You think you can get it done by five-o'clock?"

"Sure will," Tracy said. "I'll be right back. Just give me a few minutes."

Then, 'Swirl Sutra' kicked into action as Tracy walked to the IT guy's desk. The young 'Innocent' was upset he couldn't solve such a seemingly simple problem. Tracy looked at his computer screen, and He swirled around with information in flashes and a flurry of words. Then, a co-worker was on her way home and she interrupted Tracy.

"My mother loved the necklace for her birthday," she reported. "You always have the right answers. It was the perfect thing," and then Tracy returned to the computer issue.

"What did you call the printer name?" Tracy asked, and the Innocent told him. "Now, let me see how you set it up on your screen," Tracy said, and instantly, the Tall Shiny Silver Figure showed Tracy. "You didn't mess up. This wasn't your fault, and I didn't mess up with my setup, but we can fix this. WebMD decided all printers should be named with all capital letters. Your supervisor should have told you this."

The Innocent looked at Tracy with confusion.

"So," Tracy said, "kindly forward me the email from the IT Director, which showed the setup he instructed you to do, and then I'll fix it."

The Innocent did.

"Now, I need to drive from your computer," Tracy said, and he did.

It was close to five-o'clock. Tracy signed in and changed the printer's name to all caps, but the new IT Director didn't know Tracy had that authorization.

"Now print something," Tracy said, "anything," and he left. As Tracy returned to his desk, he passed the Naysayers by the water cooler.

"Do you think you have it solved?" the IT Director asked with a smirk. As he finished speaking, the MICR printer spat out a sheet of paper.

"Look behind you," Tracy said without breaking his stride, "and you tell me if I solved the problem."

The IT Director followed Tracy back to his Help Desk. "How did you do that?"

"When God tells you to take Oracle classes on the weekends, you learn stuff," Tracy said. Then, he looked the newly minted IT Director in the eye. "I also designed and set up the system."

Chapter 29

- Ed Michaels

Even though Tracy passed the test, he decided to move on. He had vacation time saved up for a trip he had planned to take with Teddy to China, so Tracy left WebMd and got a job at Global Payments. Once there, he rolled out an Oracle Implementation in thirty days for testing. It went live in sixty days, and Tracy realized God's wisdom:

While Tracy developed the Help Desk at WebMD, he learned how to be a consultant from the back end. Because Tracy solved independent contractors' issues, he learned what they did. Tracy also learned what independent contractors needed, how to manage them, and how *not* to manage them from his experience after the hostile takeover.

The end result was that 'Swirl Sutra' and the Help Desk prepared Tracy for the next level. With that completed, the Tall Shiny Silver Figure gave Tracy another directive that prepared Tracy to leave Atlanta.

"I need you to buy a desk," He said.

"But I have a desk," Tracy said.

Tracy had a drafting table, but he didn't work much at home. If he did, he used his laptop. Yet Tracy did as instructed, got in his Jeep, and went to a warehouse superstore on his lunch break to buy a desk. When Tracy got there, he was stalled.

"Sit here and praise Me," He said.

"I thought You wanted me to buy a desk," Tracy said. But the unction was strong, so Tracy didn't get out of Bruce. Instead, Tracy finished his fast food and sat in the parking lot listening to praise music.

That evening, he went over to Jack and Kathy's, which by this time was standard protocol. Tracy met Jack and Kathy after he moved to Atlanta, because Jack and Kathy's next-door neighbors were best friends with Ed Michaels. Tracy had met Ed Michaels years earlier when he lived in Chattanooga, and Ed was an integral part of the convoluted path through this season of Tracy's life.

Ed was fifteen years older than Tracy, and didn't look it. However, in gay years that was a few lifetimes. The difference between Stonewall and allowing gays in the military under "Don't ask, don't tell" was quite a gap, to say nothing of the effect AIDS had on their generations. The bridge was Ed Michaels himself, and his house. Similar to Dale, Ed was an engineer for the Tennessee Valley Authority for nearly forty years, and worked in the nuclear industry since its infancy. Ed Michaels was a tall, handsome man, who maintained carefully coifed strawberry-blond hair and made no apologies. Ed camped gay banter as well as he spun his colossal collection of vinyl, which was how the friendship started. At first, it was a small after-party once Alan Gold's Discotheque had last call. But that was all it took.

Back then, Ed lived in a modest suburban neighborhood of Chattanooga. His house was on a small rise, which allowed easy sightlines to the living room's most striking feature – a massive disco ball. Ed's furniture was also on casters, so the space could go from sitting area to dance floor in less than thirty-seconds. The 60's retractable lamp made space for the bar, once the dining room table and chairs were against the wall. The disco ball and its lights were wired directly to the switches. The adjacent spare bedroom was shelved floor-to-ceiling and wall-to-wall with records from the 60's, 70's and 80's. Very few recordings made it into the collection past that date because by the 90's, according to Ed, the music really did die.

But the house came alive when the mobile DJ booth was rolled from the spare bedroom, the furniture was moved, and the disco ball was switched on - which with the right crowd happened simultaneously. And to say Ed Michaels was colorful was so inadequate it could be considered a hate crime. He was a true child of the barefoot, hippie-turned-gay generation, and there wasn't a blind or curtain in the house. That way, according to Ed, passersby might join the party. And it was true, from the street Ed's bare chest and cut-off jeans were plainly visible dancing between his vinyl vault and full DJ setup in the living room.

On weekends, mirrored slices of light spun from the disco ball, which made the first floor twirl and flash into the night. Years later, after Ed retired and moved to Atlanta, the disco operation was moved to his basement. This had hot pink walls, and was decorated in a 1970's Pimp Daddy style where Ed did 'Disco Yoga'. However, back when Tracy was in Chattanooga, Ed Michaels was an oasis in the desert. At that time, Tracy had a mostly tragic relationship with the "Idiot Friend" as Ed called him. On the occasion of one of their breakups, Tracy needed cheering up, and it was cocktail hour on a Friday afternoon.

"Girl," Ed exclaimed. "You can't be lookin' all sad and droopy like that, you might ruin the party," and Ed looked at Tracy carefully. "I know. You need a martini. Have ya ever had a martini?"

"No," Tracy said, who was not a big drinker of any kind. So Ed fixed a dirty martini without fruit.

Tracy took the glass, held it up to the light, and wondered why it looked so boring.

"What's a matter?" Ed lilted. "You need some olives to swirl girl? 'Cause I can make it pretty. I just don't like all that loveliness to have anythin' drownin' in it."

"No, that's ok," Tracy said, and gulped it like chugging a beer.

"Oh my!" Ed screamed. "I never saw anyone do that before! Are y'all ok?"

Tracy was fine with that one, and the ones he learned to sip that followed. It was Veteran's Day weekend, so the disco ball spun with red, white and blue lights. But the cops saw fire-engine red and cop car blue, and assumed there was an emergency. Once they parked out front, the policemen realized nothing was on fire except the disco inferno. Because the doorbell couldn't be heard, they knocked. Tracy heard this, and moved his martini to his other hand to open the door. In front of him stood two officers. One was a handsome Latino, the other was a chiseled study in manhood with sandy hair, and both were buff and fresh from the academy.

"Ed!" Tracy yelled. "Did you hire strippers?"

When Ed saw the uniforms, he turned the music down to dinner party volume. The crowd meandered toward the kitchen to be closer to the rear sliding glass door. Judging by the previous decibel level the young cadets made the obvious choice, except it was Chattanooga, and it was Ed Michael's house.

"We heard a complaint about the noise from the neighbors," the sandy cop said.

"Oh really?" Ed said and giggled. "That's funny Miss Thing. Watch this…" and Ed turned to his guests and yelled: "Which one a you neighbors complained about the music bein' too loud?"

"It's not loud enough!" came from the back. "And I need another drink!"

Vindicated, Mr. Michaels turned back to face the young officers.

"Mary," Ed said. "The problem with you is, you're all brand-new. All the neighbors are here. We do this every Friday night, so you might as well get used to it."

The hot cops were a little confused, and were unplugged by Ed's easy manner that wasn't accusatory, he was just explaining.

"Now I do understand," Ed said. "Y'all saw those red and blue lights flashin' up an' down the street, an' y'all thought you needed to come an' save us," and Ed chuckled. "Which, I, personally think is just wonderful, especially as yummy as you two are. But don't worry, the lights on my disco ball will be red and green for Christmas before too long."

The cops couldn't move. Nothing close to this was in any of their training, but Ed smiled and left the door open as he went behind his DJ table.

"So," Ed concluded. "Y'all are welcome to come in an' dance if you want, but ain't nothin' gonna be turned down up in here," and the real Ms. Thing pumped the music back up to hoots and cheers.

Of course, Ed Michaels was out as much during the day as he was at night. After seeing "To Wong Fu, Thanks for Everything! Julie Newmar", he and Tracy ran home. Ed pulled the rainbow flag off his living room wall, and they went to the garage to put the top down on his blue convertible Mustang. Once they affixed the declaration to the back seat, they drove to Signal Mountain with their gayness flapping as a cape, and blasted Donna Summer to the summit and back. The important thing was, over the years Tracy met Ed's close friends in Atlanta, who routinely went up to "Chattavegas" to party. When Tracy moved down to Atlanta, they had a dinner party. It was there that Tracy was introduced to their neighbors, Jack and Kathy. They were in their early thirties, and had an adorable two-year-old daughter.

Now, Tracy went back to work, after he praised God in the superstore's parking lot. Then he told a few co-workers about his experience *not* buying a desk. That night, he told Jack and Kathy over dinner.

"That's interestin'," Jack said. "How big a desk?"

"He didn't say," Tracy said.

"We have my Dad's old accounting desk," Kathy said.

Kathy's father had died a few years earlier, and they were downsizing her mother to something more reasonable. They had emptied the house, and the desk was the last piece of furniture left.

"We would have to clean it up," Kathy continued, "but it's a nice desk. Why don't you come by this weekend? If you like it, you can have it."

"Ok," Tracy said. "I'll come by with the Jeep."

"You're gonna need somethin' a lot bigger than Bruce," Jack said.

"Ok, I'll see if I can borrow Ed Michaels' truck," Tracy said.

"This is two giant-sized bookcases and a legal-sized desk," Jack said. "You're gonna need a flatbed and some help."

"How much help?" Tracy asked.

"At least five people," Jack concluded.

The next day, Tracy tried to round up friends from work. But they were busy bungee jumping, or other extreme things. He felt he had to at least show up to apologize, so Tracy met Jack and Kathy at her family's home. The large house was on a corner lot in the outskirts of Atlanta. They showed Tracy the desk, and then Kathy looked at Jack with a tilt of her head.

"Hey Tracy," she said. "Do you mind if we talk for a minute? There's a nice garden out back."

"Sure," Tracy said, and went outside behind the house, and the backyard was lovely.

After a few moments, Jack and Kathy returned and showed Tracy the rest of the house like a realtor would. They pointed out the mellowness of the hardwood floors in the living room, the great kitchen and full basement. Nothing needed repair, with the exception of an updated paint job.

"Didn't you say you were looking for something, like a rent to buy?" Kathy asked.

"At one time I was," Tracy said, "but the market isn't too appealing right now, so I stopped."

"I know what you mean," Kathy said. "How much are you paying in rent?"

"Nine hundred a month," Tracy said.

"How about if we workout a lease-purchase agreement for a hundred more than you're paying now?" Kathy asked.

"That way we won't have to move the desk," Jack said, and Tracy felt His nudge.

"All along you thought this was about a desk," He said.

What the Tall Shiny Silver Figure meant was that Tracy needed a desk to meet with clients. From this point on, Tracy would only have consulting jobs, and work from a seated position. At the time, Tracy didn't understand the 'desk' represented his new position in life. He did think the house was everything he had ever wanted. It was on a quiet street, had a huge basement to workout in, a fireplace, outdoor patio and grill, and plenty of rooms for family to come visit. So, Tracy moved in, and for the next year Atlanta was good.

Then, almost as quickly, circumstances dried up. Once again, confusion, murk and sadness gathered strength. As the economy shrank and layoffs loomed, God led Tracy to study Psalm 91. Tracy studied it for a year before he was released from his assignment. During that time, the second dot-com bubble burst. Almost overnight the wave the tech industry rode crashed, swept many out to sea, and the party heralded by Elton John was finally over.

"This brook is drying up Lord," Tracy said, as he had said before, "and You haven't spoken yet as to what to do next."

"Start packing up the house," He said. *"Then, I want you to move in with your parents in Columbus."*

"But Lord," Tracy protested. "I can go back to West Virginia. I have the key to Granny's house right here," and Tracy picked up his keychain.

"No Tracy," He said. *"Before you can go any further, you need to understand your family bloodline, and only your father can tell you that."*

After Tracy got over the shock, he called his Dad to tell him what he heard. Harry was surprised, but agreed to the plan. Tracy packed and put everything else in storage. Then, Tracy stalled, much like he did before he left Akron for Chattanooga. Tracy stayed put in his beautiful empty house, hoping for a different confirmation.

Instead, God gave Tracy another directive, which was encouragement for something in his future. Tracy called these power pellets, and the encouragement was like bonuses in a video game that allowed the player to keep going. In terms of this world, they were rewards the flesh could understand.

"Look up Hung Ga teachers online," He said.

Tracy did, and Mo's name popped up, Tracy's friend from college days. Mo was listed as an instructor in Florida. By this time, Mo had trained at one of the number one Hung Ga Schools in the country, which was a highly specialized system of Kung Fu. Tracy called, and he immediately recognized the voice that answered.

"Is this Mo?" Tracy asked, and there was a stunned silence on the other end. "Who used to go to West Virginia Tech back in the eighties?"

"Trace?" Mo asked. "Is that you?"

"It sure is buddy," Tracy said. "What have you been up to?"

"Oh, this and that," Mo said. "It's good to hear your voice."

"I see you're teaching."

"You could say that. When can you come down? It would be great to see you again so we can workout."

"Well, I'm kind of in a bind right now," Tracy admitted. "The dot-com burst hit pretty hard here."

"I understand. It did here too."

Tracy couldn't find more to say, and Mo understood.

"But no problem," Mo decided. "Stay in touch, and when you get back on your feet, I'll be here."

"That means a lot buddy," Tracy said, and held back a tear. "I will."

Then, Tracy sat in his huge house. His birthday came and went, and Tracy waited for an alternate directive other than living with his father in Ohio. Then, at 5 a.m. on April 29, 2003, a rare earthquake shook Atlanta. The next night, Creflo Dollar explained at Bible Study. He said that whenever there was an earthquake, God released something in the earth, and a change was about to happen.

The next day, Tracy closed and locked the door of what he thought was his dream house. Before he left Atlanta, Tracy sat in the parking lot of World Changers Church, and he had communion in Bruce. Then, with the last money he had Tracy went north. He drove by Granny and Moody's house, and headed west for Columbus. A decade had passed since Tracy had left Akron. His time in the desert of Chattanooga, and the proving ground of Atlanta was finished, and Tracy finally crossed back over the Ohio state line.

- Tracy in 'Horse Stance'

Chapter 30

Harry and Lynn welcomed their son into their home, although it was an odd thing for Tracy to live with his parents at his age. Accordingly, Tracy wanted to pay rent and find a job, but his first task was to get Granny to stop calling. She couldn't understand how Tracy could pass by her house.

"Why didn't you come here?" Granny asked. "I've been takin' care of you all my life. You got the key to the house. I raised you. I know you best. Your father don't know you."

Tracy couldn't explain why he was in Columbus, other than God had sent him.

"Watch this," Granny said. "I'll get your room ready, an' I'll make sure he puts you out now. Put your father on the phone," and Tracy did. "Did you know your son was gay?" Granny cackled.

However, Granny already played that card with Harry during the famous car incident after Tracy graduated high school. Still, Harry's countenance became troubled, and he went to his bedroom with the phone to speak with Granny privately. When he came back, he handed the phone to Tracy.

"She's really upset with you son," Harry said, "but she wants to talk with you."

"Well," Granny said. "There was nothin' I could say to put you out of his house. He also said he'd take care of you, an' you were free to go if you wanted to come back."

"I know that Granny," Tracy said. "But for whatever reason, I am supposed to be here."

Moody chimed in from the other phone. "Is God really directin' ya boy? Or are ya just fuckin' up. 'Cause ya know this is crazy."

But Tracy was in Columbus to stay, and he was front and center. Harry and Lynn's home was at the entrance of their well-manicured development. It was a large stucco house with a steep roof for snow, with classical brick columns and a recessed front entryway. The family entered from the side garage, and passed the laundry and two guest rooms into a great room. The kitchen was along the back with a separating island, before white Berber carpet with a rose relief magnified the home's spacious formality. Harry's office was opposite the formal dining room, separated by the front door and hall. Harry and Lynn's bedroom suite took up the other end of the house.

Off the back of the great room was a small Florida room, which led to a patio and grill. Everything was staged over the immense finished basement, which had an informal carpeted living area and fireplace. So the dichotomy of Granny and Moody's house, compared with Harry and Lynn's, couldn't have been clearer. Yet Tracy was both, even without meeting his father's part of himself until his teens, and, according to God, that was why Tracy was in Ohio.

When Tracy returned, his little brother Bryan was in college. So it was just Tracy, Harry and Lynn in the house. But one issue had to be solved, so Harry called Tracy into his office. Unlike Tracy's meetings with Moody, Harry's meetings were more formal. Everything was in its place on Harry's large desk, and his library occupied the wall behind alphabetized by subject.

So, even in a jogging suit, Harry looked ready for a board meeting. The first conference was about the Christian fish decal with rainbow stripes stuck on Tracy's Jeep. The idea of a gay Christian son was an oxymoron to the household at the time. It wasn't something Tracy's parents wanted displayed in their driveway at the entrance of their development. Tracy recognized the roadblock the enemy put in his way. He wasn't going to let any offense hinder him, so he removed the decal.

However, as difficulties mounted, Tracy realized whatever he had to learn about his father's bloodline was important. Dark forces seemed at work from all angles. Another confirmation of this came the following week. Tracy hadn't found a job, and Lynn couldn't understand why.

She was on the kitchen side of the island in the great room. She sipped a juice she made, and Tracy sipped his on the living room side.

"This doesn't make any sense," Lynn said. "Remember how we got your first job?"

"Yes," Tracy said, "and I don't understand this either."

"I mean, I certainly don't mind you being here," Lynn said. "But you just went around the world. It seems strange you're supposed to come back here."

"This is where He told me I need to be," Tracy said.

"Well," Lynn stated. "You are a child of God, and supposed to have shelter and clothing. You're needs are supposed to be met, and the devil is a liar!"

Suddenly, the house shook gently. Tracy simultaneously broke into a cold sweat, but like someone had dropped a bucket of water over his head, to the point Tracy felt water well up in his shoes. Harry felt the tremor, ran from his office, and was uncharacteristically hyper.

"Is Tracy working out?" Harry asked, and then Harry saw Tracy. "If that wasn't you, what was that shaking?" and then Harry noticed Tracy was wet, and looked at Lynn. "What did you do? Did you spray him with water?"

Lynn shot her husband a penetrating look, but Tracy was completely doused.

"Why are you wet Tracy?" Harry asked. "Did you just exercise or something?"

"No Dad," Tracy said. "This is the first time He has ever done this."

Soon after, Tracy got a job that included travel during the week, and things settled into a routine. Tracy also enjoyed being back at Christian Assembly. The congregation was gearing up for a symposium over the Fourth of July holiday. Through their conversations about church, Harry was pleasantly surprised how much Tracy knew of the church and scripture. Harry also began to wonder about his son's relationship with God.

At the same time, Harry was uneasy with Tracy's public acknowledgement of this relationship. Harry and Lynn were both concerned how a man of God should be seen in the world. For instance, one evening, Tracy came out from his room and headed out. Lynn saw his red sneakers and shot Harry a look.

Before Tracy realized it, Harry jumped off the couch, and somehow beat Tracy to the front door. The only time Tracy saw his father move faster was during a previous summer visit. Harry came home and saw Tracy on the front steps. After he parked his Cadillac in the garage, Harry came through the house. Then he opened and closed the front door to see what was so interesting.

"Son," Harry said. "What are you doing?"

"It's fascinating Dad," Tracy said. "I'm watching this garden snake stalk this frog."

"Snake!?!" Harry shouted. "You got to kill that thing!"

By the time Tracy looked up, Harry stood behind him with a snow shovel. He had run to the garage to get it, and returned before Tracy had moved. In fact, the door alarm hadn't finished beeping from the door being reopened, and Tracy began to laugh.

"It's not funny son," Harry said, a little out of breath.

"A snow shovel Dad?" Tracy asked.

"It's the biggest thing I could find," Harry said quickly. "Now kill it!" So, Moody wasn't the only patriarch to have a snake as his kryptonite. Now, Harry managed to pass Tracy to block his exit in his very red sneakers.

"Son," Harry said sweetly. "Where are you going?" and Harry leaned awkwardly on the wall with his elbow to block the door. Although, Harry's pose made it look like he was about to get a cramp in his ankle.

"I'm going to the movies Dad," Tracy answered.

"Dressed like that?"

"What's wrong Dad?"

"Those shoes," Harry said gently. "You are going out of the house in those shoes?"

"These are my most comfortable chucks Dad."

"But, they are red son."

"So?"

"Well," Harry decided. "Your Mom and I have decided that I need to take you shopping."

"Ok," because Tracy still didn't understand.

"But, in the mean time, do you have some penny loafers or something?"

"Sure Dad, I can do that," and Tracy changed his shoes.

But their shoes represented the divide: Tracy's red sneakers, and his father's pristine dress shoes. Harry's walk with God ended up with him being a public figure as a teacher and minister. His house anchored his community, his ministry fortified his church, and Harry routinely ran into previous high school students and their growing families at the grocery store. Tracy's path took him through the southern desert, made him a cool corporate consultant, and his red sneakers had actually gone to gay bars where he watched drag performances of Kristy MacColl's song, "In these Shoes?"

To narrow the disparity Harry and Tracy went shopping, and Lynn wasn't the only one who loved clothes. Harry's passion not only made him a snappy dresser, there was a purpose. His dress shirts were pressed to perfection, and his first, middle and last name was embroidered on the right sleeve, which was revealed when Harry shook someone's hand. But that wasn't the only thing. When Tracy picked a polo shirt off a sale rack, Harry grimaced.

"Son," Harry said. "Let me show you something," and Harry reluctantly took the polo to hold it for Tracy. "Here son, feel the edge of this sleeve," and Tracy did. "This fabric will cut you."

Harry discarded the offending fabric, and grabbed an exquisite polo from a hanger behind him. "Try this one," Harry said proudly. "See, this is what you want. Something that will love you back."

So Tracy learned a few tricks, but his style was pretty much set by this time. Left to his own devices, Tracy went back to his casual ways. Later, at the grocery store, Tracy stood next to his father in the juice aisle, deciding.

"Ok Lord," Tracy said. "What's better for me after a workout - coconut water, or aloe vera juice?"

"Son," Harry said. "You could say that to the Lord silently."

"Muzzle the ox, and you will not get the results," He said. *"If you do not say it, you will not see it."*

Tracy looked at his father and wondered if he heard anything, but Harry moved on to the fresh fruit department.

"See what Lord?" Tracy said softly.

*"Remember? 'Man shall not live by bread alone, but by **every** word that proceedeth out of the mouth of God.' I am a builder. Everything that comes out of My mouth is meant to expand and cause increase. So if you do not speak our conversations out loud, there will not be a manifestation in the earth. If you just 'think' our*

conversation, the only thing you will receive from Me are dreams and visions. Building manifestations starts by speaking My conversations out loud."

"That's pretty cool Lord," Tracy said.

"If you act like I am real, than I will be real to you. If you keep Me in your mind, that is where I will stay. If you speak our conversations out loud, I will manifest out loud, and you will live life out loud. Live Life Out Loud Tracy."

"Amen!" Tracy shouted, which to Tracy felt great. But Harry was startled by his son's outburst, and looked at Tracy before he picked out the perfect box of strawberries.

Then, the Jubilee at their church was upon them. Tracy went with Harry to pick up one of the guest preachers from the airport. He was a finely dressed black man with alarmingly welcoming eyes, and had a charming English accent mixed with the Caribbean. He and Harry might have been mistaken for brothers except for the preacher's distinct, 1970's-looking clipped beard and connected moustache. When Harry got out of the car, they hugged and called each another brother anyway. The preacher's wife was impeccably dressed, had rich almond colored skin, and an easy smile. Tracy came for their luggage and put it in the trunk of the Cadillac.

"And who is this?" the preacher asked.

"This is my son Tracy," Harry said proudly. "Tracy, this is…"

"Dr. Myles Monroe," Tracy interrupted, and Harry was surprised.

"You follow Dr. Monroe?" Harry asked.

"Please, call me Myles," the preacher said.

Later, after they dropped the Monroes at their hotel, Harry was curious. "You follow Myles?" Harry asked.

"I don't really do anything but watch Christian television when I'm at home," which made Harry ponder his son. "All I know is," Tracy explained, "I am supposed to get more of Him and His word, and that's how I've been able to hold on."

During the festival, Harry and Tracy ferried the Monroes to and from the church. After the last revival, Harry drove the Monroes to the airport with Tracy as co-pilot. Myles sat behind Harry, and his wife Ruth sat behind Tracy in the back seat. They were quiet after so much church, until Dr. Monroe had to speak. His discourse was measurably Bahamian, but he wasn't the one with the message.

"Harry," Myles said, "The Holy Ghost is telling me there is something special about your son. There is a special anointing on him. Did you know that?"

Harry didn't answer.

"Is he your first-born?" Myles asked.

"Why, yes he is," Harry answered.

"Tracy," Myles said. "The Lord is telling me to sow a seed into your life. Harry, would you like to participate in this seed-sowing?"

Harry remained silent. Lynn said Harry was suspicious, which made him 'delayed' sometimes. Ironically, his son was the same way. Both Harry and Tracy liked to test the Spirit to make sure it wasn't a lie from the pit of hell. One of Tracy's favorite sports was procrastination, which, now seemed likely was inherited.

"Nevertheless," Myles said, "I shall sow it myself. Ruth, can you reach one of my books?" and Ruth pulled a book from their carry-on. "Oh," Myles said gently. "Not that one, the other one."

Ruth pulled out a different book with an eagle on the front jacket. Myles opened it, took a pen from his blazer and wrote: 'To: Tracy, May your vision be expanded by this book. God bless you. Love, Uncle Myles, Phil: 1:6.' After he closed the book, Myles held it purposefully. Then, he tapped Tracy on the shoulder with the book three times. Tracy thought Myles was trying to get his attention, but he already had his attention.

"No Tracy," He said. *"He is from the Bahamas, so he understands the English ways of kingdom and duty. He is knighting you with a title."*

'That's odd,' Tracy thought. 'We're in America. What good is a title going to do me in the middle of Ohio?' and then Dr. Monroe confirmed what Tracy just heard.

"I give you a title I have only given three other times before," Myles said, and his wife gasped hard enough to necessitate putting her hands over her mouth. "Read it when you get home," Myles said, "and study it."

As Tracy tried to figure out the spiritual significance of what was going on, Mrs. Monroe leaned up to speak in Tracy's ear.

"You are our nephew," Ruth explained. "That is the title."

When they got home, Tracy looked up Phillipians 1:6 inscribed in his book:

"Being confident of this very thing, that he which hath begun a good work in you will perform it until the day of Jesus Christ:"

To Tracy, the colon at end of the scripture said it all. Tracy still didn't know why he was in Columbus, and his father didn't seem to know why either. A week later, Harry had to go to West Virginia, because his Uncle Bob needed help fixing his plumbing. Harry asked Tracy if he wanted to go. He thought Tracy could visit with Granny and Moody for the weekend, which might calm things. On the road, the two were mostly quiet. Tracy thought about what Uncle Myles had said, and why he was sent to Ohio. Then, he was interrupted.

"Dad," Tracy said. "He's telling me to tell you this: Isn't it odd that we didn't meet until I was fifteen years old?"

Harry was caught off guard.

"Isn't it also peculiar," Tracy said, "that I have the same hand gestures, vocal pattern, and I laugh just like you do? Dad, He is telling me to tell you there is nothing that is a coincidence in Him. We have to figure this thing out in order for me to move forward."

"Ok son," Harry said. "What do you want to know?"

"Well," Tracy said. "I don't know. All He said was, in order for me to move forward, I have to learn and understand the family bloodline," and Tracy paused. "He also says that only you can tell that to me."

When they got to Charleston, Harry dropped Tracy off at Starling Drive. After their hug Granny's face fell to neutral, Moody wheeled himself into the kitchen, and the three had a pow-wow.

"Granny," Tracy said, "believe me, I'm doing what the Lord told me to do."

"Whataya mean?" Granny said.

"If I tell you," Tracy said, "do you promise not to be upset?" and Moody chuckled.

"Ya know me better than that," Granny said. "Out with it."

"Well," Tracy said. "I got a key to your house, an' I don't even have to call you."

Granny relaxed a little, "Yeah…"

"I'm there because God told me to go." Tracy said. "I told Him I didn't want to go, but that's where He sent me, an' I'm paying my own way. I have a job I know is temporary, an' God tells me I'm only supposed to be there until I learn the family bloodline."

"Well," Granny said. "I don't know what that might be, but ya better get to learnin' pretty fast. I don't like the idea of you payin' when you can stay here for free. Shit."

"Aw hell Jackie," Moody snarled. "Let's see how this works out. We got your back boy," and Moody was convinced.

It made sense to Moody that Tracy's connection with the Tall Shiny Silver Figure would come from his father. When Harry and Tracy got back from West Virginia, Tracy got another directive. He knocked on the doorframe to Harry's office, and once Harry looked up from his work, Tracy came in and sat down.

"Hey Dad," Tracy said. "I'm getting ready to do this travel. I'll be away for a few weeks, and God is telling me to ask you the proper way to do communion."

"Why is God asking you to do that son?" Harry asked.

"He wants me to do it every evening while I'm gone. So, if you can show me how to do it, I'll make sure I'm doing it right," and Tracy paused before he added, "He has never told me to do this before."

"You are coming up with the strangest things Tracy."

"I'm not coming up with them, He is. A lot of what He says doesn't make any sense - I just do it. He made me read Psalm 91 every morning for a year before I came here, and that didn't make any sense."

That statement made Harry lean back into his tall leather chair, and look off into the distance.

"Listen son," Harry said. "Your mother called me up shortly after you were three years old. You had just gotten out of the hospital with the high temperature. She told me you were talking to an imaginary friend. She asked me if she should be alarmed, and I told her no. Then I wanted to know if your imaginary friend had a name."

Tracy was surprised. This was the first time Tracy heard his parents had discussed anything about him, especially about the Tall Shiny Silver Figure.

"Well, she couldn't tell me," Harry siad. "Is this the same 'he'," and Harry paused. "Is this the same 'He' you've been talking to?"

"Yes Dad," Tracy said.

"Son, let me tell you something," and his father leaned forward and clasped his hands. "You can't be running around telling people you hear from the Holy Ghost like you do," and Harry's eyebrows went up. "They'll lock you up, and think you're crazy."

Tracy was dumbfounded. Of course, this warning made sense from the 'guns an' hound dogs' point of view when he was three. Or when he painted the vision in the sixth grade, and his class ended up doing 'the snake'. But Tracy had told lots of people in his adult life. Tracy told them how He had gotten him his jobs, helped him do his jobs, find new ones, and his co-workers believed. So at present, his father's warning rang hollow.

"Dad," Tracy said. "I really do talk to Him, and He really does talk back. I can't explain it. That's why I'm here, remember?" and now it was Harry who didn't know what to say. "You're supposed to help me figure this thing out."

"Well son, it seems to me you can't be telling people you hear from God that often. That would mean you hear from God more than Moses did," and Harry was gentle. "Now, are you saying you are greater than Moses?"

Instantly, Tracy felt the Tall Shiny Silver Figure push him aside. It was more powerful than when He took possession of Tracy's arm to make the mountain 'flow like wheatgrass'. This felt like when Tracy went to the funeral home, and the clerk wouldn't let him in to see his mother's body. Then, He said '*I am the first-born,*' and the poor woman had to bow and back her way to unlock the sanctuary door. Like then, Tracy watched the words come from his own mouth, and Tracy felt His righteousness:

"Moses' sacrifice was that of doves, goats and bulls. My covenant is of the precious Blood of Jesus Christ, and I have a right to hear from my Daddy God more than Moses ever did."

Then, Tracy was pushed back into his body, and was just as shocked as Harry. Tracy looked at his father with bewilderment.

"Dad," Tracy said meekly. "That wasn't me that just said that. I don't even know what that means. Do you know what that means?"

Because of his astonishment, Harry spoke even more slowly. "It means I have a lot of work to do, and I have to put together an entirely new message for Sunday."

240

Chapter 31

- a bamboo forest

By November of 2003, Tracy had been living in Columbus with Harry and Lynn for six months. He hadn't found out what God wanted him to know, and as the days grew shorter and colder, darkness closed in. At the time, Tracy worked with an accounting firm that did Oracle assessments.

Shortly before Thanksgiving, Tracy's supervisor lied to a client about what the company could do for them. When Tracy traveled to the job, he found himself in a situation that would compromise his integrity, and that Tracy's supervisor thought he would go along with it. Instead, Tracy told the client the truth and quit his job, and there were other demons at work behind the scenes.

Tracy spent Christmas and New Years in West Virginia, sipped apricot moonshine, and groused with Moody. When Tracy returned to Columbus, he got another contract he knew was place holding, and winter deepened. To Tracy, an antagonistic attitude grew along with the piles of snow. No one seemed to understand him, and Tracy's frustration was held captive to whatever reason he was supposed be in his father's house. The chill of the endless gray days wore on him, and, by the end of January, Tracy was incensed with God.

"Ok Lord," Tracy said. "I've been here nine months. If a woman can birth something in the natural in nine months, surely You can birth something in the supernatural in the same amount of time."

There was no answer.

"Now, I'm not trying to put a time limit on this, but my parents are also men and women of God. I'm tired of leaning on them, so You need to birth this thing fast."

More time passed, and nothing happened. Nothing was unveiled other than Lynn's frenzied preparations for Harry's surprise birthday party. Finally, on the last Sunday of January, Tracy and Lynn went to Pier One to get finishing flourishes for Harry's party. Tracy smelled a biscotti candle as He spoke.

"Repeat after Me," He said. *"Thank you Father, for my perfect job, my perfect house, my perfect body, and my perfect spouse."*

Because he was angry, Tracy replaced the candle on the shelf before he answered.

"After months of not speaking to me," Tracy said aloud. "You choose Pier One?"

Lynn turned around at the end of the aisle. "Did you find something?"

Tracy was too upset to hear her, the store went away, and it was just he and God who had it out.

"I just sat in church for two hours," Tracy griped, "and spoke to You every night for weeks."

"Who are you talking to Tracy?" Lynn asked.

She now stood next to him, but Tracy didn't see her. He continued as if he was by himself, paced, and spoke a little lower than a yell, which made Lynn look around to see if anyone else noticed.

"We were just in church," and Tracy was sarcastic. "You could have come down with a choir of angels to tell me this. The whole congregation would have gasped and adored You. Or, You could have sent that annoying angel with the clipboard but no, You choose Pier One?"

"Are you done?" He asked.

"I don't wanna be," Tracy said defiantly, "but I am."

"Repeat after Me," He said again. *"Thank you Father, for my perfect job, my perfect house, my perfect body, and my perfect spouse,"* and Tracy obeyed, albeit grudgingly.

"Thank you Father," Tracy repeated aloud. "For my perfect job, my perfect house, my perfect body, and my perfect spouse."

"Good," He said. *"Add that to your prayers."*

"What does that mean," Lynn asked. "Spouse?"

Tracy realized she stood in front of him, but ignored her for a moment. Instead, Tracy repeated the prayer again to make sure he had it, but softly and to himself:

"Thank you Father, for my perfect job, my perfect house, my perfect body, and my perfect spouse," and Lynn was stunned into her Georgia accent.

"Well I ain't never seen nothin' like that before," she said loud enough to turn a few heads. "Seen it plenty-a-times in a church pew. I even fell out a few times in the aisle myself. But I never seen the Lord speak out here in the open. Shoo!"

A week later was the first Sunday of February, and Pastor Sam had an unusual sermon. Tracy had been a member of the youth group since he first attended in 1981. Pastor Sam was an unassuming man, who ended up serving Christian Assembly for forty-one years. He had a high forehead, nicely combed hair, and a plump face that always seemed to be smiling, even when he preached on serious topics.

"Good morning everyone," Pastor Sam said.

"Good morning!" the large congregation said. They were many faiths, although primarily from the Christian and Jewish traditions, as were Pastor Sam and his wife.

"I realize this may not be what you expect this morning," Pastor Sam said. "But I am going to do what the Lord told me to do," and Pastor Sam took his seat.

The congregation stayed quiet for a moment, and wondered whether he was going to preach. Then, Pastor Sam spoke loudly from his seated position.

"For the Lord is good, and His mercy endureth for ever," Pastor Sam stated.

The congregation waited.

"For the Lord is good, and His mercy endureth for ever," Pastor Sam said again, and a few joined him for the end of the phrase. More joined on the next repetition, until the entire congregation stated the confession in unison: "For Lord is good, and His mercy endureth forever!"

After fifteen minutes of the mantra, praise broke out in the church for the next hour, and the service was done. That night, Pastor Sam held a super bowl party for members of Tracy's youth group because a prophecy had come true. Before Tracy returned to Columbus in 2003, it was prophesied the children would come home. Tracy was the first, and many of Tracy's generation followed. Some were finally out of college, or had finished their master's degrees. Others had moved away, but for one reason or another, they came home to live with their parents. Pastor Sam and his wife were sensitive to this, and hosted a super bowl party at their house. Tracy went early to meet with Pastor Sam and vented.

"Why am I stuck here?" Tracy asked. "All He said was, my father is supposed to tell me about the family bloodline. Instead, they look at me like I have three heads, which I feel like I have. I'm not used to this. I've been on my own for years. Granny and Moody could use the help, especially Moody with his wheelchair, rather than being a bother to Mom and Dad here. With my experience, I can find a job pretty much anywhere. I just want to move on. Why does God have me here?"

Pastor Sam looked at Tracy. Then he picked up his Bible from his desk. He flipped through to Psalm 27:10 and read it to himself. Then he set the Bible down and left it open.

"From my experience," Pastor Sam said, "I can't move on until I've done the last thing he told me to do. Now usually, I am the one delaying God, but this is a little tricky because it involves your Dad."

"Why can't God just tell me himself?" Tracy said. "He tells me everything else."

"I am sure He has a reason," Pastor Sam said. "But see if this helps," and he picked up his Bible and read:

"When my father and my mother forsake me, then the Lord will take me up."

Tracy was comforted a little by the scripture, even though Harry and Lynn hadn't forsaken him. Then, at the party the youth group played a game before the super bowl, and things started to move.

"If you could be any tree in the forest," Pastor Sam asked, "what kind would you be, and why."

Some decided to be an oak for strength. Others were apple or peach trees for the fruit they would bear. After a while, Pastor Sam asked Tracy directly.

"I'd be a forest of bamboo," Tracy said decisively.

"Why bamboo?" Pastor Sam asked.

"After you plant it," Tracy explained, "it takes ten years before you see anything, because the roots grow unseen. Finally, when the shoots appear, they can grow three feet in a single day. Even if you cut it down, another, stronger trunk shoots up behind you. The roots are so deep and well-connected, nothing can stop them."

Pastor Sam smiled. A few nights later, Tracy heard Him in a vision. *"Give Me forty-nine, and I will give you fifty,"* He said.

"But Lord," Tracy said. "I have a fifty dollar bill, just take it all."

"No," He said. *"I just want you to give Me the forty-nine. I do not want you to do anything for the fifty."*

Tracy had no idea what that meant, but was glad He finally heard Him.

The following Sunday was Harry's sixtieth birthday. The surprise Lynn had been planning since Tracy arrived was about to be revealed, and the whole church was involved. Before the party, and for secrecy, Tracy and Bryan went to pick up a dark black man from Barbados, and a lovely blond white woman from England. They were the main surprise for Harry's birthday, and were great faith friends of his father's. The couple introduced themselves when Tracy and Bryan picked them up at the hotel.

"But you must call us Uncle Peter and Aunt Melody," Peter said. "After all, you are Harry's sons!"

Harry's birthday party was a great success. Then, for the next week, Peter and Melody had a great visit with Tracy's parents. Tracy had to work, but he came home early in order to glean as much as possible from Harry's guests. Melody was a prophetess in the church. She saw Tracy spiritually, and both Peter and Melody were practical about God - like farmers who pushed seed into the ground. Tracy had never seen God's word used in such a way, and Peter and Melody were just as fascinated with Tracy.

Like her name, everything about Melody was sing-songy and bright. Peter was cheerfully British, even though he was from the Caribbean. He spoke about everything from being angry with God, to casual discussions of the bliss of marital sex, which made Lynn blush. After dinner one night, Melody said she talked with God all the time, just like He was standing beside her.

"I know people think it's odd," Melody sang, "when I'm carrying on, seemingly by myself as I ride the Tube. But that's how I hear back from Him."

"So, that's what He meant," Tracy said.

Melody looked at Tracy with a smile. "That's right," she coaxed. "Tell us…"

"Muzzle the ox," Tracy repeated, "and you won't get results."

"That's it," Peter said. "First Timothy, Five."

Melody immediately looked it up and read it aloud:

"For the scripture saith, thou shalt not muzzle the ox that treadeth out the corn. And, The labourer is worthy of his reward."

Melody closed her Bible, held it close to her, and looked at the ceiling.

"Our words simply fall to the ground," Melody stated. "But every living thing can feed off of us if we speak His word, and send it out into this world."

This statement made Tracy remember the last thing He said to him. Everyone was quiet, and Tracy's expression caught the attention of the room. His eyes grew more golden, and his smile couldn't be hidden.

"Just last week," Tracy said, "He spoke to me in a dream," and Melody was transfixed as Tracy sent His word out. "He said, 'Give Me forty-nine, and I will give you fifty'," and Melody got terribly excited.

"There is only one place in the Bible that forty-nine and fifty are mentioned," she said, "and it speaks about the Jubilee!" Melody opened her Bible to look up Leviticus 25, and was so exuberant she could barely breathe.

"It's right here," and Melody stopped on the page. "God is talking to Moses."

Harry's ears perked up at the mention of Moses, and was reminded of the conversation about the bulls and goats he had with Tracy as Melody read the text:

⁸ And thou shalt number seven sabbaths of years unto thee, seven times seven years; and the space of the seven sabbaths of years shall be unto thee forty and nine years.

⁹ Then shalt thou cause the trumpet of the jubile to sound on the tenth day of the seventh month, in the day of atonement shall ye make the trumpet sound throughout all your land.

¹⁰ And ye shall hallow the fiftieth year, and proclaim liberty throughout all the land unto all the inhabitants thereof: it shall be a jubile unto you; and ye shall return every man unto his possession, and ye shall return every man unto his family."

Then Melody looked at Tracy. "God's going to restore everything you lost Tracy," and she began dancing, "and He's going to make everybody see it!"

Everyone in the house was stopped except the prophetess. Melody frolicked over and handed her Bible to Lynn, who took it to read the whole chapter. Then Melody went and took Tracy by the hand.

"Would you like to go for a walk?" Melody asked gaily, and swung Tracy's hand.

"Sure," Tracy said, and Melody looked at Peter.

Melody and Tracy left for the garage, put on their coats, and walked the circle of the development. Peter came and sat down at the breakfast bar with Harry.

"Tracy told us God told him to come here," Peter said. "We think, well, Melody especially, is hearing we need to find out what he needs, and not delay his progress any further," and Harry looked at Peter.

"I think I know what this is all about now," Harry said. "I will speak with him."

The next day, Melody and Peter left for England. That evening, Harry called Tracy in for what would be the last meeting in his office.

"Uncle Peter and Aunt Melody seem to think you are here for a specific reason," Harry said, and Tracy listened. "Ok," Harry said and exhaled. "This is how it goes…

My grandfather was called into the ministry. His name was Benjamin, and the Lord told him there would be someone following him in the ministry. I was too young to realize he was talking about me. At that time, my grandfather said, 'Lord, if this is you, bless my first-born.'

God's reply was, *'Not only will I bless your first-born with a double portion experience more than what you have, I will perpetuate it. I will give a double portion experience of Me to every first-born in the following generations.'*

So my grandfather was able to hear and talk to God. His first-born was able to hear and talk to God, and do creative miracles. That was my mother, your grandmother, Lucille. One of my first experiences was when I was in college, and I came home to visit. Your grandmother always lived in Vandalia. It was a three-hour drive, and it got late. But I had to drive back to go to work in the morning. I must have left out close to ten-o'clock. So my mother prayed for me before she went to bed. An hour later she awoke, and the next morning she called me.

'How was your trip?' she asked.

I said it was fine, because I didn't want her to know I had fallen asleep at the wheel.

'Well I was wakened, because I saw your car cross the yellow line in the road,' Mother said. 'So I stayed up all night praying in tongues.'

Then I told my mother the truth. I told her I remembered falling asleep, but I didn't remember the last hour-and-a-half of my trip. When I woke up I was in my car, and the car was parked in my driveway with the motor running," and Harry stopped a moment, remembering.

"I know that may not sound like much," Harry said. "But then, Mother told me about the family blessing when I was old enough. I must have been thirteen. No, I was older, maybe fifteen."

"That's how old I was when I met you," Tracy said.

"My," Harry said. "Yes it was. How about that. Well, Mother told me what I just told you, about her father and the family blessing, and then she showed me. My mother had five sisters, and they had a prayer meeting at the house on a Saturday night. Early Sunday morning, I heard my mother and her sister in the dining room praying in the Holy Ghost. That wasn't unusual, but there was a little girl who sat in one of the dining room chairs. She was the daughter of a friend of one of my Aunts. Everyone knew she had one leg that was bigger than the other, and she walked with a limp. When I came out of my bedroom, I could tell this wasn't a normal prayer. When she saw me, my mother turned to me, and the Lord spoke through her:

'This is a witness for thy son.'

Then she and my Aunt began praying in tongues again. They laid their hands on her big leg, and as they prayed the little girl's leg shrunk down to its normal size. I saw it happen."

Harry paused again, because the miracle was as fresh to him as when it happened.

"Afterward she got up, and went home without a limp," and Harry smiled. "Then I ran to the church and got myself straightened out, and I've been there ever since."

Then Harry looked at his son sweetly. "Your grandmother prayed for you a lot," he said.

"I wouldn't have known that," Tracy said. "I remember seeing her when I was little, at that intersection. Mom yelled at her, and she pulled out like a bat out of hell."

"Well son," and Harry's eyebrow went up. "I think your mother surprised her," and he bent his head forward, "but I heard about that."

"It sounds like you were around behind the scenes, I just never saw you," Tracy said.

"I stayed away," Harry said. "Your other Granny made sure of that, but I was around. I kept my distance until you were old enough to search me out, and I knew you would."

"And now I'm here to search out the bloodline," Tracy said, but then he wanted a clarification. "Do you hear Him, I mean, like I do?"

Harry looked at his son and thought a moment. "Probably not as often, by the sounds of it. But yes, I hear Him. Like when my wife wanted to build this house," and they both laughed. "I was getting ready to retire. I didn't want to build a new house, but your mother was all about it."

Tracy remembered all the strife that went into the real cherry wood cabinets for the kitchen during construction of the house. Then Harry continued.

"So I fought against it and got angry at God," Harry admitted. "I couldn't understand why we needed a new house, and I went into a bookstore at the mall. He said, '*I am leading*,' and then I was overpowered to the point I began weeping."

Harry looked at Tracy, smiled, shrugged his shoulders and held up his hands. "And that was that. Once I recovered and gave it over to Him, there was our house on the cover of a magazine. The contractors fell into place and before I knew it, the house was built and we were living in it."

"That all sounds familiar," Tracy said. "I snot and cry at God all the time. Once I stop, He asks me if I'm done," and Harry laughed with his son. "Then He makes it plain, once I get out of the way."

"Hmm," Harry mused, and had another revelation.

"But it sounds like there's more," Tracy said.

"There is," Harry said, and began to understand why this conversation was important. "The house was a small thing really, and there is a reason my ministry is with the elderly."

Tracy didn't understand.

"You see," Harry said. "Lucille's blessing was creative miracles, like when she healed the girl with the big leg. But there was more...

When Ben died, my grandfather, he was in the living room sitting in his chair. Ben had been dead for a while and my grandmother, Lily, was praying over him, so we stayed with her. Then she was overcome with grief and asked the Lord, 'Let me speak with him one more time.'

Ben rose up and said, 'It's alright Lily,' and he fell back again into his chair."

Then, the first-born of the third and fourth generations took in that moment of the blessing.

"Now," Harry continued. "I was in Columbus when my mother Lucille died. She was fairly young at age sixty-two, and went into the hospital for a routine surgery. The night before she died her nurse called the family in, but I was in Columbus. The nurse called in the morning to say she had gone, and that they would leave the body in the room until I got there. When I did, I went to the window to pray. I thought of my grandmother, and what happened with Ben after he died, but the Lord interrupted me.

'She does not want to come back,' He said. Then Mother's nurse came in to confirm this. She told me how tired Lucille was, and that she didn't want to come back, and I understood. But all of this makes me think about what Lily said."

"What do you mean Dad?" Tracy asked.

"My grandmother only asked to speak with my grandfather one more time," and Harry's eyebrows went up. "What if Lily had asked for more? What if she asked for a year?"

"Or his youth to be renewed," Tracy said.

"Exactly son," Harry said, "which makes me wonder what you will do," and Tracy smiled at his Dad, and was at peace.

Selah.

Chapter 32

- at the river

Tracy was at the river behind Granny and Moody's house. It was a beautiful summer day. He sat on his haunches on the shore, and picked up rocks and threw them in the water. When Tracy looked down the river, he saw a man walking on the water. He had on a shiny robe, and Tracy recognized Him to be the Lord. He was in His human form, called Jesus, in order to show what Tracy could do within his own human form.

When Tracy saw Him as the Tall Shiny Silver Figure, He was Elohim - all God - the created One. At those times He was all light, nothing could stop Him, and everything belonged to Him. Now, Jesus walked in the middle of the river, but He wasn't walking toward Tracy. His path was down the middle. He looked at Tracy, although He didn't say anything. In fact, the Lord appeared not to pay Tracy too much mind.

Tracy thought, 'Hey, I've got enough experience in these visions to recognize I can ask for some stuff – 'you have not because you ask not'.'

Tracy wasn't afraid because it was peaceful. But this also wasn't the Tall Shiny Silver Figure - the jovial 'imaginary friend' from when he was three. This was Jesus, a grown man like himself, which made Tracy reluctant. Tracy didn't want to step out of the boat only to sink. Instead, Tracy tried to think of something Peter didn't think of in the storm, and then he was encouraged.

"Give a man a fish, and he will go hungry the next day," the Holy Ghost said. *"Teach him how to fish, and he could earn his own living, and have his own business."*

By this time, Jesus was adjacent to Tracy, and Tracy realized the Lord would keep going if he didn't say anything. Tracy also understood the Lord must be recognized, and His goodness must be acknowledged. So Tracy mustered his faith as Jesus passed him.

"Hey," Tracy said, and waved.

Jesus stopped and looked, because He was hoping Tracy would say something.

"Show me how you do that," Tracy said.

Jesus was impressed with Tracy's words. Jesus could teach from a distance, as a lecturer does in front of a chalkboard, or from a boat before a crowd. However, Jesus' preferred method of teaching was being present with a student, so He could show them how to do something. That way, the lesson would be understood by experience and could never be taken away.

"Come on," Jesus said.

At Tracy's first gesture to get up from his haunches to obey, he immediately stood in front of Jesus in the middle of the river. Tracy wondered how he got there so fast, but he didn't get distracted. Tracy kept his eyes fixed on His as they walked down the river. And the Lord's face was a beautiful outline of His human form in light – His beard, His warm smile and flowing hair.

But His eyes were a flame – literally, like the flame a common lighter produced. Tracy wanted to ask, but his thought was interrupted.

"That is a different lesson," Jesus said kindly, "which I believe you already know," and Jesus looked at Tracy with a knowing glance. "I believe He already told you," and Tracy knew the 'He' Jesus referred to was the Holy Ghost. "He can't keep a secret."

Tracy thought Jesus was funny and 'had serious jokes', which helped him relax. However, Tracy was still walking with Him down the middle of the river on water, so he didn't take his eyes from Jesus' face. As they walked, Tracy knew they went where the Lord had been, and the path was where Tracy was headed. Jesus had walked this path earlier, to make sure it was secure before He came back to get Tracy. After this revelation, Tracy was emboldened, but he still didn't take his eyes off the Lord's.

"Lord," Tracy said. "This is good and all, but I asked you to show me how you do this."

"Ok," He said. "Look down."

"Oh no," Tracy said. "Not me. That's how You got the last one," and Tracy laughed, referring to Peter.

"And You know how I feel about "Jaws", and how I can't put my hands in soapy dishwater, and You want me to look down?"

"No really," He said. "Look down."

"Are you sure I'm not going to sink?"

"Really Tracy," and He said it a third time: "Look down."

Tracy looked. Under his feet was a series of stone columns that weren't connected. As Tracy walked, a single column of stone rose to meet his foot. Each column stopped just below the surface of the water, so only the soles of Tracy's shoes got wet. The pillars couldn't be seen from shore, but they were always out there in the deep, waiting to be called.

Tracy was made to understand he walked on stones of revelation knowledge, which were built through praying in the spirit. As Tracy stepped, he received another revelation, which instantly built the next column of stone to meet his footfall. As each revelation came, Tracy made a step, which made another column ascend from the deep to meet his foot. If Tracy hesitated, nothing met his progress.

The more Tracy walked, the more he understood. Soon, he saw a pathway of disconnected stones form ahead of him, with spaces of water the length of his stride between them. The columns were of stone, built of Rhema word, and were directed by Tracy into physical existence. Tracy was made to understand the gates of hell could not prevail against his walking, because it was written on the columns of stone themselves. So, from the shore, it appeared as if Tracy walked on water. In truth, Tracy was stepping out by faith on His Word.

As for Tracy the man, the experience felt like when he learned to ride a bike, and the training wheels were off. Tracy was shown how to walk on water, and he was doing it. He felt that moment of freedom, knowing he could balance and not fall. And, just like Moody was there to catch him if he fell, Tracy knew he could get up again, and walk on water again without failing. Then, Tracy heard joyous hollering and clapping. Tracy looked behind him, and it was the Lord who was in the distance cheering him on.

Tracy was astonished, but knew he had succeeded. Tracy had learned how to walk on everything Jesus and the Holy Ghost showed him, and he was well on his way.

"Aren't You coming with me?" Tracy yelled down the river.

"My Grace is sufficient," Jesus yelled back.

Tracy was incredibly grateful, although that felt woefully inadequate. Tracy wanted to thank Him, but knew that thanking Jesus was only doing what He said to do. So, Tracy kept walking, for without faith it was impossible to please Him, but that still didn't seem enough…

"Just tell everybody how to do it," the Lord answered. "They all need to start walking on water!" and with that, Tracy woke up.

Selah.

- Momma Ro

Chapter 33

After Tracy learned his family's bloodline, his assignment was complete. The next day a recruiter called. Tracy traveled to Dayton for an interview the following day, and the next day he went to work there. By the end of the week, they asked Tracy to work from home while they got a contract ready for a project. The following week, Tracy was handed a company credit card, and, within two weeks of learning the family bloodline, Tracy was off to Washington, D.C. with a job, traveling expenses, and a new direction in life.

As Tracy drove from Columbus, decades of memories filtered through his mind. Although D.C. wasn't Tracy's first choice for his next move. It reminded Tracy of the time when He told him to put his waterbed together. Like then, Tracy knew God was up to something, and welcomed the opportunity. At the same time, Tracy dreaded what was likely to be involved. In the back of his mind, Tracy thought returning to D.C. meant reconciling with Bobby. He hadn't seen Bobby since Freddie died eleven years earlier. The time before that was at Vera's funeral two years before that. Now that they were gone, Tracy didn't want to revisit his childhood memories of D.C.

On the other hand, Tracy didn't want to return to Columbus after his two-week contract was finished either.

"Lord," Tracy said. "I'm grateful for the progress, and I recognize what You are doing behind the scenes. But if this is what I'm supposed to do, You have to help me."

Tracy waited for an answer. None came, but that wasn't unusual. Tracy knew He wasn't under any obligation to respond to his crazy thought patterns.

"But, Your thoughts are higher than my thoughts," Tracy added.

Little did Tracy know, God had him on a fast-track. As Tracy neared D.C. he realized he would be there for dinner, so he called Todd. Over the years, the college roomies caught up with one another every month or so. Todd's diligent study habits transferred into promotions and career advancements, and Todd now lived in a wealthy suburb in a house worthy of manse status.

"Hey Todd," Tracy said. "What are you doing for dinner tonight?"

"Nothing," Todd said. "Why?"

"It happened so fast I haven't had a chance to tell you," Tracy said. "But I'm on my way to D.C. for a two-week contract."

"How wonderful," Todd said. "Once you get settled in your hotel come over. I can't wait to show you the house. Then we can go somewhere for dinner."

After he checked in to his hotel, Tracy changed his clothes to match his red sneakers. Then he drove through the planned curves of Todd's neighborhood of three thousand square foot homes. Todd answered the doorbell and gave Tracy a big hug.

"It is so good to see you," Todd said.

"You too," Tracy said, but was distracted by the height. "Your pictures didn't do the house justice," and Tracy looked down at the shined Brazilian hardwood floors, and bent to take off his chucks.

"You don't need to worry about that," Todd said.

"Yeah right," and Tracy took off his shoes.

"So," Todd said as they toured his home. "Sabrina lives down the street. I am sure she would love to come to dinner."

"That would be great," Tracy said.

"Good, because I already invited her. It's been a long time."

"It sure has," Tracy agreed, and they headed upstairs to finish the tour.

"Just after I spoke with you I called Granny," Todd said. "We hadn't caught up in a while. She told me about you living with your Dad and Mom in Columbus, and about your contract here in D.C."

Tracy listened, because Todd was obviously going somewhere in his careful way. After he showed Tracy his bedroom suite over the garage, they headed back over the catwalk to the opposite end of the second floor.

"I know this is only a two-week contract," Todd said, "but after talking with Granny," and Todd stopped to face Tracy. "There are plenty of jobs here that could use your skill set. You don't have to go back to Columbus," and Todd opened the door to the large guestroom like a game show model would gesture to see what was behind door Number 2. "So, this is your bedroom until you buy a house."

Tracy's mouth dropped open as Todd showed Tracy his room. Then, Todd's voice went away as Tracy daydreamed.

Of course Tracy was flabbergasted by the opportunity, and he knew there were many jobs in the area. If a contract ended, he could pick up another. More importantly, now he would have the security of a place to live while he saved up money to buy a house. Meanwhile, Todd went back downstairs, and he showed Tracy the details he would need to know as a housemate.

'So this is why You were so quiet Lord,' Tracy thought. 'You got all this set up while I drove here,' and then Todd stopped talking. They were standing by the alarm system at the front door.

"Tracy," Todd said curtly. "Come back to reality."

Tracy smiled, and thought it was great to be in the company of a friend who knew him so well. Todd was kind of like Freddie, Tracy thought, but it was more than that. God gives you your family, but *you* get to pick your friends.

"Tracy," Todd said again. "Do you remember the code?"

"The code?" Tracy asked, and then he saw Todd's fingers poised over the alarm keyboard. "You know I don't," Tracy admitted. "But show me again, and I promise I'll stay right here."

That night, Tracy, Todd and Sabrina had dinner together. The last time the friends gathered was after Todd's college graduation. In that tradition, Tracy did a dramatic re-enactment.

"Ok," Tracy said, and got up from the table. "I have to go to the bathroom. But before I go, there is a topic I would like you to discuss. You're both gay. Now talk amongst yourselves."

"How did we not know each other was gay?" Todd giggled.

"And now I sell pharmaceuticals to gay boys," Sabrina laughed. "I guess we have come a long way."

But that wasn't the only reunion in store. The next night, Tracy called another lifelong friend - the one he met in first grade.

"What are you doing?" Tracy asked.

"Child, the Lord must have put me on your heart," Tori answered.

"Why do you say that?" Tracy asked.

"Well," Tori said, "I have all my friends here supporting me except one, an' now you called."

"What happened?" Tracy asked. "Is it serious?"

"Not that serious," Tori said. "I just wanted to be a little thinner, an' everything is fine. I just have to be careful what I eat for a while."

"Well," Tracy said. "Guess where I am?"

Tracy told her, and Tori was beside herself. They had kept in contact over the years, but hadn't seen each other. So the first grade classmates reunited while going to restaurants to try new foods. On Wednesday they went to church together, where Tori spent all of her free time. Tori didn't tell her mother Tracy was in town, or Bunky, so the two planned their attack. After church, they headed to Momma Ro's house for Sunday dinner. Tori went to the front door and started banging.

"Bunky," Tori cried. "Come open this door!"

"Girl," Bunky yelled as he came through the living room. "What are you doin' bangin' on *this* door? You know we always come in on the side."

By the depth of his voice, Tracy realized he hadn't seen Bunky since he was a teenager.

"Quit your stallin' an' let me in," Tori yelled.

"Didn't your Momma raise you right?" Bunky chided. "Actin' like a hoodlum in this neighborhood," and he opened the door.

Tori stood broad chested with her hands on her hips to hide Tracy, but Bunky's voice belied his adult body. As Tracy peaked through Tori's elbows, he marveled at the towering six-foot, seven-inch man, who was easily two-hundred-and-fifty pounds of muscle. Before Bunky could figure it out, Tori slid to the side and Tracy stood up. Bunky looked as if he had seen a ghost, and then he picked Tracy up and tossed him around like a rag doll. He carried Tracy into the living room before he let go, and Momma Ro came out of her kitchen.

"What in the world?" Momma Ro crooned. But her tall self couldn't believe it, and the room couldn't hold her joy. Eventually, everyone settled down and Charlie came over.

"Good to see ya," he said, and grabbed a soda from the fridge.

Then they ate - fried chicken, green beans, collards, macaroni and cheese, cornbread, and a big sheet cake. Nothing had changed in Momma Ro's rancher except Tracy's size, which made the house seem small. After dinner, they went to the finished basement that brought back happy memories.

"Child," Momma Ro sang. "I've been prayin' for ya. But shoo, it's good to lay eyes on ya," and she hummed a little. "Last time I spoke to Granny, she was sayin' you were out at your father's in Ohio. I bet it was good for you to get to know one another."

"It was good Momma Ro," Tracy said, "an' it's truly great to be back here."

"Your Momma always wanted you to get to know your father," Momma Ro said. "But I didn't even know you were comin' to town sugar," and Momma Ro took a sip of her grape soda. "Have you seen Bobby yet?" and a hush fell over the room.

"Actually Momma Ro," Tracy said. "I was praying about that very thing on the way here. I know there's a reconciliation comin' between him and I. But if the Lord don't arrange it, I'm not gonna try an' birth an Ishmael. In the meantime, I'm gonna stay right where I am, an' enjoy all y'all."

"Well shug," Momma Ro said, "that sounds Biblical. Come on over here an' get yourself another piece a cake," and Tracy smiled. Momma Ro was always in the Bible, and if his answer was good enough for her, it was good enough for him, and it was great to be home.

Chapter 34

- the perfect house

Tracy's two-week contract turned into six-months, and by July he got the rest of his things from Columbus. Living with Todd was like college days, only with less drama. The D.C. market was plentiful, and Tracy got another job before his six-month contract was up. Tracy found a church home with Tori's congregation, and went to Momma Ro's every Sunday afternoon. Then, in November, the preacher at Tori's church confirmed what Tracy heard in Columbus.

"God has a perfect job for everyone," the preacher said. "Sometimes we have to find it," and the congregation cheered with 'Amens'. "And know that God has your house, the one especially picked out for you in his perfect plan," and the organ swelled. After a while, the preacher spoke of everyone's health. "And expect God to restore your body, the body Christ paid for on the cross…"

Finally, after another few minutes he said, "Oh yes, God knows your partner, sometimes even when you don't. It may even be someone you know, and had no idea was His plan. But know this: God has the perfect spouse waiting for you for the right time," and Tori squeezed Tracy's hand as a chorus of praise rang through the hall.

The preacher's words were confirmation of the four promises God gave Tracy in Pier One, although he kept that fact under his hat. As Tracy and Tori went to Momma Ro's for dinner, Tracy got an unction to swing into a new subdivision under construction.

They drove by a freshly dug pond, and then a sections of roads, sidewalks and townhouses that were built, but not finished.

"Where are we going?" Tori asked.

"I felt an impression to pull in here," Tracy said.

"Did you just hear from God?" and Tori was excited.

"Not exactly," Tracy said, "but I think we should see what's here."

"Well," Tori said flatly. "This is odd. There's nothing around here but a bunch of woods."

They stopped by the office for information. A realtor gave them pamphlets, and showed them various models and floor plans.

"I have a townhome I could show you," she offered.

"Let's take a look," Tori said.

They went to the backside of the development. The row-homes were two stories high with an untouched forest behind. The realtor went to the middle one, and Tori turned to Tracy as the realtor fooled with the lockbox.

"You always want the end unit," Tori said through her teeth. "There's more light, an' you'll only have one neighbor that shares a wall." Then, Tori said loudly, "Can we see the one on the end?"

"Well, it's not finished," the realtor said, "but you will get the idea."

The realtor went to the end house and opened the door. Tracy's first thought was that it was comfortable, because it had a lot of light. Then he looked deeper inside. There were no kitchen cabinets, countertops, carpet or flooring. The wiring wasn't finished, so there were no light fixtures, and wires spat out from boxes where sockets and switches would go.

"Do you like your house?" He asked.

Tracy was stunned. The realtor began her tour, but it was difficult with so much unfinished.

"How will I know what this is going to look like?" Tracy asked.

"You can go to the showroom," the realtor said. "It's not open to the public, but it's in the shopping area in the middle of…"

"Oh," Tracy said, completely sidetracked, "there's a basement?" and the realtor took them to the basement where bare bulbs hung helter-skelter in the large empty room.

"This will remain mostly unfinished," the realtor said.

"I can finish this off," Tracy decided, because he liked the open space to workout in.

"Do you like your house?" He asked again, and Tracy became intrigued.

When they went back upstairs, Tracy paid attention to the way the staircase ended at the small half-bath. The main hall also went from the front door through to the living room, and things became familiar from Tracy's vision. When he looked through the kitchen where the refrigerator would be, Tracy could see where Granny Berger had sat on the sofa that wasn't there yet. When Tori and the realtor toured the living room, Tracy went upstairs by himself.

Tracy went into the master bedroom, and recognized the shelf running above the doorframe at the odd angle. Tracy went into the master bath where there was a space for a Jacuzzi tub. It also had a double sink and a shower, both of which he always wanted.

"Do you like your house?" He asked a third time.

Tracy smiled, bit his lip and wondered. He left the master bedroom, and went down the hall to the guest bedroom. Tracy half-expected to see Freddie lying on the bed in his white sweat suit with his hands behind his head, but the room was empty. Then, Tracy understood Freddie was resting. He did what was allowed in Tracy's vision, so Freddie wasn't there in real life, yet.

"Yes," Tracy finally answered. "I do like this house. But how do I know what's ordered for it?"

"Go and check it out," He said.

"Ok," Tracy said. "I will."

Tori and Tracy went back with the realtor to her office. She asked questions in quick succession, and noted everything on her computer screen:

"Are you employed? How much money do you make? Are you a first-time buyer? What is your address? How much do you currently pay in rent?"

Papers suddenly flew out of the printer. After a few signatures Tracy thought were permission for a credit check, she was done.

"Congratulations Mr. Staples," the realtor said, and she stood to shake his hand. "You just signed a contract for a new townhouse."

"What?" Tracy asked. "What does that mean?"

"If all the numbers work out," she said, "and I didn't see any alarms, you just bought a house."

"I don't even know what it's going to look like inside," Tracy exclaimed.

"Well," the realtor said. "You can go to the showroom and see everything picked out for it."

"What if I don't like it?" Tracy asked.

"Of course, you can change things," the realtor said, "but it will cost $1,000 per change order," and she made a boo-boo kitty face. "Sorry about that."

At Momma Ro's, Tori explained in great detail how Tracy bought a townhouse basically sight-unseen. Then, Tori decided Tracy needed to plan. They went to Pier One that afternoon, where Tracy first heard about his perfect house. He always envisioned his kitchen with a copper-colored scheme. Limited edition copper charger plates were on clearance, so he bought them. The next day, Tracy told his co-workers the whole story: the vision of the townhouse, repeating the promises, buying the townhouse before it was finished, and buying his charger plates.

"You matched plates to your house before you moved in?" his co-workers asked.

"I bought them on faith," Tracy said. "The Lord told me to."

"That's really cool."

Because the realtor thought Tracy might change his mind, she made an appointment for him to see the showroom after work. Everything was exactly what Tracy wanted. There would be wall-to-wall carpeting in every bedroom and on the stairs. It had recessed lighting, a plush beige living room carpet, maple floors in the hall and dining room, gray granite countertops, cherry wood cabinets, and stainless steel appliances - all of which were masculine. Because Tracy skipped the living room on the tour, he realized God provided the fireplace and mantel he always wanted as well. When the design team finished showing the samples, Tracy giggled and thought, 'God does know the secrets of your heart', and he didn't want to change a thing.

But not everyone agreed with the plan for Tracy's new house, specifically, Tracy's project lead and the Director of Human Resources. Since his visions in Chattanooga, Tracy recognized demons and evil spirits more easily. They tried to manifest themselves in those who allowed such manipulation. They could inhabit so-called 'friends', and oftentimes family.

However, particularly in contract work, the spirit of jealousy was busy. The fact that God was no respecter of persons allowed the spirit of division to flourish, disguised as racism. This circumstance, along with jealousy, made Tracy a perfect target.

Five months earlier, Tracy had a contract that didn't make much sense. Accounting anomalies kept appearing, and Tracy couldn't fix them. After a few months, the H.R. Director called Tracy in to announce he was being put on a Performance Improvement Plan. Her name was Dixie, who was a small painted woman in a business skirt, blouse and blazer, topped with well-appointed brunette hair and blond highlights. As Tracy sat in her office, he detected a veneer about Dixie, which reminded him of the dart in the eyes of the demon he slew with the help of the annoying angel.

In speaking with other co-workers, Tracy learned the project lead's father was on the board of the company. This was also the project lead's third assignment in four months. The project lead was from Alabama, and was more racist than anyone Tracy had ever met. Tracy also figured out that the project lead planned to use him as the fall guy for his own incompetence.

The upshot was that Tracy knew the Performance Improvement Plan was bogus, and that Dixie's H.R. Department was the reason the project lead was still employed by his father's company.

Months later, and about the time Tracy was led to his townhouse, Tracy worked with a lovely woman from Canada on the project. She didn't understand racism, and wasn't familiar with American mores. They had been working together for weeks when Tracy found out the truth: the racist project lead that hired Tracy directly lied to him, and the accounting anomalies had occurred months before Tracy arrived on the scene. Tracy was furious, so that night he prayed.

"What should I do Lord?" knowing He knew everything about it.

"Let them have it," He said.

So, Tracy stayed up all night to fix a process two teams had tried to fix over the past five months. 'Swirl Sutra' kicked in, and by morning, Tracy had written five different manuals. He laid them out at work, which took two eight-foot tables to spread out the documentation - from legacy mapping, to testing and training, to go-live; all of which included screenshots for each individual step with idiot-proof arrows. When Tracy finished his presentation, the team of eight looked at him in absolute awe.

"Yeah," Tracy laughed. "You won't see me after this, because I just finished the project for you."

Then, Tracy and his co-worker from Canada presented the new accounting process to the client. They were astonished. After the meeting broke up, Tracy and his Canadian co-worker waited by the elevator.

"I think that went well," Tracy said.

"You know it did boy!" she screamed, and thoroughly grabbed Tracy's tight round black ass.

Tracy immediately looked at everyone through the glass of the boardroom, in order to confirm they saw what happened. Sexual harassment was a real and present danger in the highly politicized world of contracting in the nation's capitol. So, Tracy placed his cards of racism, and the pronounced smack on the ass by his co-worker in an imagined sealed envelope in his breast pocket. Then, Tracy got on the elevator with his Canadian colleague, and they had a great lunch together. Later, as Tracy brushed his teeth and got ready for bed, Tracy got another directive.

"If you have any work you want to keep on that laptop, get it off." He said. *"Then clean the laptop, change every password to Live Life Out Loud, and make sure you capitalize the L's."*

"What's going on Lord?" Tracy asked.

"Tomorrow they are going to terminate your contract."

"Really?" and Tracy was surprised at first, although it started to make sense as he listened to God's plan.

"But I want you to be ready for it. Dress in casual clothes, do not show up to work before ten, and make plans with Tori to have lunch at eleven."

Because the project lead and his father's company had been so openly hostile to him, Tracy took God at His word - particularly about the 'Loud' part. He put on a powder blue shirt, ivory bow tie and pants, and the woven slip-ons he bought with Harry. Looking ready for at least nine holes, Tracy went to work precisely at ten-o'clock carrying his freshly wiped laptop.

"You look snazzy today," the secretary said. "Let me see what cubical they are putting you in for the next project," and she searched her schedule.

"I don't think I'm staying," Tracy said, "but please verify that."

The secretary made a call and looked at Tramele – the name Tracy now used at work – because she was surprised.

"You're right," she said. "H.R. would like to see you now."

"Good," Tramele said. "I was counting on that," and Tracy went to the H.R. Director's office.

"Have a seat Tramele," Dixie said.

She was wearing a different version of her power skirt and blazer. Tracy took a seat in his ivory pants, put the laptop down next to his chair, and crossed his legs to accentuate his woven slip-ons.

"How did you like your last project?" she asked.

"It was ok," Tramele stated. "A little challenging, but I made it through successfully. Yet I am grateful it's over, and I am ready for the next new thing."

"Well," Dixie said, "that's exactly what we want to talk to you about. We have put a separation package together for you. We are going to terminate your contract," and Tracy wondered if she had a mouse in her pocket.

"Well good," Tramele decided. Dixie looked up. "I did hear you correctly, didn't I?"

"Excuse me?" Dixie asked, and was perplexed, but Tracy recognized the enemy.

'The Blood has already been spilled', Tracy thought. 'Here's my time to testify, and I can watch Satan be defeated in all of this. I can kick the demons of jealousy and racism's ass right in front of her heathen eyes', and Tracy smiled. 'You think you have me cornered?'

"So," Dixie said. "We have drawn up a separation letter, and we will forget all about that Performance Improvement Plan."

"Which I passed successfully," Tramele stated.

"Yes," Dixie said. "Right," and went on as if that had no bearing on the matter. Then, she produced a large business check from her folder, and laid it next to the separation letter. "We will also give you a separation check for seven thousand dollars."

Tracy knew what Granny would say: 'You can keep your damn check!' Instead, Tracy looked at her, unfolded his legs, folded his hands and leaned forward to see her eyes.

"The Lord is telling me not to sign that document because it has a string attached," Tracy stated. "And the string is that check, to ensure I can't sue your company for sexual harassment."

The H.R. Director was stymied, and the enemy was frozen.

"So," Tracy explained, "I am going to have to decline your offer and give you back your laptop, tell you the password and leave, because I have lunch plans in twenty-minutes." Then, just to mess with her, Tracy pulled back his powder blue sleeve and looked at his wrist as if a designer watch was there.

"Excuse me?" Dixie repeated.

"Again," Tracy said from his seated position. "I prayed about this last night, and God revealed to me your plans. So, if we're done here, can I go?"

Dixie looked at him, blinking.

"Do you actually think I dress this way to come to work?" Tracy added.

Then, Tracy picked up the company laptop, stood, went to the desk, and put it on top of the unsigned agreement and check. The eyes of the H.R. Director watched but she was powerless to move, just like the darting eyes of the doomed demon. Then, Tracy calmly took a post-it note and pen from her desk. He wrote: 'Live Life Out Loud', stuck it to the computer, and went and opened the office door.

"You have a great day," Tracy said without turning.

"Sorry you won't be able to get your townhouse," Dixie taunted.

"Stop Tracy," He said. *"Shut the door,"* and Tracy did as he was told. *"Turn around and say this:"*

"Excuse me?" Tracy asked, the same way she had.

"Well," Dixie said acerbically. "You have to have a job to buy a house."

"Say this Tracy:" He said, and Tracy did:

"Who says I have to have a job to get a house?" Tracy asked.

"Every mortgage requires you have employment," Dixie said lawfully.

"Move over Tracy," He said, and Tracy watched these words come from his own mouth:

"Those are Man's words. God's words were before the foundation of the world, and He says He will give me goodly houses that I did not build, wells I did not dig, and vineyards I did not plant. I am going to get this house, and, expect a phone call from me rejoicing with a follow-up testimony of just how good the Lord is!"

Then Tracy opened the door, walked out, and got to the parking lot before he asked.

"Lord, what just happened?"

"You were supposed to go to closing on the house today, and they knew it."

Now, it was Tracy who was shocked at the depth of their deviousness.

"Do not worry about it Tracy," He said. *"They are not going to be ready for closing today or tomorrow. It will be next week."*

"So what are we going to do?"

"Well," and the Lord smiled. *"We are going to start this car and have lunch with Tori, and talk about all the good things I have done."*

"Yeah," and Tracy smiled. "Let's do that."

Chapter 35

- Tracy at the Soirée

After lunch with Tori, Tracy went back to Todd's and prayed. He acknowledged what God had done, and that he was about to own a house. Tracy also wondered how he would pay for it, so he asked.

"Go back to repeating what I promised you," He answered, *"and thank Me for it every morning. Whenever you feel uneasy through the day, say it Out Loud."*

"That's gonna be a lot of prayin' Lord," Tracy said.

"It will be a lot of saying to see it," He said.

So Tracy did. He said his prayer before he searched for a job. If anxiety hit as he waited for people to call, he said it again. Tracy said it while he worked out, and during lunch. Sun up to sun down, Tracy repeated God's promises for five days. However, when Todd was around in the evenings, Tracy didn't say it aloud. Tracy knew Todd wouldn't understand until he saw God get Tracy his house. Todd was also distracted, because at the end of January he was hosting his fortieth birthday party.

After Thanksgiving, Tracy and Sabrina had stuffed translucent pearlized envelopes that announced "*La Noire Elegant*, (also known as) The Old Black Stank Soirée". The party was a multi-day event, and Todd had prepared all year. The basement's remodel included a grotto style bath. The back wall of the niche was lit for a life-sized Grecian woman who carried cement fruit, and her nude beau held towels for the shower.

There was only one thing left to install, which blocked Tracy's entrance when he came back from an interview. The large red leather couch took up the front hall, and was stuck at an absurd angle into the white leather couches of the living room. Todd stood behind it.

"Ta-da!" Todd said. "What do you think?"

"It's awesome," Tracy said, "but I'm not sure it looks good here."

"Silly," Todd said. "I had it custom made and delivered for the basement." Tracy wondered why the couch wasn't fully delivered, but Todd was undaunted.

"Come on, put your stuff down and help. Then we can go eat dinner real quick, and sit on my new couch and watch TV on my new flat screen."

But the stairs to the basement were as grand as the rest of his home in style elements only, and the couch got stuck at the first turn.

"Careful with my leather," Todd said. "I can patch a wall."

Four hours later, Tracy called a time out.

"I think somethin's wrong with this process."

"I guess you're right," Todd admitted.

"So, are you gonna send it back?"

"Hell no!" Todd exclaimed. "This bitch is going into the basement," and when Tracy came home the next day, the red leather couch was gone. Tracy followed the trail of fine white dust to the middle landing, and Todd stuck his powdered face through the couch-sized hole.

"She's in here," Todd said. "She looks good too!"

But there was another problem, which Todd explained over dinner.

"Tracy," Todd said. "I don't mean to be rude, but you're going to have to find somewhere else to be on Thursday."

"You mean, because of your out-of-town guests?" Tracy asked.

"No. They have their hotel rooms," and Todd hesitated. "But the Closed Door Party on Thursday is my inner circle, and you don't know them."

"Do not worry Tracy," He said. *"You will be in your new house."*

"Don't worry," Tracy repeated. "I understand. I'll find a place to be."

"Thank you," Todd said.

Tracy wasn't totally convinced, but he stood in faith. Then, on the Wednesday of Todd's birthday party, the title company called. They were ready to close, and wanted Tracy to come in the next day.

"Lord," Tracy said. "I don't have a job yet."

"Have you not understood anything by now?" He asked. *"What have we been saying?"*

Tracy said it: "Thank you Father, for my perfect job, my perfect house, my perfect body, and my perfect spouse."

"*Good,*" He said. "*It is time to see what you have been saying, and you will see it tomorrow.*"

"Lord, I'm not tryin' to go there an' lie."

"*Just go to the bank for the certified check, take Tori to the closing, show up on time, and shut up.*"

'Show up and shut up,' Tracy thought.

That was pretty clear, so Tracy called Tori. Both knew the realtors were supposed to do a forty-eight hour check on employment, but when Tracy told Tori His directive, she became his aide-de-camp.

"Now remember," Tori instructed. "All we gonna do is show up an' shut up. Just sign, an' when all this is over with we're gonna rejoice, because God got you a house without a job."

They went to the small office in a non-descript building to meet with the title agency. No questions were asked of Tracy except for the check, which he handed over and signed the receipt. Tracy was handed more papers that were explained, and he signed. Explain, sign, and repeat went on for about half-an-hour, and Tracy left the office with the key to his new townhome. Because God believes in overflow, Tracy also left with a three thousand dollar check back from the closing costs, which he knew was to buy furniture.

As soon as Tracy and Tori were back in the Jeep they screamed and rejoiced, and as they went to the townhouse it started to snow. Everything was in place - the maple floors, granite countertops and cherry cabinets. Then, Tracy noticed the knobs and looked around. He went to the front door and went upstairs. Every knob and fixture in the entire house was brushed nickel, and Tracy laughed at God's joke. He loved brushed nickel, and five was the number of Grace. When they were finished rejoicing, Tori looked at Tracy.

"What are we gonna do now?" she asked. Tracy stood in the living room in front of the fireplace and mantel he always wanted. He got pensive, turned in a circle, and looked around in thought.

"We're gonna have dinner real fast," Tracy said. "Then I'm gonna take you back home, because I have my own private praise an' worship session to do."

"Why's that?" Tori asked. "Didn't we just have one?"

"I feel like there's more to this," Tracy said, still turning slowly in the middle of the living room. "I just have to ask. So I'm gonna stay here by myself tonight."

"Well," Tori decided. "You at least need a shower curtain an' a towel, 'cause there ain't no blinds."

So they left, and had a light dinner because snow had set in. Tracy dropped Tori off, and he bought toiletries, milk, bread, peanut butter and jelly. He made a quick sandwich, and put the groceries in his virgin refrigerator. Then, he flicked the switch that turned his fireplace on and sat in the middle of the floor. He thanked the Lord, drank his milk, and ate his peanut butter and grape jelly sandwich. When he finished eating, he got up and danced for joy.

"*Stop!*" He said abruptly.

"What Lord?" Tracy said.

"*You are rejoicing over the wrong thing.*"

"What do you mean?"

"*Go outside,*" He said.

Tracy looked through his windows, and it was snowing hard.

"Will I need a coat?"

"*No,*" He said. "*You are not going to be out there that long.*"

Tracy put his shoes on, because there were a few inches of snow on the ground.

"What now Lord?" Tracy asked as he stood outside.

"*Grab that stake in the ground,*" He said.

Tracy was shown the plain wooden stake at the corner of the lot. He went and wriggled it out of the ground, and the bottom was covered with mud and ice.

"*Now take it, and run back in the house,*" He said, and Tracy did. "*Shut the door and lock it,*" and Tracy did. "*Go into the living room by the fireplace,*" and Tracy did.

Tracy held the stake so the mud and ice were over the hearthstone, warmed himself by the fire as he waited, and the mud and ice melted.

"*You are rejoicing over the wrong thing,*" He repeated.

"What should I be rejoicing over?" Tracy asked.

"*Remember back in Atlanta? When I had you reading Psalm 91 every morning for a year, until I released you from it?*" and all of His words came back to Tracy, as easily as he knew his name:

Psalm 91:

He that dwelleth in the secret place of the most High
>   *shall abide under the shadow of the Almighty.*

2 I will say of the Lord,
>   *He is my refuge and my fortress: my God; in him will I trust.*

3 Surely he shall deliver thee from the snare of the fowler,
>   *and from the noisome pestilence.*

4 He shall cover thee with his feathers, and under his wings shalt thou trust:
>   *his truth shall be thy shield and buckler.*

5 Thou shalt not be afraid for the terror by night;
>   *nor for the arrow that flieth by day;*

6 Nor for the pestilence that walketh in darkness;
>   *nor for the destruction that wasteth at noonday.*

7 A thousand shall fall at thy side, and ten thousand at thy right hand;
>   *but it shall not come nigh thee.*

8 Only with thine eyes shalt thou behold and see the reward of the wicked.

9 Because thou hast made the Lord, which is my refuge,
>   *even the most High, thy habitation;*

10 There shall no evil befall thee,
>   *neither shall any plague come nigh thy dwelling.*

11 For he shall give his angels charge over thee, to keep thee in all thy ways.

12 They shall bear thee up in their hands,
>   *lest thou dash thy foot against a stone.*

13 Thou shalt tread upon the lion and adder:
>   *the young lion and the dragon shalt thou trample under feet.*

14 Because he hath set his love upon me, therefore will I deliver him:
>   *I will set him on high, because he hath known my name.*

15 He shall call upon me, and I will answer him:
>   *I will be with him in trouble; I will deliver him, and honour him.*

16 With long life will I satisfy him, and shew him my salvation.

Tracy smiled, but still didn't completely understand.

"Well," He said. *"Welcome to the secret place."*

"What?"

"Remove the dirt from the bottom of the stake."

Tracy tapped the stake on the hearthstone carefully so not to stain his new carpet, and all the mud and ice fell off as a piece. On the end that had been in the ground was clearly marked in a contractor's black marker: Lot 91. Tracy smiled, marveled at the Lord, and spent his first night in his secret place of peace.

Selah.

The next night was Todd's Welcome Party. When Tracy signed the guest book with the feather pen, he wrote his new address for the first time, and Todd came over to give Tracy a hug.

"Thank you for understanding about last night," Todd said, and then he noticed what Tracy was doing. "What are you writing?"

"My new address," Tracy said.

Todd looked at him, because Todd was still not convinced of Tracy's connection to the Lord. Todd never understood why Tracy left N.C. State, and Todd couldn't believe Tracy could buy a house so soon, particularly without a job and nothing saved.

"Really," Tracy said. "This is the address of my new townhouse."

"How do you buy a townhouse in two days?" Todd exclaimed.

Tracy shrugged his shoulders.

"How come you didn't tell me?" Todd asked. Tracy looked around at Todd's guests.

"You were busy," Tracy said. "Happy fortieth birthday my friend. You have always been there for me, and I am so grateful."

On Saturday, over a hundred revelers swarmed the house for the Old Black Stank Soirée. At some point, Tracy and Sabrina stood and admired the new red leather couch. With all the time that had passed, the long friends shared a moment of reflection amidst the din. A large platter of hors d'oeuvres was on a stand outside the VJ booth next to them, which matched the display of fruit the Grecian nude held in the niche of the grotto.

"Tracy," Sabrina said as she ate a grape. "If you could make a million dollars, how would you do it?"

"I'd write a book," Tracy answered.

Sabrina picked up a strawberry.

"Well, what's stopping you?" and she bit her strawberry and walked off, and Tracy felt a confirmation.

After Todd's party, Tracy moved into his new house and used his three thousand dollar check to buy furniture. Once he got a phone number, Tracy called Dixie, the H.R. Director - the carefully painted one with the tight business skirt and brunette hair and blonde highlights. Tracy told her the details of his brand-new townhouse before he told her his name. Before she could hang up, Tracy told her that God loved her and something happened. Tracy's praise report affected her, and Tracy heard her softly crying on the other end of the line.

Then, Tracy settled into his house. He spent evenings in front of his fireplace, or in his Jacuzzi as he praised God, and thanked Him for the good things he had done. Tracy took refuge in the dwelling meant for him, shielded from the noisome pestilence, where no evil could befall him, and Tracy lived there - just he and the Lord.

- Sifu Mo and Tracy

Chapter 36

Tracy loved his house and thought his perfect job would follow, but it didn't. He sent out résumés, had face-to-face interviews, and February came and went. Tracy had saved enough money to last through April. By mid-March the spirit of fear tried his resolve, but Tracy kept his mind on Him. He watched Christian television, held the stake with Lot 91 written on it, and held onto his four promises, but God wasn't talking. Tracy recognized the test of his spirit, and knew the Lord wouldn't take him this far to leave. Besides, it wouldn't make sense to get his perfect house without a job only to lose it - what kind of testimony would that be?

Then, Tracy received his first mortgage bill that was wrong. The amount was twice as much per month than his contract stated. He called the lending company who told him not to worry about it. They instructed Tracy to make his first payment, and said they would straighten it out later. After Tracy got off the phone, His interruption was abrupt as it was surprising.

"Do not pay the mortgage until they get the payment amount correct," He said. *"Otherwise you will affirm their error, and they will hold you to it."*

"Thank you for that confirmation Lord," Tracy said, a little miffed it was the mortgage company that got His attention. "Now, what about a job to pay for all these bills?"

There was no answer, and Tracy knew he was back on radio silence. Another week went by, and Tracy's frustration grew. He sat in his perfect house alone without the three other promised goods, and his 'secret place' began to feel like a desert.

"Lord," Tracy said. "This is really weird. So, if you are a friend that sticks closer than a brother, I'm gonna start treatin' you like one."

For the next two days, Tracy argued and fussed at the Lord. When that didn't work, Tracy went 'Granny Moody on God.'

"How dare you," Tracy yelled, "put me in this situation and not talk me through it." His words rang off the empty living room walls. "You're my father. When I call You, You're supposed to answer!"

Tracy went from rage to weeping. He beat the floor in front of his fireplace one minute, and was 'snottin' an' cryin' the next. He thought he had passed all his tests. Tracy was tired and at the end of yet another rope, but the end of this one was too close to everything he was promised. Tracy spent all night in his empty house 'carryin' on.' Finally, in the silence before morning, he stopped to catch his breath.

"Are you done?" the Lord asked.

"Yeah," Tracy said, and wiped his eyes.

"You know it does not take all that. I am always here."

"Then why weren't you saying anything?"

"Because you were doing so well. You were doing fine, and you were not sinking," which made Tracy remember walking on the water in his vision at the river. *"This is how I strengthen your faith for the next round, because we are going higher than this townhouse Tracy."*

"Ok," Tracy said, and was intrigued. "What shall we do?"

"You spent the last few months working for Me," He said. *"Now, it is time for you to take a vacation."*

"What?"

"Call Mo in Florida. You have wanted to workout, and wanted to get back to your Kung Fu for a while. You have lain that on the altar long enough. Now, I am going to give it back to you in a straight way."

Tracy was speechless because this made the least amount of sense, so the Lord clarified.

"Call Mo in Florida. Take a vacation there, and workout with him for your birthday weekend in April."

"Lord," Tracy protested. "My entertainment budget for April is $500, which doesn't include a plane ticket, or expenses while I'm in Florida."

The Lord waited.

"Ok," Tracy said flippantly. "You're gonna have to help me understand this one. Show me in the Bible where somebody needed something really bad, and You told them to go on vacation."

"Fine," He said. *"Remember Peter?"*

"Yeah," but Tracy didn't follow.

"When he needed money to pay his taxes?"

"Yeah..."

"I told him to go on vacation and go fishing," and as He said it, Tracy saw it, which was the revelation:

Even though Peter's profession was a fisherman, fishing was also his hobby. So, when the Lord told Peter to go fishing, Peter didn't take out his boat with his nets and crew. Instead, Tracy was shone Peter on vacation. He had on a straw hat, and sat on the bank of the river behind Granny's house fishing for catfish.

"Can you see it?" He asked.

"Yes Lord," Tracy said. "I see it."

As Tracy looked into the vision, he stood in the middle of the river on a stepping-stone that came from the deep to meet his foot. As before, when Tracy took another step toward the revelation, Tracy was reassured the gates of hell could not prevail against the next pillar.

"Now that you can see it," He said. *"Look closer."*

Tracy took another step. As he did, another stone came up to meet his footfall. Then, Tracy saw Peter the way he was – relaxed, as he lazily cast his line into the river.

"Do you see? Peter did not put a bait on the hook because I did not tell him to."

Tracy saw the hook was bare when it went in the water, and Tracy looked at the Lord, who now stood beside him.

"With the first fish Peter caught there was a gold coin enough to pay his taxes, My taxes, and plenty left over for Peter as a reward for obeying the first thing I told him to do: Go on vacation."

As He spoke, Tracy understood. By that time in their relationship, Peter knew the Lord well enough to only do what He had told him. Peter took one step at a time, faith upon faith, without adding or subtracting anything.

"Exactly," the Lord said. Then, He looked at Tracy with great intensity and said, *"What are you going to do?"* and Tracy smiled.

"I'm gonna call Mo an' go on vacation," and Tracy sighed, because it was finally time to reconnect.

Tracy thought of Mo's round face and high top fade, and realized they hadn't seen each other since college days. Then, even though it was just dawn, Tracy decided to call. Mo worked out early and besides, Tracy thought, the Lord told him it was ok.

"Hey buddy," Tracy said. Mo knew exactly who it was and laughed.

"Wow it's good to hear your voice," Mo said. "How long has it been?" and Tracy laughed.

The last time Tracy called Mo was right before he left Atlanta, and Tracy left behind what he thought was his dream house. Now, two Aprils later, Tracy sat in his perfect house, and was following God's instructions to go on vacation for his birthday. So, the 'power pellet' from 2003 worked. Tracy was sustained until the realization of owning his townhouse by 2005, and unknowingly, Mo was about to help Tracy manifest two more promises.

For now, Tracy told Mo the whole story – from getting his house without a job, to Peter fishing by Granny's riverbank. Mo laughed, but not as a scoff. To the contrary, Mo looked forward to what was to happen, because he was familiar with Tracy's relationship with God.

Mo was originally from New York, although you couldn't tell from how little he said. He was innately easy-going, which hid his understated, surgically precise humor. He was an average-sized black man whose stature belied his physical power. Mo also observed and remembered everything. Now, he lived outside of Fort Lauderdale, was married, and had two boys who were three and five. He had his master's degree in computer science and a good job. Mo was excited Tracy was finally coming for a visit, and when Tracy hung up, he booked his plane tickets.

Then Tracy called Tori. They hadn't spoken much the last few months, other than seeing each other in church on Sundays. When Tori asked for news, Tracy answered like the Shunammite woman answered, 'It is well,' when her only son was dead, and she went to fetch Elisha:

"Are ya likin' your new house?" Tori would ask.

Tracy would reply, "It's all good."

"Did all your blinds fit?"

"Good enough."

"How's the job search goin'?"

"It's goin'," and Tori was kept away from the period of testing Tracy went through.

So, Tori was surprised when Tracy called to say he was going on vacation. The next day, they shopped for workout clothes Tracy needed for his trip. Tracy caught Tori up on what the Lord was really up to, and at the end of the week, Tracy left for Florida.

When Mo picked Tracy up from the airport, it was as if the decades hadn't happened, except for their closely shaved baldheads. After they caught up, the discussion quickly regressed to the guttural pops and grunts that ensued when one spoke of Kung Fu. They both loved it - all of it – the discipline, diet, body awareness and philosophy. When they arrived at Mo's house, Tracy got settled into the guestroom. Then Mo had to go back to work.

"I have a few things to wrap up in the office," Mo said. "Why don't we swing by, and I can show you where I work."

"You can take strangers into work?" Tracy asked.

Mo chuckled in his little boy way. "I'm the boss," he said. "They work for me."

"I guess it has been a long time," and suddenly, Tracy's cell phone rang. "Sorry, I thought I turned this off," and Tracy didn't recognize the number.

"Aren't you going to answer your phone?" Mo asked.

"Nah, they'll leave a message," Tracy decided. "Right now I'm here with you, doing what God told me to do."

"Suppose this is your first fish?"

Tracy went blank as the two worlds collided.

"Remember?" Mo asked. "You didn't even have a chance to put bait on your hook, and you just started your vacation."

Tracy recognized the accuracy of Mo's words, and jumped to answer his phone. "This is Tramele, how can I help you?"

"Mr. Staples?" the man asked.

"Yes sir," Tracy answered.

"Are you still in the job market, and available for an interview?" the man asked.

"Yes sir," Tracy said, and looked at Mo and whispered, "First fish!"

Mo smiled widely, and went into the kitchen for some coconut milk.

"Do you have time to talk with me about this offer I have?" the man asked.

"Yes sir," Tracy said. "However, before we get started, I should tell you my plane just landed. I just started my vacation, so I am not in a place to write anything down."

"I understand," the man said.

"But if that's ok with you," Tracy said, "I have a little bit of time right now."

"I realize you're on vacation," the man said, "but do you have any other job offers pending?"

"No sir," Tracy said. Then the man spent a few minutes explaining to Tracy what the job entailed.

"Can you start work on April fifteenth?" the man asked.

"Yes," Tracy said.

"Well, I don't want you to be the fish that got away."

Tracy laughed aloud, but the man acted as if he didn't hear him.

"What compensation are you looking for?" he asked.

Tracy held the phone to his thigh.

"He's asking me to name my price Lord," Tracy said. "No employer has ever asked me to name my price. What should I do?"

"What do you want that gold coin to be?" He asked. *"It will be whatever you call it."*

At the time, the highest salary Tracy experienced was $85,000.

"Ninety-eight thousand," Tracy said, because it was just shy of six figures.

"Done," the man said.

"Really?" Tracy said before he could think. "All of that happened in ten minutes?" and at first, Tracy thought he was talking to the Lord.

"Really," the man answered. "I like your personality. If the rest of the team I am putting together have the same, we will have a great time on this project."

Tracy needed more time to process what happened, and the man knew it.

"So," the man said. "Enjoy your vacation, and I'll be in touch with you when you get back."

"Thank you," Tracy said and hung up.

Mo reappeared from the kitchen. "And?" he asked.

"You were right. That was the fish with the gold coin in its mouth."

"How much was the gold coin?"

"Ninety-eight."

Mo was impressed. "And in less than an hour."

"What?"

"You've been on 'vacation' for less than an hour, and you got your job."

"Yeah," Tracy said. "I guess I did," and the weight was lifted so Tracy could enjoy his vacation.

On Saturday morning, they went to Mo's studio lined with mirrors. He taught an adult class in the morning, and a kid's class in the afternoon. Immediately, Tracy was back in his element, and just like the old days, he didn't want to stop. That night, Mo and Tracy ordered Chinese food, watched Kung Fu movies and carried on with horrible 'Kung Fu' accents. They had to stop the action at almost every turn to catch more lightning-fast techniques. On Sunday morning, they went back to Mo's studio alone.

"Trace," Mo said, "do you have any questions for me?"

Tracy was surprised because Mo was so advanced. His previous teachers would never have offered this question. Tracy had been taught by trial and error before he was corrected, so this approach was new to him.

"Yeah," Tracy answered, "but I'm a little hesitant to ask them."

"How about I start," Mo said easily.

Tracy sat cross-legged on the floor, and for the next two hours Mo gave him an overview of the Hung Ga system, from the first form to the last. Tracy had yearned to learn this system his whole life, and it was beautiful and moving his old friend was the one who showed him. During the demonstration Mo hid nothing, and for Tracy it was like reading an open book. When Mo finished, Tracy was humbled.

"Would you take me on as a student?" Tracy asked.

"I already have," Mo answered, and with that, Tracy's path was straightened.

On the plane ride home, Tracy's past, present, and future collided. As he felt the soreness of his muscles, Tracy thought back to how his training started, when Granny decided he needed a hobby.

"Somethin' you're good at," Granny had said, "an' you can do into your old age. I got my bowlin'."

Now, Tracy smiled because God had returned him to Kung Fu. He provided the perfect teacher to guide him, and for the first time in a long time, Tracy was sore but content. Tracy felt he could finally breathe as he returned to his own house and started his new job. Then Tracy laughed, and remembered his four promises. Somehow, without him knowing it, God had pulled everything together: he got a job on vacation, he was in his new house, and he was working his body in the way that he loved. So, even though there was one left to realize, Tracy delighted in God's ways.

Chapter 37

- Freddie in Bobby's chair

When Tracy returned from his vacation in Florida, he finished the preliminaries for his security clearance. Then, he began his career as a consultant for the FAA through an independent consulting firm. Unlike many of the previous jobs that catapulted him to this level, Tracy loved every minute. He enjoyed the encouraging environment, and the fact his coworkers appreciated his knowledge and experience.

At the end of the month Tracy was paid, which caught him up on his mortgage, utilities, and filled his cabinets and fridge with money to spare. To celebrate, Tracy hopped in his Jeep and headed to Pier One. There, he got plates to match the chargers he bought months before. As he went through the aisles, Tracy remembered when he first heard the four promises in Columbus. He remembered carefully replacing the biscotti candle, before he yelled at God as Lynn looked on. Now, he was grateful for how much God had blessed him.

"What about that car you always wanted?" He asked.

"Lord," Tracy said. "I just got my first mortgage, started a new job where I actually know what I'm doing, and have finally caught up on my bills. I'm happy where I am, and I'm not looking to add another payment."

"But what about that car you always wanted," He repeated. *"Was it some kind of Australian thing?"*

Tracy smiled as the Lord dug into his imagination, and knew exactly what Tracy forgot he wanted.

"It wasn't an 'Australian thing' Lord," Tracy answered like a little kid being teased. "I thought about a Subaru when I was in Australia, because it was called an Outback. I liked it because it had all-wheel drive, and it would be a good, all-around utilitarian vehicle."

"Yes, and what do you want on it?"

"Well, I travel a lot in the wintertime to see Granny. I know the Outbacks have a winter package. While the Jeep is nice, electric windows and a sound system with a CD player would be cool."

"Yes, and what else?"

"Lord," Tracy protested. "I'm content where I am, and I'm trying to get out of debt, not add more."

"But I want to fulfill the desires of your heart, so I am searching it to see what else I can do for you."

"But Lord," and Tracy was silenced, because He was adamant.

"Move your butt out of the way so that I can bless you."

Tracy understood the 'butt' was the 'but' of his words, because what He had for Tracy was greater than he could imagine. All Tracy had to do was receive what the Lord had for him, and He confirmed this.

"Do not tie my hands, now that we are on a roll."

"Ok Lord, I remove the but," and instantly, Tracy's cell phone rang.

Tracy recognized the number. It was the recruiter he worked with through the spring to find a job. Tracy was grateful for his diligent work, so he pulled over to catch the call on the second ring. Tracy parked Bruce in the well-lit parking lot, and he thanked the recruiter. Then Tracy told him he had gotten a job and wanted his name removed. But Tracy told the recruiter he would definitely use him when he looked for his next gig.

"And let that job go to someone else more suitable," Tracy prayed, "in Jesus' name."

Tracy ended the call, put Bruce's clutch in reverse, and looked behind to back up.

"Stop," He said. *"Park the car again and look up."*

Tracy did as he was told. He thought something was wrong until he looked up and saw the huge illuminated Subaru sign, and the fact that he was parked in front of the showroom window.

"Lord, you've got serious jokes."

"Tell me what you want," He said.

Feeling had, Tracy thought he would make this game hard for God.

"Ok," Tracy decided. "I want everything my Dad would have, but in my style. That means it would be white, have heated leather seats, a CD changer, a sunroof, but not an automatic," which Tracy was sure an Outback couldn't possibly have at the same time.

"So, I want a stick-shift with all those bells and whistles," Tracy decided.

"Can I help you?" a salesman said through the Jeep window. Tracy was startled, but opened his door and got out of Bruce.

"I think I'm looking for a Subaru Outback," Tracy said.

"We have many Outbacks," the salesman said.

Tracy looked around. "None of these speak to me."

"We have more in the back," the salesman said. "What are you looking for?"

"A white one," Tracy said.

"Ok. I believe we have five in," the salesman said.

As they headed to the back lot, Tracy recognized five was the number of Grace. When they got there, Tracy saw the white Outbacks scattered among the other colors. Even though Tracy knew where his car was, he thought it would be fun to look at the others along the way. Like the 'Hot/Cold' children's game, Tracy knew the path, but decided to take his time. The first three white Outbacks didn't have sunroofs, and as Tracy passed them he waved his hand at them.

"Nope. Nope. Nope." Tracy said, and the salesman looked at Tracy more closely.

'Over here!' Tracy's car said eagerly. Tracy stopped in his tracks and turned to the salesman.

"Did I just hear that?" Tracy asked.

The salesman cocked his head and spoke slowly. "I'm not sure…"

Then they went to the fourth white Outback that had a sunroof, but the seats were cloth.

"This is fine Lord," Tracy said aloud, "but not what my father would drive," and Tracy thought of his father's advice - 'That material will cut you son,' and Tracy laughed aloud.

'Don't make me wait!' Tracy's car pleaded from the back of the lot.

"You have got to be kidding me," Tracy said.

Now the salesman truly wondered with whom Tracy was speaking, and Tracy answered the salesman by looking him directly in the eye.

"Well, God saves the best for last," and they went to last row. There, Tracy's car sparkled like the final reveal in a showcase showdown.

"Surely Lord, you are joking!" Tracy said, and he walked around the outside. He noticed the moon-roof and stick shift, and turned to the salesman. "I want to test drive it."

"I'll get the keys," and the salesman ran back to the showroom.

Tracy opened the door and sat in the beige leather seat. It had the winter package with heated seats and mirrors, a rear-window defroster, CD changer, electric windows and locks. It also had wood-grain trim like Harry's Cadillac. So, Tracy thought it was neat and tidy like his Dad, but durable and sporty like himself.

"That car is not supposed to be unlocked," the salesman yelled louder than he realized. "How did you get in the car?"

"It was unlocked," Tracy said, and the salesman handed him the keys.

"Well, it can't be," the salesman said. Then he tried the doors to the surrounding cars that were locked. In a panic, the salesman went to the other side of Tracy's car, and he tried more locked doors to be sure. Tracy rolled the passenger's side window down.

"Would you like to come with me on this test drive?" Tracy asked.

The salesman was completely flummoxed, and looked at Tracy much more closely as he got in the passenger's seat.

Tracy loved his new car, and realized what it meant to have 'God do exceedingly abundantly above all that we ask or think'. Then, without trading in Bruce and with only five hundred dollars down, Tracy drove his white Subaru Outback home that night. On Friday, he headed to West Virginia to visit Granny for Mother's Day in his new Subaru.

Then, Tracy returned to his townhouse and spent the summer settling in. As September came Tracy was given his next directive, which wasn't as pleasant. He was on his way home, although he was stopping by Momma Ro's to have dinner.

"Hey Tracy,' He said. *'It is time.'*

Tracy let out an audible groan. "Really Lord?"

"Yes Tracy," He confirmed, *"Now is the time,"* and Tracy sighed heavily, and took time to meditate on what had to happen before he responded.

"Ok," Tracy said. "I knew this was coming, I just didn't look forward to it. Now, if You confirm it and set it up, then I won't have a problem doing it. All I ask is that You go before me and make it plain, and that whatever is done in the dark, let it be brought to the light."

"I will," He said.

When Tracy arrived at Momma Ro's, he found out Bunky and Tori were coming for dinner. As the family ate, Momma Ro confirmed what Tracy was told.

"Tracy," she said. "Do ya think it's time to reach out to Bobby? 'Cause he was askin' about ya at the breakfast on Sunday."

Momma Ro spoke for Charlie, even though he sat and ate at the other end of the table. He actually had the conversation with Bobby. All of the husbands who didn't go to church with their wives met at the same restaurant for breakfast. They arrived just before the first service got out. That way, the food was fresh and hot, and they got a good seat at the window. Then, they had two hours for 'man-gossip' until the second service got out, and they had to beat it back home before their wives got there.

"Momma Ro," Tracy said, and he sat back. "That is confirmation, so I am ready."

"That's great sugar," Ro said. "He says he has some pictures he wants to give ya. He thought it best to give them back directly, an' I thought so too."

"Besides," Tracy agreed. "We're approaching the anniversary of Freddie's death, an' I know he thinks about that. We're also coming up on Yom Kippur, an' we just finished celebrating Rosh Hashana."

"Tracy," He interrupted, *"look at everyone's faces. They have no idea what you are talking about. Feed them slowly."*

'I do sound crazy, don't I Lord,' and Tracy smiled before he spoke aloud.

"Hey guys," Tracy said. "The same voice I heard an' followed, that got me back here to Maryland, an' surprised everyone with getting' me the townhouse an' the new car, He spoke to me on the way here from work. He told me it was time to meet with Bobby, an' Momma Ro, you just confirmed it. I also realized the timing not only coincides with Freddie's passing, it lines up with the Jewish Holy Days of the New Year and Yom Kippur, which is the Day of Atonement."

Charlie, Momma Ro, Bunky and Tori stared at Tracy, because it made such perfect sense.

"So yes," Tracy said. "I am ready, just say when," and the silence held for a moment.

"You ain't gonna breakout them knives, or any nunchucks are ya?" Bunky asked.

"Bunky!" Momma Ro scolded. "You just stop it!"

"No," Tracy said easily. "This is not that. I won't have to spring any Kung Fu moves on him."

"Mercy!" Momma Ro cried. "I should hope it doesn't come to that," and she hummed a hard "Mmm-hmm," for emphasis.

"But since you're ready," Momma Ro concluded, "Bobby said ya should come over to his house anytime after work. He doesn't go anywhere, but he asked ya give him a call before ya come."

"You won't recognize him," Bunky said. "I was in the store a while ago, an' I heard a familiar voice call me. When I turned around, there was this frail man standin' in front of me. I didn't know who it was."

"An' you'll feel pity for him," Tori said.

After dinner, Tracy checked in with his father.

"I don't think that is a good idea son," Harry said. "I wouldn't advise it."

"Well, Momma Ro has all but set it up," Tracy said. "I can just stop by his house on my way home."

"You're going to his house?" Lynn sputtered from the other line. "Why can't you meet in public? Because you can forgive that man from a distance. You don't have to see him at home. That's just ridiculous."

"Mom," Tracy said calmly. "It will be fine, an' believe me Dad, this wasn't my idea."

"Well son, I understand He is telling you to do this, and He has prepared you," so Harry relented. "I guess we should see where this leads. But call me before this happens, so we can pray over it."

"I will Dad," Tracy said, and he did.

Midweek was close to the time Freddie died, so Tracy called his father. They prayed a prayer of protection, and that anything done in the dark would be brought to the light. The next day, Tracy called Bobby when he was about to leave work. He also stopped by Momma Ro's on the way, so she would know where he was. It had been seventeen years since Tracy had left his mother's split-level house, when he had milk tea with Granny and Vera, and they laughed at Helen Keller jokes.

Now, Tracy parked on the street. He walked up the driveway to see the man who may have willfully, or inadvertently let his mother die. The lawn was mowed, but there was tall grass in broken cracks of the driveway. Numerous oil stains on the cement hadn't been washed, which was unusual for the mechanic who had kept his cab and cars immaculate. On the walk from the driveway to the front door, Tracy noticed a box of Christmas lights stranded in the unkempt bushes in front of the house. The railing along the front steps was rusty. Cracked caulking squeezed from the window seams, and the aluminum trim was loose with moss growing on it. When Tracy pressed the doorbell, it didn't work. He knocked, and Bobby opened the door a little too soon.

"Glad you made it," Bobby said. "I wasn't sure you'd remember where the house was."

Tracy was immediately put off. Of course he knew where his Mom's house was, but Bobby looked tiny and withdrawn. He didn't look the sailor who navigated the world's seas in the Navy, had more cars than he could drive in a workweek, or captained his yacht on the Potomac to great bravado. However, Bunky and Tori's words hadn't prepared Tracy for what he saw – a scared, sleepless, timid man, who's personal lack of maintenance matched his house.

Inside the house it was dark, even though it was late afternoon. The carpet rolled with age, and looked not to have been vacuumed for seventeen years. Tracy's wingtip shoes stuck to it as he walked, and the living room was still setup for the Christmas party Vera hosted before she passed. The space where the Christmas tree stood was vacant in front of the picture window. The table that was usually there was still pushed into the corner. The spider plant Vera had kept in the big green pot was long gone.

Instead, the holiday candleholders and Christmas candy dish stood next to the empty pot, as if to guard the silence. Then, instinctively, Tracy went to the kitchen. The decorative fork and spoon with his Mom's fruit garland were overgrown with hamburger grease and dust, and the air was a far cry from the smell of cinnamon toast and milk tea.

"I got some pictures for ya," Bobby said. "I was goin' through the photo albums downstairs."

Tracy turned back to Bobby. He stood in the gloom of the living room, and Tracy was again taken by how small he was.

"Yeah, Momma Ro told me," Tracy said, "but before we get to all that, how have you been?"

"I've been tryin' to hang in there," Bobby said. "I haven't had a good night's sleep..." and Bobby stopped, and it was as if Tracy wasn't standing in front of him.

"Since when?" Tracy asked. Bobby looked at him.

"Since Bootsie died."

"Well Bobby, that's not good. Nobody should greave that long," and they headed downstairs to the family room Bobby had finished off for Vera.

It was incredibly dark as they descended. Bobby flipped a switch, and two lights came on by the TV. It was the same set with rabbit ears that Tracy and Freddie watched when they were in elementary school. The same brown knitted oval rug they played on as kids lay before it. Bobby took a seat in his orange cloth recliner, which looked like Archie Bunker's. By its vintage the chair could have watched a current episode, except now, it was held together with patches of duct tape. Tracy sat on the couch, but kept forward for fear of what might happen to his suit if he leaned back.

"Yeah," Bobby said. "I keep gettin' woke up at one-o'clock in the morning by these loud noises outside. It's like an army goin' down the street, an' there are helicopter searchlights all around the house."

"It always happens at one-o'clock?" Tracy asked.

"And at three," Bobby said, and Tracy thought this was odd. Those were the times his Mom woke up the morning she died, when she asked for more water, and Bobby and Freddie went back to sleep. Tracy got the sense that Bobby was chased by those demons.

"What do you do about that?" Tracy asked.

"I used to go into the corner an' pull the mattress over me, but I got past that."

"You should probably talk to someone about that," Tracy said, "because you should get your sleep."

"Yeah. I got a prescription I got to pick up at the pharmacy. But I don't have any money, so I have to wait until my check clears."

"When is that?"

"The end of the month."

"That's two weeks away. How much is your prescription?"

"Ten dollars. Why, are ya gonna pay for it?"

"I believe the Lord will allow me to do that," Tracy said.

"Oh, the Lord," Bobby said. "That's right. I heard about you and," but Bobby couldn't think of how to say it, "the church. I heard that you an' Tori go to church all the time with Rosetta," and Bobby turned into his old self a little. "If anybody could turn ya around, Tori could," and Bobby looked at Tracy the way he did before he made the boys take their bikes back to Moody's truck. "Although she might be too much woman for ya."

"Bobby," Tracy stated, who was so much greater than the little boy Bobby had known. "Tori and I are just friends," and Bobby became timid again. "Now, how about those pictures."

"Oh yeah," Bobby said. "Here they are," and he reached into the side pocket of his recliner.

Bobby pulled out an envelope, and sat up to hand it to Tracy. Then, Bobby sat back and pulled a steak knife out from under his chair. He placed it on the side table next to an open can of cashews. Tracy wondered if Bobby used the knife to open the can, but it was already open, and had a pull-tab. Then, Tracy opened the envelope and thought they would reminisce, but there were only eight pictures.

'I didn't come here for eight pictures, did I Lord?' Tracy thought. 'But maybe he just wants to hear the stories behind them, and have a little company.'

So they went through the pictures and talked like old friends, even though they weren't. They laughed about Freddie's antics, skipped over the bad parts, and managed to pass about fifteen minutes.

"I got some more upstairs," Bobby said. "They're in a plastic baggy if ya wanna see 'em," and they went back upstairs to the living room. "I've been meanin' to clean the house up, but I haven't had any gumption to do it. I've also been meanin' to get cable installed, but I couldn't get up on the roof."

"Bobby," Tracy said, "the cable people go on the roof when you get it installed."

"Well, I bought this dish off this guy. I knew all I had to do was point it at the sky. But I couldn't get my buddy to go up on the roof with me an' help, so I just let it go."

Tracy looked at Bobby in disbelief. Bobby sat down in the corner chair of the living room. Tracy carefully sat on the edge of the loveseat and looked at the material. The furniture was the set his Mom had wanted for so long, and had kept immaculate. Now it was covered with dirt, and yet more oil stains. When Tracy looked up, Bobby had forgotten about the other pictures. Instead, he reached under his chair to pull out another steak knife. He placed it on the side table between them, and there wasn't even the charade of cashews to explain the behavior, so Tracy asked.

"Bobby, are you ok?"

"Yeah man," Bobby said. "Don't mind me. I just get scared here all by myself."

"Well, turn some lights on, an' get rid of those dark corners. Get yourself some nightlights you can put all over the house."

"An' who's gonna pay for all that electricity?"

By this time, Tracy was done with him. "Are you ready to go to the store? Because it's gettin' late, an' I have to go to work tomorrow."

"Yeah, Charlie was tellin' me about that nice job you got with the FAA. An' I heard you bought a brand-new townhouse not too far from here. So you're doin' good."

"The Lord is good," Tracy said, "an' he's not finished yet, so let's go get that prescription."

Bobby locked up the house. Then they walked down the driveway and got into Tracy's car.

"Man," Bobby said, and inhaled deeply. "It still has that new car smell to it."

Tracy smiled. Bobby used to get a new car every two years, and Tracy's new Subaru was all he could talk about.

"These leather seats are heated?" Bobby asked, "an' the mirrors have defrosters in 'em too?"

As they drove, Tracy realized that was why the Lord got him a new car before he had this meeting – a meeting with the man who told him he would never amount to anything. But that was all water under the bridge, and Bobby was the worse for it.

"You should come 'round sometime," Bobby said, after Tracy dropped him off.

"I don't live too far away," Tracy said. "But I'm gettin' busy with some projects."

"Well, if you can," Bobby said, and went into his dark house, and didn't turn on any lights. When Tracy got home, he called his father.

"Son," Harry said, and he was upset. "I don't want you going there anymore. It bothers me to hear that is what you went through. You are my son, not his, and you need to tell Momma Ro about this too," which Tracy did.

"He did what?" Momma Ro screamed. "He used me to set you up, an' then pulled steak knives out on ya? Oh no shug. You ain't ever goin' back over there again. We're done with that man for good!" and they were.

In February, Bobby's son David called Tracy at work.

"Hey buddy," David said. "I don't want to bother ya, but I think ya should know Bobby died. I'm gonna have to go view the body to identify it."

"I'm sorry to hear that," and Tracy thought a moment. "But you shouldn't have to do that alone."

"Oh I'll be alright," David said, "he wasn't your father."

"But I'm your brother, an' I'm going with you."

"Well," and David sighed. "We have to go to Lynchburg."

"Why do we have to go there?"

"Because that's where he died," David said.

"Oh," Tracy said, because he knew anything with Bobby was complicated, even if he was dead. "You can tell me on the way," Tracy decided, and David did.

Bobby visited his girlfriend for Valentine's Day, which was why David got the call from the hospital in Lynchburg, Virginia. So that night, Tracy, David, and his wife drove through the night in David's black SUV. They got up early at the motel in Lynchburg, and David's wife needed some caffeine before they went to the funeral home.

"I need to stay awake," she said at the coffee shop. Then she looked at Tracy. "An' you look like you need one too."

"That's probably too strong for me," Tracy said. "Caffeine really affects me. I probably shouldn't."

"Get out," David's wife said, and hit Tracy's arm hard. "You just let me," and she stepped up to the counter. "Yes, this man wants a mega super-charged latte," which Tracy finished before they reached the funeral home, and he was affected.

After David and Tracy identified the body they met Bobby's girlfriend, who was forty years Bobby's junior. Then, David, his wife, Tracy, and Bobby's girlfriend sat in front of the funeral director's desk. As the director spoke of transportation matters, he handed David a small bag with Bobby's personal effects. As the funeral director continued, David went through the bag and handed each item to his wife, one of which was a prescription bottle.

High out of his mind on caffeine and sugar, Tracy feverishly sought out the contents listed on the bottle of pills. He thought they would be blue, but these pills were pear-shaped and yellow.

'C, I,' Tracy thought as he read. 'But her thumb is in the way. What is that other letter? An L?'

Tracy screamed and turned to David. "What's he doing takin' a sex drug? He's not supposed to be takin' that. He has a heart condition!"

"Calm down Tracy," David said. "What are you talking about?"

"That's the new weekend sex drug," Tracy said rapidly in caffeine mode. "You can take it Friday night, an' be good Sunday all the way up to when you have to go to work Monday mornin'! But Bobby's not supposed to be takin' those while on heart medication, which I know for a fact he's on, because I tried to drown his nitroglycerin pills a long time ago."

David's wife stared at Tracy, but David asked. "But why would he be takin' a weekend sex drug in the first place?"

"Well," David's wife said. "It was Valentine's Day," and she shot her husband a look with a neck crook. "Which would have been nice," she said, because Bobby's death had messed up her plans.

"But that doesn't make any sense," David said.

"Oh yes it does," Tracy said, who realized there was a fourth person in the room. Then David, his wife, and Tracy simultaneously turned to look at Bobby's girlfriend, who shifted in her chair and was Valentine's Day red.

"I got to go," Tracy said, jumped up, and got back to David's car before he fell apart from laughing.

David and his wife soon joined Tracy, and they 'commensed to 'hootin' and hollerin'. Then, David opened the bottle to check the pills, but there were others wrapped in foil inside. When he unwrapped those they were blue, which made them laugh and rock the black SUV harder. Finally, David screamed the truth:

"Pops didn't die of a heart attack, he died of a hard-on!" and that was the end of Bobby.

Chapter 38

- the Moody tractor

There were two times in Tracy's life when Moody acted like the Tall Shiny Silver Figure. The first was when Tracy was in elementary school. Moody gathered Tracy and his 'runnin' cousins' together to take a picture. Right after, he grabbed Tracy by the hand, and they hopped in his newly refurbished black 1950 Chevy Bel Air. Moody spent years restoring the car, including the original red and black-striped leather interior. Granny could have put makeup on looking into the chrome, except she wasn't allowed to drive it. Moody knew she would mess up the wide whitewall tires in some parking shenanigan.

"You're comin' with me," Moody said, and closed Tracy's heavy door. Moody got in on his side and manually rolled his window down. Tracy did the same, because it was hot and there was no air conditioning. Moody kept the original column shift, but had installed the necessary update of an eight-track tape player. At first, Tracy thought he was in trouble because Moody was so serious.

"I took this picture so you would remember this day," Moody said, and pointed at the Polaroid snapshot developing between them in the wide seat. Then they drove to Dupont City and went to a strange house, where Moody got out without hesitation.

"Get out of the car boy," Moody said.

Tracy went with his grandfather who knocked on the door. When the white man opened it, Tracy realized they had business with each other.

"Here," Moody said, and handed the man an envelope. "This is the last thing I owe ya. In thirty days, I expect to see my title in my hands free and clear or I'm comin' back." Moody leaned over to speak with Tracy. "You remember this. This is the day your grandfather paid off his house, an' he 'owes no man nothin' but to love him'."

Moody stood back up, and cut a figure with the stub of his cigar under his Eroll Flynn moustache and stingy-brim hat.

"Thirty days," Moody said into the man's eyes. "Ya hear me?" and Moody looked at Tracy and warmed his tone. "Come on let's go," and they got back into Moody's faultlessly black hardtop coupe, started her up, and proudly backed out of the driveway as "Mustang Sally" played them out at a respectable volume.

The second time Moody acted like the Tall Shiny Silver Figure was also serious, even though Tracy wasn't sure why at the time. Moody had called a Jewish man to the house, and this was the second time Tracy had seen him. The first time was a year earlier, just after Tracy moved in with his grandparents. Granny and Moody wanted to adopt him. Vera wouldn't hear of it, so the attorney drew up papers for them to be Tracy's legal guardians.

The next time the attorney came to the house was after Moody came home in his wheelchair. Bonnie was a puppy, and Moody had just finished signing an official-looking document at the kitchen table. The tri-fold legal document was on rigid paper, and Moody held it up for Tracy to see. The only thing legible was "Last Will and Testament" printed in an English typeset across the top.

"Tracy," Moody said sternly. "You're not gonna know what's in this, but remember this day, the day it was signed."

Granny, Moody and the family attorney were at the table in the meridian blue kitchen, and Tracy stood in the doorway. Then, Moody looked at Tracy from his wheelchair.

"If anything happens to me, you get in touch with this man," Moody said, and he pointed the document towards the attorney. "He'll take care of everything else," and Moody meant business.

"Ok Pawpaw," Tracy said, and studied the attorney.

"You contact this man," Moody repeated.

The severity of Tracy's Pawpaw couldn't have been clearer, or the trust that Moody put in the Jewish man who sat at his table.

Now, almost three decades later, Tracy went to Rand shortly after his birthday to visit Moody for Easter. In May, Tracy visited Granny for Mother's Day. By that time, Moody was in the V.A. Hospital in Huntington because of the gangrene on his foot. By Memorial Day, Moody was moved to a nursing home in South Charleston to be closer to home. Tracy went to visit him, and like the 'meetin's' they held through the years, Moody spoke freely.

"Hey Trace," Moody said. "Can you get me some of that ginger extract? I've seen ya usin' it with your Kung Fu trainin'. I think it's supposed to be good for settlin' you're stomach. Mine's gettin' upset from all this medication."

"Sure Moody," Tracy said.

Tracy also noted Moody had gone 'old school', returning to homeopathic remedies his family had used at the farm. Then Moody sat up and got serious, like when they went to pay off the deed to the house, or the day Moody made his will.

"Look in there for my book," Moody said, and pointed to the drawer in his nightstand. "You're gonna need this, but give it to me now so I can call her."

Tracy got the black leather address book from the drawer. Moody always carried it in his pocket protector for important numbers, and the pages were only slightly spattered with the oil and grease of a mechanic's fingers. When Tracy handed Moody his glasses, Tracy noticed his teeth weren't in. Moody always wore his dentures when he was awake. This made Tracy realize Moody had been awake for some time, and Moody noticed Tracy looking at his teeth.

"Yeah," Moody said. "They don't fit anymore, since I lost a little weight in my gums," and he fumbled though his address book. "The family attorney died some time ago, an' his daughter took over."

With those words, Tracy realized the gravity of the situation. Moody found the number, and then reached for the hospital phone and dialed. When she picked up, Moody spoke so Tracy was included in the conversation.

"Yeah, this is Kindel," Moody said. "I was callin' for you to bring those papers in," and there was a pause while she spoke.

"I'm ok," Moody said. "They got me on some new medication that makes my stomach upset, but that's not what I called about. I got Tracy here with me, my grandson. You'll remember me talkin' about him, an' now, I'm talkin' to him about you. He'll know how to contact ya if somethin' happens to me, 'cause I'm givin' him your name an' number."

She spoke again, but Moody interrupted.

"No, I know you're busy, so you don't need to talk to him. But I expect you'll be hearin' from him soon," and when Moody hung up the phone Tracy was shocked.

Things became blurry in this world for Tracy. But as Moody gave Tracy his attorney's information, he was forced to make peace with the same thing Moody already had. Later, as Tracy drove home to D.C. he asked the Lord for more time. Tracy meant he wanted Moody to live longer, but the Lord granted his request in a different way.

Two weeks later Tracy was laid off from his contract job, which couldn't have been more perfect. By June, Tracy spent weeks at a time in Charleston visiting Moody. Tracy only came home to the townhouse to cash his unemployment checks. By the time the Fourth of July came around, Moody was moved to the VA Hospital in Richmond, Virginia. Moody trusted them, and his brother Dris lived in Richmond. Tracy also realized Moody had moved himself closer to the farm and the family cemetery. Then, things seemed to become blurry for Moody. On one of Tracy's visits, Moody said something odd during one of his check-ups, and it wasn't the first time.

"Hey Doc," Moody said. "Remember when black was white, and white was black?" and Moody went on like that until the exam was over. After Tracy pulled Moody's wheelchair out of the doctor's office, he took Moody back to his room and shut the door.

"Moody," Tracy said, and sat on Moody's bed to face him. "No one knows what you're talking about. Now, the medical power of attorney was just signed over to Granny an' me. So you need to tell me what this is all about, or not mention it anymore. Granny is tryin' to claim you as unfit, and I'm not about to let that happen. So tell me what you're talkin' about."

Moody got an odd, far away look. "Beware of the time when they call good bad, an' bad good," and he never mentioned it again.

By the time fall came, Tracy had a good amount of time to cope with the process. Tracy had spent a lot of time with Moody, so he went to visit Granny. It was October, and Granny loved Halloween. She spent all year 'yard salein' and collecting creepy doodads to spread around her porch and yard. For some reason, there were more witches in her collection than most. Granny also liked to put everything up early so everyone could admire her display.

Moody hated the process, but liked the decorations once they were up. However, Moody's real beef was with the Christmas lights, which Tracy thought about as he and Granny stuffed the scarecrow. It always sat to the right of the front door in an old webbed lawn chair, and was made from Moody's old work clothes. Tracy smiled as he remembered...

"Why does she have to wait for the coldest day of the year to do this?" Moody griped. "We coulda done this in October when we put up Halloween, an' just not lit 'em 'til now."

Granny spookily appeared in the front doorway with a box of Christmas lights.

"Aw hell no," Granny stated. "I'm not gonna leave lights up like they've been left up all year. Nor do I wear white after Labor Day," and she dropped off her box, and went back into her warm house.

A year or two later, when Tracy was in high school, Moody decided to get on Granny's nerves. It was a particularly cold and windy day after Thanksgiving. Tracy was on the ladder, and Moody sat in his wheelchair on the front porch handing him the lights.

"Here we go again in this damn cold," Moody muttered. But he stayed silent when Granny came out to get the mail. Tracy prepared himself, because he knew if they were both quiet when they were together, somebody was 'plottin' a scheme'. As Granny went down the walk to check the mailbox, Moody saw his opportunity.

"Hey Jackie," Moody said. "Since you're down there, can ya get me my hammer?"

Granny was halfway to the garage before Tracy asked the obvious through tight lips:

"What's that got to do with hangin' these lights?"

"Shhh," Moody hushed. "Don't say nothin'."

Granny got it, came back up the walk, and laid the hammer at the foot of Moody's chair. She turned back down the walk because Troy, the mailman, had just arrived. He liked to chat with all his clients, sometimes twice. There were only three houses past Granny's before he would come back down the other side of the street. That would only be a few minutes, depending on how long Barbara caught Troy's ear.

For now, Granny said hello, and only got a few tidbits of gossip before she walked back to the house.

"Hey Jackie," Moody said, "since you're goin' in the house, there's a screwdriver on the steps by the back door," and Granny went into the house with the mail.

"She must know somethin's up by now," Tracy said from his ladder.

Moody stayed mum. Granny came back with the screwdriver and handed it to Moody, who put it at the foot of his wheelchair with the hammer.

"Thank you," Moody said, and Tracy grimaced.

'You know you messed it up now,' Tracy thought. 'You never say thank you,' but Moody continued on his quest.

"Down in the basement, there's that pair of yellow-handled pliers," Moody said, and Granny went back down the walk, passed her mailbox, and went back down into the garage.

"Maybe she's quiet because she's feelin' the joy of the holiday season," Tracy mentioned.

"That, an' she wants her lights up," Moody mumbled.

About that time, Troy reached William Russell's house, and William Russell came out to get his mail. Granny waved and came back up the walk with the pliers, and put them by the hammer and screwdriver.

"Oh, an' ya know what?" Moody said. "I forgot to tell ya, while you're down there…"

"Aw shit Moody," and Granny straightened up. "Get up an' get it your own damn self!"

Troy and William Russell watched Granny slam the door to her warm house, delighted to witness the pair in action, and Moody and Tracy broke into snickers.

Now, twenty-five years later, Granny looked at the finished scarecrow.

"Ya know," Granny said. "Y'all always wanted to hang the Christmas lights at Halloween-time."

"I was just thinkin' about that," Tracy said. "An' the time Moody had you runnin' everywhere."

"An' I told the man in the wheelchair to get up an' get it his own damn self?"

"That was classic Granny," Tracy said and Granny smiled, but not for long.

"You wanna hang the lights up now?"

"No Granny," Tracy decided, "because I know you hate that. Besides, I plan on comin' back before Christmas. I can hang them then," and Granny nodded.

"But I was thinkin'," Tracy said. "We should all go down and see Moody - the whole family. We can all pile in our cars an' just go," and Granny agreed.

So, Tracy spent the next two weeks rounding up the family, and then he helped drive everyone down to Richmond. His other cousin Demi and her family drove up from Charlotte. Then, all the 'runnin' cousins' had a great visit with their Pawpaw over Columbus Day weekend. When they returned, Tracy spent the night in his room, and when he came in for breakfast Granny had just hung up the phone.

"That was Moody's doctor," Granny said. "He said Moody woke up this mornin' an' told the doc he felt really good. Then he asked when he could go home," and she paused. "'I'm ready to go home', was what he said."

Tracy looked at her.

"Now Tracy," Granny said. "The doctor said that in his experience, when he an' the other docs have seen this happen, they have anywhere from eight to twenty-four hours."

Immediately, Tracy stood even though he was numb. He picked up the phone and called Moody to keep his spirits up.

"Well Moody," Tracy finished, "I'll make plans to come down there tomorrow."

But the next morning, Granny got the call Moody had passed. The man who had stood next to the Tall Shiny Silver Figure when Tracy was three went to be with Him. 'Pawpaw. You. Pawpaw. You.' Tracy remembered when they stood side by side, except Moody didn't know that until now. Now, Moody was with Him in the heavens.

Back here, Tracy covered his pain with urgency. He and Granny systematically told his cousins, particularly Mia, who was a nurse. Tracy knew she had to be told in person, because she and Moody were so close. Tracy went and spoke to her supervisor first.

"Now she's going to know why I'm here," Tracy told the charge nurse. "So, as soon as I come around the corner an' she sees me, I'm gonna have to take her home. She'll be no use after that."

In terms of the funeral arrangements, they were taken care of by the veteran himself. Moody was to be buried at the farm, and Dris, Moody's remaining brother, just had to be there to open the gate. So Tracy headed to the farm in Virginia. Dris met the family at the motel by the lake, because no one had lived in the farmhouse for years. They had a big dinner at the restaurant, and as Dris and Tracy carried on the family realized how close they were. The two had also spent a lot of time together in Richmond with Moody the past few months.

The next day, everyone went to the small white church founded by the great Mr. Moody where his son lay in the casket. There was a respectable congregation, but all of it was a blur to Tracy. Granny ran around as if she hosted a tea party, but Tracy couldn't let go. After the service, the funeral directors asked everyone to leave to close the casket. Tracy stayed behind with Demi. The cousins sat in the center of the middle row as they turned the crank to lower the body. When Tracy couldn't see Moody's face anymore, he broke into a cold sweat and cried more than he ever had.

As the funeral procession made the last turn to the farm, nothing was familiar to Tracy. The watermelon field was covered with twenty-year-old Virginia pine. The tobacco-drying shed was hidden in young woods, rather than the hand-built building of logs that had stood at the end of the neatly planted field. When they pulled up to great Pawpaw's house, it seemed much smaller than Tracy remembered. Mrs. Moody's rocking chair still sat on the front porch, but her chicken house was gone. When they pulled into the circular drive, Tracy thought of her funeral. He remembered the tables of food, and the long procession that walked from the meadow after the rain stopped, before the bees resumed their work in her peach trees.

Now that it was fall, everything seemed tired and dying. The small family of twenty arrived, including the new generation of cousins. They were the same ages as Tracy and Freddie when they had first visited the farm. Then, just past the house, Tracy noticed a line of cars parked in the other end of the circular drive.

As the family got out of their cars, what seemed a small army got out of theirs. The distinguished black men wore black tuxedoes with white gloves, and a white apron with a triangular pattern embroidered in gold. Some had large necklaces with medallions, one had a top hat, and all had a golden 'pocket protector' on the outside of their breast pocket bearing the insignia of the freemasons. A tall elder of the group came over to Dris and shook his hand.

"We saw that one of our own was goin' home," he said. "We got everybody together. If we had known, we could've done a better job. We just found out from the obituary in the paper a few days ago."

"Moody was a Mason?" Tracy asked, who couldn't believe he didn't know this.

"And has been for a long time," the gentleman said. "He was one of our eldest fellows, and, if you don't mind, we'll take care of him from here."

The group of thirty formed a line to take Moody's casket to the gravesite where they performed the burial rite. And it made sense the son of brick maker who lived in Virginia close to one of the oldest black lodges in the country would be a freemason. Tracy also remembered when Moody commented when Mr. Wilson died, the one who taught him to be a mechanic. Moody saw the Mason insignia by his obituary in the paper. Moody said that he didn't know Mr. Wilson was a Mason, but that was the only clue he ever gave that he was one as well.

Now, what followed was the pageantry and precision of a perfectly executed service. It was a meaningful tribute to a man who had done so much with his life, and, as with so many things with Moody, it was more than anyone expected.

Once the Masons said their goodbyes, the family went through the house and time had taken its toll. Without the presence of Emma or Richard, what remained seemed shrunken and decayed. Much of the furniture was gone, and it was clear no one lived there. Before he left, Tracy went over to the equipment shed where the family tractor stared blankly at him. He thought of Moody's 'rabbit huntin', when he had shot out the tire. Then, it registered how easily Moody fell asleep at the farm. Now, his Pawpaw was finally laid to rest where he began, and his course was done.

After that, Tracy left Granny in Virginia to take care of paperwork. As he drove back to West Virginia his thoughts wandered. Moody was there for him so easily, Tracy thought, and they were such kindred souls. Moody always supported him unconditionally, and helped let him live his own life. Now that he was gone, Tracy was surprisingly lost, and Tracy realized how much the fact Moody was in this world had steadied his existence.

When Tracy got back to Rand, he headed to the house to spend the night in his room. However, when his hand touched the latch on the gate, he saw the scarecrow on the front porch. Because it wore Moody's clothes it was Moody's size, and the fact the scarecrow sat in a webbed lawn chair on the dark porch made things surreal.

So, Tracy took his hand off the latch, and decided to walk down the street to spend the night at his cousin Marie's house. He was exhausted, but as Tracy turned a rabbit came from the side of the house by the garage. Tracy wasn't sure if Moody was 'messin' with him', but the rabbit came right for him. Between that and Granny's witches, Tracy beat it to Marie's house, and the rabbit chased him the whole way.

- Moody, before he passed

Chapter 39

- Tracy in his townhouse

"Tracy," Granny said. "Come here an' tell me if you see this too."

Granny was at her sink. She looked at her cherry tree, which still had the rusted pulley attached to the trunk from when she terrorized Moody with the rubber snake. Tracy had just gotten up, and he came and stood next to Granny.

"He's looking right at us," Tracy conferred, and Granny was surprised.

"How you know it's a he?" Granny asked.

Tracy laughed. "Well, either it's the same rabbit Marie saw down in her yard yesterday, an' Mia saw across town on her lawn, or we've got an infestation."

"But he's just sittin' there, starin'," she said in amazement.

"I can't explain it either Granny. But it looks exactly like the one that chased me down to Marie's house when I first got back," and Tracy got some coffee. Granny had stayed an extra day at the farm, and Tracy wanted to get her settled before he had to get back to D.C. Once Tracy got to Rand, he got a call from his recruiter. He was to start his new contract job on Monday, and Tracy recognized God's perfect timing. He had been unemployed since June, which afforded him as much time as possible to spend with Moody until he passed. As soon as that was finished, Tracy got a job before he could ask for it, and he was grateful.

However, when Tracy returned home and went back to work, he became angry with God. He knew his contract with D.C. Metro wasn't permanent - the problem was his empty house. When he returned alone, the emotional pain of Moody's passing that had built up in Tracy came unleashed. Tracy didn't see the point of going on, and thought he would rather be with Him, Moody, Freddie and his Mom.

"Lord," Tracy prayed. "I know this new contract isn't my perfect job, and I'm glad I have a job," and he sobbed, as the grief of Moody's death overpowered him. Then, Tracy exhaled quietly:

"I am tired of going through life experiences alone."

Tracy heard what he said and cried more. As Tracy waited, he sat in the middle of the hollow living room in front of the fireplace. The house was still empty, except for the end tables on either side of his burgundy couch, which matched the circular black walnut coffee table Moody made for Granny as a wedding present. Tracy sat cross-legged on the floor, and the emptiness grew in every direction until it engulfed him. The loved ones who had showed him his townhouse were gone - Granny Berger, his Mom and Freddie. Now that Moody was gone, it seemed to Tracy there was nothing left, and that he got something wrong.

"Where's my wife?" Tracy yelled, and he hit the carpeting. "If you can't produce the perfect wife that the four boxy walls of the church says I'm supposed to have, then I don't want to do this anymore! I'm still alone, I don't have the desire for a woman or a family, and I'm approaching forty. I should have been settled by now," and Tracy punctuated his words with more carpet hits, "and not be alone!"

There was silence, except for the echo off the blank white walls and tall ceiling.

"Everybody tells me to settle down," and Tracy sobbed. "Momma Ro and Tori are all about it, because they, 'know me so well.' Lynn, and even Dad… 'It's about time son,' he said," and Tracy stood up. "Time for what?" and Tracy looked upward and screamed. "I don't want to go through any more of life's experiences alone!"

Then, Tracy panted and spun in a circle, the way he did when he first praised God for his house.

"And Lord," Tracy clarified. "We already know shopping can be a life experience. Remember Pier One and the four promises? So change me. Make me desire a wife," and Tracy took a breath. "Because I can't make that up. I don't rap. I'm not LL Cool T, or even MD Cool T. I don't know how to rhyme. It's not my poem, it's Yours! But there's something not working right, so I must be doing something wrong."

"Are you ready for this?" He said like a remix DJ.

"Yes!" Tracy cried. "Bring it on!" and was so relieved to hear His voice. "I am ready for You to give me the desire for a wife!"

"Sit down," He said.

Tracy went over to the burgundy couch and prepared himself.

"Are you really ready for this?" He asked. *"For real?"* and then, in the process of sitting down, Tracy felt Him push Tracy into the couch with His presence of an overabundance of love. *"Am I the creator of everything?"*

"Yes Lord," Tracy answered. "Everything I see and don't see. You have created it all, and I am ready for You to create me anew," and Tracy thought of Adam and his rib that made woman, and that somehow God could change him so he would suddenly like girls.

"No Tracy," was the immediate answer, and He asked again, *"are you REALLY ready for this?"*

Tracy cleared his mind as best he could, so he could receive His peace.

"Am I the creator of the universe?"

"Yes Lord. You created it all."

"What about the languages, you know, like the 'words coming out of your mouth'?" and Tracy saw those exact words come out of His mouth in smoke as He spoke them. The wispy words swirled around Tracy's face, as if they came from the caterpillar's pipe.

"Yes Lord. All of that," and Tracy was impatient.

"So, what did I promise you?"

As Tracy said it, the Tall Shiny Silver Figure's robe became vaguely academic, and He had a pointer in His hand. He floated a foot or so above the living room floor, and stood in front of a chalkboard. As Tracy spoke, the words became a poem on the board, and He tapped each line as they were heard and became manifest:

"You promised me a:

Perfect Job,
Perfect House,
Perfect Body, and a
Perfect Spouse."

Tracy added "In Jesus' Name," and as he said it, he realized it: "And those were *Your* promises, because it has *Your* name on it. So where's my wife?"

He turned around quickly and spoke faster. *"I never promised you a wife Tracy, I promised you a spouse."*

"What?" Tracy asked, and instantly, Tracy felt Freddie's excited whisper in his ear:

"Chicken-butt! - Take a slice an' eat it up - two-cents-a-cup - don't try your luck - Chicken-butt! - Say what!?!"

Then, just as quickly, Freddie cackled with the satisfaction of decades, was gone before Tracy could turn around, and the Tall Shiny Silver Figure smiled.

"Freddie has been waiting to do that to you in your new house," He explained, *"ever since I allowed him to show it to you in that vision."*

"How is that even possible?" Tracy asked.

"Do you really want more pearls?" He asked.

"Yes Lord," Tracy said dogmatically. "More pearls please."

"Ok, I will give you two," He said. *"The first one is, 'Absent from the body, present with the Lord.' The other is that you should praise the Lord, because 'He inhabits the praises of His people',"* and He leaned into Tracy again. *"When I come to inhabit - meaning to live there, I do not come alone,"* and Tracy felt a wink. *"I come with a cloud of witnesses, and Freddie is amongst them thanks to you and Lynn,"* and remarkably, that explained both pearls.

"But enough of that for now," He said, and went back to His chalkboard. *"Back to this poem,"* and Tracy's four promises reappeared along with His pointer as He turned.

"Now," He stated. *"If I am the creator of the universe, and I created all the languages, and the 'words that come from your mouth'* (and the words appeared again in smoke around Tracy's head). *Do you not think I could come up with a word that rhymes with house?"*

Tracy didn't understand, because the conventions of this world were too calloused in him.

"Do you not think I could come up with a word that rhymes with house, yet means wife?" and the Tall Shiny Silver Figure pointed to the word 'spouse' on the board as He said 'wife'. Then, He turned to Tracy with great love in His heart.

"I do not have a wife for you Tracy, I have a spouse," and this time, Tracy was shown what He meant.

"Ok," Tracy said. "This goes against everything I have ever been taught in this world," and Tracy recounted the hours he spent in church. "They always told me out of *Your word* that homosexuality was an abomination. So, I don't know how to go forward with what You are tellin' me right now. I need You to order my steps Lord, and show me where this is in Your word."

"Fine," He said. *"Open your Bible to First Timothy, Chapter Four."*

Tracy reached for his Bible on the end table, and he and the Lord had Bible study.

"So, Paul is writing along," the Tall Shiny Silver Figure explained. *"When he is suddenly interrupted,"* but Tracy didn't understand. *"Read the first line."*

"Now the Spirit speaketh expressly," Tracy said, and understood who was speaking. "You're right Lord, the Holy Spirit interrupts Paul."

"I allowed the Holy Spirit to interrupt Paul at that time specifically for this day in age, and for this revelation to get out at this time."

Instantly, a giant pillar came up underneath Tracy's feet. The pillar stopped and became an ottoman, and because his feet were lifted up Tracy was forced to recline.

"And you can rest in that," He said, and Tracy understood the scripture inscribed on the pillar:

Psalm 110:1

The Lord said unto my Lord, Sit thou at my right hand, until I make thine enemies thy footstool.

Then, as Tracy looked at the pillar he understood who his enemy was, and the Lord explained the revelation He had saved for this present day:

1 Timothy 4:

4 Now the Spirit speaketh expressly, that in the latter times some shall depart from the faith, giving heed to seducing spirits, and doctrines of devils;

2 Speaking lies in hypocrisy; having their conscience seared with a hot iron;

3 Forbidding to marry, and commanding to abstain from meats, which God hath created to be received with thanksgiving of them which believe and know the truth.

4 For every creature of God is good, and nothing to be refused, if it be received with thanksgiving:

5 For it is sanctified by the word of God and prayer.

"Who is speaking?" the Tall Shiny Silver Figure asked.

"Paul was," Tracy said, "but he is interrupted. So now, it's the author of the Bible - the Spirit, not Paul who is speaking expressly."

"When is this going to happen?" the Tall Shiny Silver Figure asked.

"In the latter times," Tracy answered.

"And who is departing from the faith, and giving heed to seducing spirits, and doctrines of devils?"

Tracy found this hard to believe, but there was only one true faith spoken of in the Bible.

"Who is speaking lies and hypocrisy Tracy?" He asked.

"They do Lord?" Tracy asked.

"Yes. They mean well, but their conscious has been seared."

"I don't understand," so He showed Tracy as He said it:

"You see them at every Pride gathering," and Tracy saw the protesters chanting hate. Their "S's" hissed, and Tracy saw the sin consciousness that was seared onto their foreheads.

"They are not acting like Me," He explained. *"Did you ever see Me do that? They are today's Sadducees and Pharisees, and I am not in that. They are the ones forbidding to marry, and commanding to abstain from meats, not realizing that I, the creator, created marriage and food to be received with Thanksgiving. I not only created the marriage feast, I blessed it in Person!"*

A tear fell onto Tracy's cheek, and He became serious.

"But if you do not believe this truth, it will not set you free, and you will stay in bondage."

"Really Lord?"

"Yes!" He said with a great shout. *"Because every creature of God is good, and nothing is to be refused. So, I need you to receive this word with thanksgiving in your heart, because verse five is the Grace to walk in it."*

"Wow," Tracy said, and sat back to take it all in. "How many people have You shown this to Lord?"

"I have shown this to a lot of people, but they have not seen it."

Tracy wanted to receive it for himself, but was still unsure. "You need to help me out with this some more Lord," and the Lord's patience was inexhaustible.

"If I am in you," He said sweetly, *"and you are in Me, there is no escape. Could Noah fall out of the ark?"*

"No…" Tracy answered.

"Noah fell down in the ark, but he could not fall out of the ark. Noah was in Grace floating upon Grace. Therefore Tracy, you can not fall out of Me, because if you could, that would mean you would be stronger than Me, and you would be stronger than the Blood…"

And suddenly, the Tall Shiny Silver Figure became inflamed. He spread His arms like the angel when he smote the demon in Tracy's vision, and the train of His robe filled the room with glory. Without a shadow present, the Tall Shiny Silver Figure looked like He did when fighting Satan: He was Christ on the cross, and the Holy Spirit was aflame about Him. The Holy Spirit's wings were spread as a Phoenix, and there was a flame like feathers above His head. Then, Tracy was made to understand that when the Holy Spirit descended at Jesus' baptism He came as a dove, which ate worms. Now, in the end times, the Holy Spirit was a Phoenix to slay the dragon:

"…AND NOTHING IS STRONGER THAN THE BLOOD."

As quickly, the Tall Shiny Silver Figure's all-consuming light, and the Holy Spirit's fire was retracted. Then, as if blowing across a feather, the Tall Shiny Silver Figure breathed into Tracy:

"So get this revelation Tracy, and walk in it:

Galatians 3:

28 There is neither Jew nor Greek, there is neither bond nor free, there is neither male nor female: for ye are all one in Christ Jesus."

"Neither male nor female," Tracy repeated. "So you mean..?"

"This is your revelation Tracy," He said. *"Why? Because you are all one in Christ Jesus,"* and He pressed into Tracy the most and whispered. *"So, are you ready to find your perfect spouse?"*

All of a sudden, Tracy's mind was changed and the world could not tell him no. Because Tracy received his revelation with thanksgiving, he became determined. Tracy knew in his heart that he had the freedom Christ's Blood was shed for him to walk in, and the word 'wife' was no longer part of his thinking.

"Good," He said. *"So, are you really ready for this?"* He repeated. *"Because I am about to shake the foundations of your world Tracy. It will blow your hair back, and it will take a while for the dust to settle. All you have to say is yes."*

"Yes," Tracy said. But then he wanted to know.

"So, how do I find my perfect spouse Lord?" and as Tracy said it, he became lighter. "I mean, you have to tell me who the right one is, because I don't have time to pick an Ishmael. I have a bad track record in terms of my past boyfriends, as you know, otherwise I'd be happy by now."

The Tall Shiny Silver Figure's board and pointer went away. His robe became normal because the schoolmaster was finished with the law, and He looked at Tracy.

"You pick him out," Tracy said.

The Tall Shiny Silver Figure smiled because He already had, which made Tracy realize that fact.

"But how I will know who he is?" Tracy asked.

"Do you remember when you and Tori went shopping at Pier One?"

'Oh, here we go with Pier One again,' Tracy thought.

"You are the one who likes that store," He said. But He went on, *"and I told you to buy that wrought iron artwork?"*

"Yes…"

"And you came home, and hung it on your foyer wall?"

"Yeah, and I hung it too close to the ceiling. I wanted to move it down to center it on the wall, but you wouldn't let me."

"The reason I would not let you move it, is because the perfect spouse I have for you will put something beneath it."

"Really Lord?" and Tracy wondered what would fit there, because it was such a narrow space.

"That is My will for you, and that will be the spouse I have chosen for you."

Tracy wanted to go look at the wrought iron décor hanging on the foyer wall, but He wasn't done.

"But you can not tell anyone. That is between Me and you, because if you tell someone Tracy, anyone, they will put something there, and you will have created an Ishmael."

"Yes Lord," Tracy said. "I understand. But how do I look for my perfect spouse?"

"Put an ad on the internet for the desires of your heart," He said.

Then, for the next two days, Tracy got ready for his new job, and prepared to meet his perfect spouse.

313

Chapter 40

- Tracy's wrought iron artwork

Tracy's first week at his new job was typical with orientation. More importantly, Tracy was free to find his perfect spouse. Several men answered his ad, and Tracy found it easy to weed through most of them conversing by email. The first person Tracy met was not a good fit, which was obvious when they got together over coffee.

The second candidate was a good match, and they dated a few times. Their careers were compatible, and he spoke of the future they could build together. He was a college quarterback, a man's man the way Moody liked Pete, and was effervescent like Justin. As time went on, Tracy was ready to place a pause on his website profile.

Before he did, Tracy decided to spend a weekend alone with God because he didn't want to run blindly into another bad relationship. Besides, there still wasn't anything under the iron décor in his foyer. On the other hand, Tracy thought, he hadn't checked his profile in a while. After work, Tracy got some dinner and decided to watch a movie. When he logged in there was a new email that seemed to fit and Tracy answered. As the conversation continued it seemed the feeling was mutual.

What are you doing tonight? the third man typed.

I am just staying home to spend some time by myself, Tracy responded, because he had purposed not to go anywhere or see anyone.

Well that's fine, I work mostly on the weekends, and I have to get up early tomorrow. Would you like to meet tomorrow night?

'That's not pushy or overly aggressive,' Tracy thought, 'and he seems genuinely interested.'

Well, I'm not going anywhere, Tracy typed, *if you want to stop by.*

I have another few students, the third man said, *and then I could come over, if that would be ok,* and it was.

Tracy met Bob late on Friday, November 10, 2006, and they watched a movie together. Bob was Tracy's age, white, and average height. He had a crew cut and wire glasses, which Tracy thought made Bob look intelligent and that he had potential. The next night, Bob came for dinner. It got late, and Bob had to get up early on Sunday to direct his church choir.

"Why don't you stay over," Tracy offered. "My house is much closer to your church, and that way you won't have to drive home. I'll make breakfast for you," and he did.

Over the next month, Tracy continued dating the second candidate, and saw more of Bob. Then, Tracy visited Bob's voice studio at his church and became more intrigued. A few weeks before Christmas Tracy had a project to finish that required him to work late, and he wouldn't get home until after dinner. It was a Tuesday, which was one of Bob's odd days off, so Bob offered to cook dinner. Because Bob had a roommate he asked to cook at the townhouse, and Tracy checked in.

'Why does he want to cook me dinner while I'm not there?' Tracy asked. 'Nobody has a key to my house. Todd doesn't. Neither does Tori, who I've known all my life.'

Tracy didn't get an answer, and understood he was on his own.

'But he does work for a church,' Tracy reasoned. 'I know where to find him. It's not like he's going anywhere, and he's been here before.'

So Tracy gave Bob the key to his perfect townhouse, and left for his long workday.

As for Bob, he had his weekly meeting with the Pastor in the morning. That was followed by rehearsal plans and edits to the church bulletin. Then Bob was free for the afternoon, and he headed to Tracy's townhouse. By mid-afternoon, Bob was at the grocery across from Tracy's development, and he went to work in his kitchen.

By evening, Bob had pâté, cornichons, Gruyere and apple slices plated on the kitchen's granite countertop. He had Parmesan encrusted pork chops holding in the oven, garlic mashed potatoes and minted baby carrots waited on the stove, and the banana pudding cooled in the refrigerator. Bob borrowed the CD player from the Jacuzzi, and set it up in the kitchen to play Mel Tormé - the 'Velvet Fog'. But nothing prepared Bob for the reception he received.

Around eight-o' clock, Tracy entered his well-lit house. When he looked at his foyer wall, Tracy slumped against the front door. He dropped his briefcase involuntarily and began to cry, which Bob didn't realize at first. Tracy couldn't move and continued to sob. When Tracy gradually slid down the door to sit on the floor, Bob became concerned. It was the first time Bob had ever been in Tracy's house by himself, and he wasn't sure what was happening.

"Are you ok?" Bob asked, but Tracy wasn't reachable.

Unknown to either of them, as Bob locked his studio door something caught his eye. Bob had all his worldly possessions in the voice studio he built off the choir room of his church. Before he left to cook Tracy dinner, Bob grabbed the framed needlepoint his grandmother had given him. It bothered Bob that the first thing seen in Tracy's home was a wrought iron décor hung too high. Bob thought there would be just enough room, and decided if Tracy didn't like it he would take it down immediately. When Bob let himself into Tracy's townhouse, the first thing he did was hang the needlepoint. To Bob's surprise, it fit perfectly between the ironwork and the light switch, and the wall seemed complete.

That was the first thing Tracy saw when he entered his perfect house, as someone stood in his kitchen. Then, what had God promised Tracy washed over him, and he was overwhelmed. All Tracy could do was look at the needlepoint underneath his wrought iron artwork that read, 'God Bless Our Home' in red letters with a pink yarn background. Bob's Mom-mom made it for him for Christmas when he graduated college, with hopes Bob would settle down and start a family.

"If you don't like the Velvet Fog, we can put on En Vogue," Bob said, but there was no response. "Is it the Gruyere?" Bob tried. "Because I know a lot of people aren't familiar, although it's a great cheese, especially with apples." Tracy kept sobbing.

'I can't believe this is him Lord,' was the only thing Tracy could think. 'How is this possible?' There was no answer from Him.

Bob came over to collect Tracy's briefcase and set it to the side. Then, he tried to help Tracy slide himself back up the door to stand. Bob knew that whatever was happening, it was cathartic. Bob also knew that Tracy, the person who had awakened more within him than he thought possible, was at a crossroads. So, Bob didn't say any more, and waited until Tracy was able to stand. After, Bob wiped Tracy's eyes with a tissue.

"I thought you liked pork chops," Bob joked, and Tracy smiled a little.

"You don't understand," Tracy said.

"That's ok. But let's get this coat off, and we can get you settled down."

"That's just it," and Tracy looked at Bob as tears ran down his face.

Bob had no idea what Tracy meant. But Bob did want Tracy to be ok that he was in his house when Tracy came home, and that he felt safe. Bob also didn't want his pork chops to dry out, so he took Tracy's coat and hung it in the hall closet. Then he helped Tracy into the kitchen, and offered him something to drink to go with the hors d'oeuvres.

"I think I need to go upstairs," Tracy said, without having anything.

"Ok," Bob said.

"And maybe I'll take a shower to get the day off," Tracy decided.

"That's fine, take your time," Bob said, and Tracy went upstairs to his bedroom. Bob turned off the oven, and went to wait on the burgundy couch and watched TV.

'Are you for real Lord?' Tracy asked, as he took off his suit and tie.

There was still no answer. The proof was on the wall, but Tracy decided not to tell Bob. The two hadn't known each other that long, and they hadn't had a chance to talk about God other than their churches. Tracy didn't want to scare Bob, so he kept what he was experiencing to himself.

Although, Tracy decided to explore the idea Bob might be his perfect spouse. A few days later, they went to a community Christmas concert. On the way home they passed Tori and Tracy's church, and Tracy decided to find out.

"So, what's you're relationship like with God?" Tracy asked.

"I'm not sure what you mean," Bob said. "Do you mean in terms of my work with the church?"

"Maybe," Tracy said. "But I was thinking of your personal relationship with Him."

"Well," and Bob had to think a moment. "I feel closest to Him through music. I feel close to God when I sing, and I always know what hymns to pick for each service before I know what the sermon is about."

"Well, that's something," Tracy said, although what Bob said didn't seem much, compared to being in His presence as often as Tracy had.

"I also know when I'm not in the right place," Bob said, "which is where I've been a lot the past few years," and Bob realized he was considerably lighter, because there was grace in Tracy that Bob hadn't experienced in many years.

"But that's how I know what to teach," Bob continued. "Whether it's a private student or my choir, something comes over me. Then I say things that are more brilliant than I understand, or, I move people emotionally before I know what I said. That's when I know He helped me unlock something. I feel His Spirit come through me, He helps the choir sing, and we inspire the congregation."

Tracy kept listening.

"I feel like a conduit when I conduct," Bob said. "It's my job to pull out the love and beauty that is inherent in the music, in order to bless the congregation with it."

"Like a connection between the two worlds," Tracy said.

"The two worlds?" Bob asked.

"Well, this world and," and Tracy hedged, "the heavens."

"That's it exactly," and Bob smiled. "I have always felt I could help people experience God through music, especially choral music, because a choir literally speaks the truth."

"I wonder," Tracy said, and then he thought, 'what are you putting together Lord?'

"What?" Bob asked. Tracy was wary, but took a step.

"I wonder if God is putting together a Praiser and a Worshiper."

"I'm not sure what that means," Bob said. "But I know our church experiences are different. I'm not very familiar with the charismatic church. I've only known 'traditional' churches. I was drawn to the National Cathedral because the music was so good."

"It is different," Tracy said, and decided to take another step. "So, have you ever heard from God?"

"You mean, heard His voice directly?"

"Yeah," Tracy said.

Bob was about to say no, but then he remembered something he hadn't thought about in decades…

Bob was born in New Jersey, but moved to Maine when he was eight. He spent his summers on Hurricane Island, where his parents worked for the Outward Bound School. He listened to readings of Thoreau and Nietzsche on the 'Morning Meeting Rock', and learned about his 'inner child'. Then, Bob had an odd experience. Hurricane Island was a marvelous but dangerous place. The purpose of the month-long course was to push students to find themselves, which included capsizing a pulling boat for safety training.

The double-ended boats were like Viking ships, and were stripped for the drills. Only the built-in rowing benches, and a small deck for the helmsman remained. In that deck was a two-foot square opening for a portable compass. The boats were wooden and heavy, and the 'Watch' of twelve college kids capsized the boat on top of them. For safety, a pair of divers was in the water. They guided students into the air pocket, or cleared them to the surface. As a teenager, Bob ran a small outboard skiff kept on standby for years. He watched boat after boat turn onto its occupants. Then, Bob heard the divers explain to panicked students how to dive back down, and get out of the air pocket under the capsized boat. The summer after his freshman year of college, Bob decided to become such a diver.

The day for his training was overcast. At first, Bob observed the two divers in his wetsuit, and his weight belt made him otherworldly in the water. Before the second capsize, Bob's instructor suggested he hold the edge of the boat as it came over. This would effortlessly push him down from the weight, and then Bob could resurface.

Because the other divers needed to be by the students, Bob did this near the stern of the boat to stay clear. What Bob or his teacher didn't realize was the eddy of the tide. In the small cove, the current's circulation was strong a few feet below the back of the boat. As the pulling boat came over, Bob put his hand up to catch the rail, which pushed him under the water as planned. When Bob thought he was in the air pocket, he hit his head. It was dark and disorienting, and he reached up and felt the flatness of plywood. Then Bob realized he had drifted up into the steering deck. So he tried to push himself down to have the tide carry him out from under the boat, but the funnel of the tide was too strong. Bob realized he was quickly running out of oxygen and options, and that he was at an unmistakable crossroads.

Then, Bob was made to understand there was air in the compass box. He reached up to feel the deck again, and found the small square hole. He put his hands in and felt air rather than cold water. At that point, Bob knew he had to trust Him more than himself. The question was whether Bob's head would fit, and if there would be enough air trapped for him to take a breath. It was also an all-or-nothing deal, because Bob knew he had to expel all his air before he ripped off his mask to breathe inside the box. Then, as Bob hung weightless three feet underwater, he felt a warmth hold him as He guided Bob under the two foot box. So, Bob exhaled all his bad air and ripped off his mask. Then he felt the shock of Maine water, tilted his head skyward and took a humongous breath into darkness.

Immediately, it was if a light was switched on. Bob saw his head inside the compass box as if he watched the scene in a movie. But it seemed to Bob he was with someone, and Bob took several breaths. His energy was replenished and then some, which made Bob laugh. Totally refreshed, Bob tilted his head to get out of the box. He inadvertently let go of his mask, and swam blind because of the salt water. But Bob knew how far to get out from under the boat, and that he had passed the test.

When Bob surfaced, he heard the other divers helping students out from under the boat's air pocket. Once everyone was out from underneath, Bob's instructor came around the stern of the boat with his mask.

"Are you ok?" his instructor asked.

"I'm great," Bob said. "I guess I lost my mask in the process. Thanks for getting it for me."

But Bob was glad he lost his mask, and from then on, he knew how much God had his back...

Now, as they drove, Bob couldn't believe he had forgotten.

"I think I did," Bob said.

"You think you did what?" Tracy asked, because a bit of time had passed during Bob's reverie of twenty years, and the revelation was strong.

"I think I have heard God," Bob realized, "although not directly, like a voice. I just felt His presence, and He showed me what to do, and He saved me."

But He wasn't done with Bob. In fact, He was just getting started.

- Mom-mom's needlepoint

Chapter 41

- Granny's Christmas, 2006

Once Tracy entertained the idea that Bob might be the one, a rapid series of events were set into motion. The first was Todd's Christmas party the following weekend. Moody's declining health subsumed most of Tracy's year. A few people knew that he had moved into his townhouse the previous January. Justin had heard Tracy had moved in with Todd, but he didn't know that Tracy had moved out, and this created a circumstance worthy of any soap opera.

When Justin called Todd to inquire about Tracy, Todd only informed Justin that Tracy wasn't there. Todd did say Tracy would be attending his Christmas party. So, Todd invited Justin to his party, but didn't tell Tracy in order to surprise Tracy. Justin had called because he was coming to D.C. for a caucus, but he had also recently broken up with his partner of fourteen years. Unbeknownst to Todd, Tracy planned to introduce Bob to some of his friends. On the night of the party, Tracy called to make sure it was ok if he brought a guest.

"Hey Tracy," Todd said. "You're coming, right?"

"Of course I am," Tracy said. "But I wanted to make sure it was cool if I brought someone."

"You know I have plenty of room. Is it Tori?" but Todd got distracted. "Move that over there. No, on the other side," and Todd came back. "Sure Tracy, I'll see you when you get here," and Todd hung up.

"What kind of party is this?" Bob asked.

"It's a Todd party," Tracy said. "You'll see."

When they pulled up to Todd's house, the red carpet went from the front door to the driveway, then down to the sidewalk for guests arriving by chauffeur. Once inside, the serpentine revolving tree of live poinsettias captured guest's attention. The next eye-catcher was the two-story Christmas tree in the living room. But every room had a tree including the garage, which was decorated with vintage matchbox cars. However, before all of that, Tracy and Bob went to sign the guest book and Todd came over.

"Hey Tracy," Todd said, and he looked at Bob.

"And this is," and Tracy thought a moment. "This is my friend, Bob."

"Well hey Bob," Todd said. "It's nice to meet you." Then Todd looked at Tracy, and cocked his head a little before he whispered in Tracy's ear. "I have a surprise for you."

"Oh?" Tracy said loudly, and looked around. "Where is it?"

"Well, 'it' will arrive shortly," Todd said, "but I didn't realize you were bringing a date."

"Did you hire a stripper?" Tracy asked coyly, although he really hoped Todd hadn't.

"You'll see," Todd said, and walked off.

"Tracy!" Sabrina yelled from the living room. "Oh my gosh, I haven't seen you in forever!" and she ran over, and practically jumped into Tracy's arms.

"Hey girl!" Tracy said. "I know I've been busy this year." Sabrina stood back to look into Tracy's eyes.

"I'm so sorry to hear about Moody," Sabrina said. "I know that must have been rough on you."

"It was," Tracy said, "but I'm here."

"Yes you are," Sabrina said, and she looked at Bob.

"And this is Bob. We met a month ago."

"Hi Bob," Sabrina said, and smiled. "It is very good to meet you," and they hugged.

"Glad to meet you too," Bob said. "I've heard stories, but it's good to actually meet you."

Sabrina laughed. "What did he say about me?"

"Nothing too incriminating," Bob admitted. "But it's clear you two go back a while, which is always a good thing."

Then Sabrina's entourage of power lesbians decided the gay boys were monopolizing too much of her time. Before they succeeded luring Sabrina back, the doorbell rang and no one answered it. Then it rang again.

"Why isn't Todd answering the door?" Tracy asked.

Sabrina shrugged. Then Todd sauntered over with a grin and looked at Tracy.

"It's for you," Todd said, and gestured toward his gránd entránce.

"Is this my surprise?" Tracy asked. "My surprise can ring the doorbell?"

Todd just smirked, before he was whisked away by the caterer for a food-related emergency.

Tracy went to the door, and wasn't sure whether the stripper would be a sailor, a cop, or a sexy black Santa. When Tracy opened the door he saw Justin, caught his breath, and promptly closed the door. Tracy hadn't seen Justin since Vera died, and the disconnect was too much for him.

'What is going on Lord?' Tracy asked, but there was no answer. Tracy realized he shut the door on his past abruptly, so he re-opened it.

"What are you doing here?" Tracy asked. Justin smiled, because he understood.

"I was in town for a meeting," Justin answered sheepishly. "I called Todd to ask about you, and he told me about the party tonight."

"Oh," Tracy said, and then Justin laid more on the line.

"I also wanted to see you," and Justin leaned into Tracy, "because I broke up with my partner."

"Oh," Tracy said, and thought of the awkward scene in "Brokeback Mountain".

"Surprise!" Todd yelled, running for Tracy. "I see you got your present. Do you want to introduce him to Bob?" Todd asked with mischief.

"Sure," Tracy said, and came back to the situation with fresh eyes.

"Bob," Tracy called, and motioned for Bob, who was still with Sabrina. "Come over here, I want you to meet someone."

Bob came over, and Tracy made the introduction by the revolving poinsettias.

"Bob," Tracy said, "this is Justin, the first guy I ever dated," and Tracy searched before he knew what to say. "Justin, this is Bob," and Tracy smiled, "my fiancé."

"What?" Bob asked.

Out of nowhere, Todd's cousin Dana came screaming on tiptoes.

"Did you say fiancé?" Dana inquired, who was obviously the most fabulous gay man in the room. "Because if you are about to be family, we need to know if we approve."

"What?" Bob asked again, but his question was obviously of no importance.

"Come with me," Dana said, and grabbed Bob's hand to drag him to Todd's office.

"Did you just say fiancé?" Bob asked.

"Yes," Tracy said, and Bob was surprised.

"Do you mean it?" Bob asked.

"I think so," Tracy answered, which was good enough for all that was going on.

"Come," Dana demanded. "You need to be interviewed," and he went down the hall waving for Bob to follow. Bob looked at Tracy.

"Dana's a good friend," Tracy said, "and he really is Todd's cousin. I've known him a long time, and he wants to get to know you because we're together."

So, Bob was fully vetted from college work experience to favorite color. Dana actually wrote things down, once he found a pen and a yellow-lined pad in Todd's desk. Later, Bob met Justin, and with Tracy the three had a good talk away from the din of the party. As time went by, Bob saw why Tracy loved Justin. Justin's memories of Vera and Moody also enlightened Bob as to who they were in Tracy's life. The next to win over was Granny.

Christmas was on a Monday, so Bob and Tracy packed up the car before they headed for Christmas Eve Service. Bob's church service started at five, would be done and dusted by six-thirty, and then they could head to West Virginia to surprise Granny. Before they went, Bob wanted to know what to get Granny for Christmas.

"Granny has everything she needs or wants," Tracy said.

"But what does she like?" Bob asked.

"You really don't need to get her anything. She won't use it, and she won't like it if you go out and buy her something."

"I can't meet your grandmother for the first time empty handed."

"Well, you've talked to her on the phone, why don't you ask her?"

"Then she'll know something's up," Bob decided.

Then, the plant in the corner caught Tracy's eye. Bob got a potted Norfolk Island Pine for the dining room the week before. It came with silver glitter and a few ornaments, and Bob added white lights and red bows. Bob got it as a surprise and cooked dinner again. When Tracy came home from work he was arrested again, and got a tear in his eye.

"What's wrong?" Bob asked.

"Nothing's wrong," Tracy said. "It's just that you put up a Christmas tree."

"I'm sorry, I thought you would like it," and Bob came over, and they looked at the young green tree together.

"I haven't celebrated Christmas in this house before," and then Tracy was surprised at himself. "And I haven't decorated for Christmas in years," and he looked at Bob. "My Mom died right after Christmas."

"Oh, I didn't realize," Bob said, and thought he had been insensitive.

"No, it's ok. I just hadn't thought about it. I used to love Christmas," and Tracy smiled. "Maybe it's time to change that."

"Or, maybe I should stop bringing things over here if it always makes you cry," Bob said, because Tracy still hadn't explained the significance of his Mom-mom's needlepoint.

A week later, Tracy looked at the little tree and got an idea. "Granny does like her houseplants."

"She does?" Bob asked.

"You'll see," Tracy said. "She has them in front of the windows in her living room."

"Is there a lot of light?" Tracy looked at him, because he didn't understand. "In Granny's living room, is the light the same amount as here in the dining room?"

"It's about the same," Tracy said.

"Done," Bob said.

The next day, Bob repotted a peace lily in his studio because he knew it needed more light. Then, after Christmas Eve Service, Tracy and Bob hit the road. They spent the night at a downtown Charleston hotel, and in the morning, Tracy gave Granny a call.

"Merry Christmas!" Tracy said.

"Merry Christmas to you Tracy," Granny said. "You're up early."

"Granny, you know I'm always up early. So what are ya doin'?"

"I'm not rightly sure yet Tracy."

"Are ya dressed?" and it was hard for Tracy to hide his excitement.

"Now, why do want to know that?" and Granny paused, "but I'm not runnin' 'round the house naked, if that's what ya wanna know."

"Well, I have a surprise comin' for ya, an' I wanted to make sure."

"Tracy, I'm sittin' here in my robe an' slippers, like I have for the last fifty years."

"Ok Granny," Tracy said. "Just keep an eye out, an' have a Merry Christmas."

"Alright," Granny said, "I'll be right here. The kids aren't comin' 'til this afternoon."

After they got dressed, Tracy took Bob on a driving tour of Charleston. He mentioned the cows as they headed around the curves of the highway, which followed the Kanawha River up to Rand.

"An' there's a farm on the way to Granny's" Tracy said. "It has these cows that are black, with a big white stripe in the middle."

"You have Belted Galloways here?" Bob asked. "We called them oreo cows growing up."

"I don't know what they're called, but we have them."

"But that's impossible," Bob said. "We have them in Maine near our house, and the sign on the barn says they're the only farm in the U.S. that raises them."

"Well, you tell me," Tracy said, as they drove by the pasture full of Belted Galloways.

"Yep," Bob said. "Those are oreo cows."

Then, Tracy and Bob realized both of their high school's colors were blue and gold, and their mascot was the panther. They both played various brass instruments at basketball games in band, and both wore a banded collared shirt for their senior picture. As they meandered through Rand, Tracy pointed out his schools, the little church he went with Aunt Z, and the community center.

Finally, they drove down Starling Drive to Granny's house. Bob stayed close behind Tracy as they went up the walk, even as Bob carried the large peace lily between them. Granny opened the front door as they got to it.

"I thought ya might be doin' this," Granny said. Tracy gave her a big hug. Then Granny stood back, and Tracy stepped aside to reveal Bob.

"An' this must be Bob," Granny decided with an odd smile, "with a plant." Granny looked at Bob more to study him, except the plant was in her way.

"This is for you," Bob said, but to Granny, that was obvious.

"Well," Tracy said, "let's put this in the living room," and he grabbed the plant.

"Yeah Trace," Granny said, "just put it over there somewhere," and she pointed absently as she looked at Bob fully. "Now, come on in here an' give me hug."

Then, Bob spent the rest of the day meeting most of Tracy's 'runnin' cousins'. He met Marie, who lived down the street, and had a little boy and girl in elementary school. Demi had driven up from Charlotte with her boy and girl. Mia's three boys were there, although she was with her husband's family in Kentucky. So, kids from three to eighteen arrived mid-afternoon with lots of funny stories about Granny. But most stories were about Moody, because it was the family's first Christmas without him.

After opening presents, the group sat on the large sectional sofa until they spilled into the large space in front. They all had a memory, and everyone had a tear to shed about something Moody said or did that changed their life. Bob was also moved, because even though he was the only one in the room who wasn't family, he was completely welcomed, and made to feel as familiar as Granny's furniture.

"How about the two dollar bills?" Tracy asked. "It didn't matter what time of day or night, or where ya were, Moody could pull a two dollar bill out of his pocket."

Everybody talked at once about how many they had gotten in birthday cards, or found hidden in a present they wouldn't find until they got home. Then, Marie got a big grin on her face.

"Y'all know why Moody always had two dollar bills, don't ya?" Marie asked.

Everyone's expression went blank except Granny's, but she didn't say anything.

"No, why?" Tracy asked, and Marie looked directly at Granny.

"Well, Moody told me you always thought it was the devil's money," Marie stated. "So, he kept buying the bank out of two dollar bills, 'cause you wouldn't touch 'em."

Granny looked forward as if she wasn't being addressed, but Marie continued with her indictment.

"An' then, Moody said as time went by, an' you saw all us kids were able to spend 'em, you wouldn't use 'em out of spite. That way, he could keep some cash on himself."

Everyone looked at Granny.

"Huh," was all Granny said, and the family laughed until it hurt.

- Tracy and Marie

Chapter 42

- Mia with her beer

The next day, Bob and Tracy left Rand for the townhouse so they could repack. Because they had the week off, the new couple decided to continue introducing each other to their families. On Wednesday, they hopped a plane to visit Bob's family, who lived in the mid-coast region of Maine. Compared to West Virginia Maine was colder, but for Tracy it was the darkness that was astounding. It was pitch black outside by the time the "Oprah Winfrey Show" aired at four-o'clock, and there were other stark contrasts to the Christmas at Granny's.

Bob's grandfather had passed a few years before at ninety-five. A little before Christmas, it was necessary for Bob's parents to put his Mom-mom into assisted living. Bob's younger brother was in Egypt, serving in the Army Reserves. He had recently divorced, and his young kids were with their mother's family. Over the past two years, Bob's older brother had come out, divorced his wife and moved in with his partner, which made Christmas anything but traditional for the family.

Where the two-story great room once held uncles, aunts, cousins, and great-grandchildren vying for space around Pop-pop's recliner, there was a vast emptiness. The huge Christmas tree usually stuffed with ornaments from Bob's great-grandmother's flower shop lay cold in the basement. Bob's his parents were shell-shocked, as they still took care of Bob's fifty-six-year-old Down-Syndrome uncle. They tried to keep the status quo, but the new reality couldn't be avoided.

Now, Bob's parents sat with their two gay sons and their new partners - who had somehow replaced their parents, daughters-in-law and grandchildren, and any familiar memory of Christmas. Yet the small group had a good time - although dinner was like a scene from any movie where the history of the room was much too big for the disjointed guests left at the table.

When they got back home, Bob and Tracy's family introductions were done with one exception. Then, once again, Tracy's father dropped in unexpectedly. It was now March, and Harry called to let Tracy know that his Great Uncle Bob had died.

"Are you going to the funeral?" Tracy asked.

"Yes," Harry said, and he was solemn. "Your Mom and I are going. It's this Saturday."

"I'll meet you there," Tracy said. "I have someone I want you to meet," and Harry took that in. "Are you going to be ok Dad?"

"Yeah son," Harry said. "I'll be alright. I'll see you there."

On Friday night, Tracy and Bob drove to West Virginia and stayed at Granny's house in Tracy's room. The next morning as Bob got dressed, Tracy went in for another cup of coffee. From Tracy's expression, Granny knew it was the two of them that had to 'have a meetin'.

"What's wrong Tracy?" Granny asked.

"Granny," Tracy said. "I'm concerned about Dad meeting Bob."

"Why's that?"

"Well, Dad an' I never really had the conversation," and Tracy paused. "It's always been implied, an' we've prayed against it. Now, I have a new revelation about that, an' I've been set free."

Granny turned to look at Tracy.

"I can see that," Granny said, and got quite serious. "I wasn't sure the first time I met Bob. Moody died recently, an' you coulda still been in your euphoria about a new relationship. So I was concerned whether you were gonna make it through that patch. But now that I'm seein' Bob a second time, an' seein' you again, I'm ok, because I know you're ok."

Tracy could hardly believe it, and just looked at Granny.

"I was really concerned," Granny said. "But now I see you're gonna be ok, an' we *all* like Bob."

With that statement, Tracy knew that meant everybody – Jinny, Alvin, his cousins, and everyone in the little neighborhood of Rand.

Then, Granny grabbed a knife off the kitchen counter, pointed it at an imagined foe and her voice went hard.

"An' if your father don't like him, then he can kiss my ass. An' you can tell him I said so."

Tracy smiled for a variety of reasons, but Granny wasn't done.

"We like Bob," Granny established. "He brought me a plant."

Tracy had to laugh.

"Now go on an' get yourself dressed," Granny said, "so you won't be late."

So the two left for the funeral in their suits, and Bob had his first real taste of West Virginia. Uncle Bob's church was up in a 'holler' - but not like the swale that held the street between Granny and William Russell's house. This was a dead-end holler with hairpin turns, which required the Subaru be downshifted into first gear.

When they reached the tiny white church, it was cantilevered from the mountain. The back of the church nuzzled into the slope, and the entrance steps dangled over fallen rocks at a forty-five degree angle. It was also apparent steel beams weren't considered, because of the long cracks in the cement block foundation. As Granny predicted, Bob and Tracy were late and the service had started. After they scaled the loose shale to the front steps, they entered the small vestibule. Every seat was taken in the wooden pews that held about fifty.

Because the church doors were open to the sanctuary, Tracy and Bob stayed put. As they did, a few congregants turned to see who came in. Bob realized he was the only white person there. Although that wasn't uncomfortable, because he had often been in such circumstance. The unnerving part was adding the weight of two people to the unbalanced end of the church. Bob had already visualized the church breaking loose and skiing down the mountain, as in any scene from the "Pirates of the Caribbean" franchise.

Yet Bob was comforted when the choir entered. Tracy already mentioned that Great Uncle Bob was a person of stature in height, width and depth, and the fact his oversized casket was directly underneath the narrow stage for the minister was a relief. However, after seven women of like stature entered in oversized robes, and stood behind the minister to sing their choir selection, Bob breathed a little easier. Then Bob wondered.

"Where are your parents?" Bob asked in a whisper.

"Do you see the tallest head," Tracy hushed. "Right in front of the casket on the left side of the aisle? And do you see the carefully combed hair of the woman sitting to his left?"

Bob looked. "You mean the man in the handsome suit, and the woman in the fire-engine red jacket?"

"That's them," Tracy confirmed, and Bob had to stifle a laugh.

"What?" Tracy asked.

"I'll tell you later," Bob decided.

Tracy looked at him. They were in the vestibule, and no one could really hear them.

"Ok," Bob whispered. "Do you remember me telling you about my best friend Jim, even though he's forty years older?"

"Your professor at Ithaca?" Tracy asked.

"Yeah, who taught me how to do the Madrigal Feasts. Anyway, he had a lot of colorful expressions, because he was originally from Fort Deposit, Alabama."

Tracy had no idea what this had to do with anything.

"So, that's your step-mom up there, right?" Bob asked. "The one in the red?"

"Yup," Tracy said, "although I just call her Mom, and she only wears St. John, so that is a top-of-the-line wool suit."

"Well that may be," Bob said, "but I know what my good friend James Edward would say."

"What would he say?" Tracy asked, and he thought he was ready. But Bob pulled out a perfectly bent southern accent that would have made Lady T blush:

"Honey, there are only two kinds of women that should wear red, and she is not a Spanish dancer."

Tracy took it in for a moment. Then, he emitted a high-pitched squeal, stomped the floor with his size-thirteen dress shoe, and immediately ducked down. Not knowing any better, Bob stayed standing in the middle of the vestibule. The very black West Virginian congregation turned around and saw Bob, who looked back at them like a D.C. albino deer in headlights. Then, the congregation looked at each other to see if anyone knew Bob. They wondered if the little white boy was lost, or whether he meant to laugh at an extremely revered black man's funeral. They also considered whether Bob would fit next to Uncle Bob in his casket, if it were necessary to hide the body.

Tracy realized Bob needed to be claimed, so he grabbed Bob's hand and told him to get down.

"What are you doing?" Bob whispered.

Tracy still had a scene from the inverse version of "Get Out" playing in his mind, but quickly stood to the amazement of the back half of the congregation.

"Come on let's go," Tracy said, hearing banjo music, and he dragged Bob out of the church, and down the loose shale to the car where they could safely laugh their asses off.

After the funeral, Tracy and Bob followed the procession down the holler, across the highway that split Charleston, and onto the opposite high ridge. It was threatening to rain, but the view was breathtaking down the long curved valley of the Kanawha River. The gravesite service was short, and because there were fewer people Bob got to have a look at Tracy's parents. Harry and Lynn also saw Tracy. Afterward, Harry came over and gave Tracy a hug.

"I've missed you son," Harry said.

"I've missed you too Dad," Tracy said, and they separated. "Dad, I want you to meet Bob," and Tracy presented Bob in such a way that Harry knew who he was.

Harry reached out his hand, and Bob could clearly read Harry's first, middle and last name embroidered on his cuff, which was something Bob had never seen before.

"Hello," Harry said in his trademark way, and they shook hands.

"It's nice to meet you," Bob said. Then he stepped back, because he was the stranger at a funeral.

"Where are you two staying?" Harry asked Tracy.

"We're staying at Granny's," Tracy said. Harry raised an eyebrow.

"Really?" Harry asked. "And what does Granny say about that?"

"Actually," Tracy replied, "she told me tell you that we *all* like Bob."

Harry's eyebrows went higher and then, Lynn finished her conversation with a relative and came over.

"Who is this Harry?" Lynn asked quickly, referring to Bob.

"Hey Mom," Tracy said, and they hugged before Harry continued.

"Honey, this is Tracy's friend Bob," Harry said. "Bob, this is my wife Lynn."

"Nice to meet you," Bob said, and shook Lynn's black leather glove.

Lynn smiled back, and Bob went back to stand by Tracy.

"Honey," Lynn said quietly and to the side. "What is this?"

"Later," Harry said softly, "but Granny says we *all* like Bob."

"Oh," Lynn said, and began to process what that meant. Then Harry and Lynn had to get back to Ohio, so they said their goodbyes.

After that, Bob and Tracy were off to Mia's. She was having the family over for dinner to watch a bootlegged Pacquiao fight. Because Mia was away for Christmas Bob hadn't met her, even though he met her three sons. This made Tracy realize something as they drove up the steep holler to her house.

"Now I haven't mentioned this before," Tracy said, "but all the women in my family have a switch."

"A switch?" Bob asked.

"Yeah. I didn't know about it until Marie explained it to me. But they all have a trigger, and Mia's is the worst. So, if you see her get a strange look in her eye, or she says something strange, just give me a yell."

"A yell?" Bob asked, as they pulled up to the house.

"You'll be fine," Tracy said. Then he jumped out of the Subaru and ran into the house to see everybody, but mostly because of the height issue with Mia's house.

Bob lagged behind, because he was taken that Mia's house was situated the exact opposite of the little white church from that morning. This holler was just as steep, but it was the road that clung to the mountain. From the road's edge, Mia's house had two steep steps down followed by a small bridge, and somehow, the house clung to the mountain without tumbling into the gorge and small stream a hundred feet below. Fortunately it was getting dark, so Bob was able to get to the front door before vertigo set in. Once inside, the small living room opened to a large, dimly lit dining room. There steam pans hissed full of fried chicken, collards, corn bread and mac and cheese. Granny put down her chicken wing and came over.

"How'd it go?" Granny asked at point-blank range.

"It was good," Tracy said, but Granny didn't stand down. "Really, I think they like Bob too."

"Huh," Granny said, and went back to her fried chicken.

Tracy re-introduced Bob to the group from Christmas, and they all said, 'We all know Bob,' who smiled because he was old news.

"Well I don't know no Bob," Mia said, with a tilt of her head.

Tracy went over to his cousin for a hug. Mia's husband filled the doorframe from the kitchen, who had been a professional football player before his shoulder had trouble.

"Yeah," he said. "Where's this 'Bob' we've been hearin' so much about?"

Bob was introduced, and learned more about Tracy's family. The first lesson was how to drink beer.

"Here ya go Bob," and Mia said, and she handed him a can. "You wanna straw?"

"A straw?" Bob asked, and Mia showed him the bendy straw sticking out of her twenty-ounce.

"It get's ya there faster," Mia winked.

Then she walked into the dining room drinking her beer like a sippy cup. And she was right about the straw, because a little while later Mia was on a roll.

"Oh yeah," Mia said. "You ain't gonna find me gropin' around tryin' to find no bat. That's why I got my pool balls lined up."

"What is she talking about?" Bob asked Tracy, but Mia heard him.

"What?" and Mia turned and asked Bob. "You don't have protection?" and Bob's mind went immediately to condoms, and somehow Mia read his mind.

"An' I'm not talkin' about no condoms," Mia confirmed. "Although, they're in the same drawer right next to my pool balls. No, I mean if a woman is alone in the house, an' ya hear somebody bumblin' around downstairs, ya don't have no time to be searchin' around for no baseball bat, that coulda rolled too far under the bed."

"That's right girl," Marie agreed.

"No, you need somethin' ya can put your hands on," Mia said.

Bob looked at Tracy, but he just grinned.

"You don't believe me?" Mia asked. "I'll show ya. I'll be right back."

Mia went upstairs, opened the drawer to her nightstand and came back. What she had in her hand was a white gym sock with red stripes. Two pool balls were obviously stuffed into the toe, and the sock was stretched to the point it looked like it needed a truss.

"That's what I'm talkin' about," Marie said.

"An' if you whip this thing around, you can crack a skull," Mia said, and she started slinging her sock, but her husband ran over as if he had a flashback.

"Easy girl," he said. "We're all family here," and took the loaded sock from his wife. Then everyone had some dessert. But as the evening progressed, things got more dangerous than Bob anticipated.

Granny and Marie went home. Just Tracy and Bob, Mia, her husband, and her teenage boys got ready to watch the boxing match. For some reason, Bob ended up on one of the two gray velour loveseats in the tiny living room. Bob sat on a loveseat on one wall, and Mia sat on the other. Then Mia got a strange look, even though Bob had been there for over four hours.

Tracy was in the kitchen talking with Mia's husband. Mia cued the fight, and the announcers discussed Pacquiao. Mia didn't say anything, and Bob stared blankly at the TV. Mia sipped her twenty-ounce through her straw and took a sideways look at Bob, who pretended to watch the TV. Bob snuck a peak back, and Mia quickly stared at the screen. Then Mia looked at Bob again, and cocked her head as she sipped her beer loudly through her straw. When Bob looked back, Mia snapped back to the TV, and this happened a few more times before she spoke.

"Now, I know I should know this," Mia said, and took a long slurp. "An' I don't mean to be rude or nothin', but who are you, and what the hell are ya doin' in my house?"

Bob didn't wait for the pool balls. Instead, he recognized the switch and yelled, "Tracy!?!"

Chapter 43

- Granny's squirrel lunch

But the family introductions didn't stop. In April, Bobby's father died. Tracy's Bob went to the funeral, and met some of Tracy's cousins from that branch of his past. Tracy hadn't seen them since Freddie died. Bob also met David, who happened to live a stone's throw from the townhouse. So, in less than six months since Bob hung his Mom-mom's needlepoint on the wall, everyone knew the phrase 'Bob and Tracy'. Then, the pair went to Granny's for Mother's Day to surprise her again. Tracy called her on the way.

"Hey Granny," Tracy said. "What are ya doin'?"

"Thinkin' you're up to somethin'," Granny said. "You comin' this way?"

"Well," and Tracy laughed, "Bob an' I are half-way there to see ya."

"What time?" Granny asked.

"A few hours," Tracy said. "Do you want us to stop for some chicken? We can get a bucket of extra crispy on the way."

"Actually," Granny said, "I had a couple of squirrel defrostin' from the freezer. Ask Bob if he's had any squirrel," and Tracy saw the look on Bob's face.

"I don't think he has Granny," Tracy said.

Bob shook his head no.

"Well, I think it's about high time he had," Granny said. "I only had three left. But I'll get William Russell to shoot another couple off the wire."

337

"It's no problem to stop and get some fried chicken Granny," Bob offered.

"I don't want ya to go to any trouble," Granny said, and she was on a mission now. "What time you say you'd be here?"

"By lunchtime," Tracy affirmed.

"Ok," Granny said. "I'll be ready," and she was.

Granny had her cast iron skillet piping hot when Bob and Tracy walked through the door, and the squirrel was almost done. Then Granny had to make the squirrel gravy.

"This is the best part," Granny said, and she was right.

Bob thought squirrel tasted exactly as one would expect – hyperactive and like acorns. However, squirrel gravy was pretty good smothered over white bread, and Bob tried to eat another piece. Because the animal was small, the only thing edible was the legs. To Bob, once the legs were splayed and smashed flat to fry, it seemed clear he was eating squirrel ass.

When Tracy spit something out that made a 'ting' on his plate, Bob was done.

"What's that?" Bob asked.

"Oh," Tracy said. "I forgot to tell you to be careful of the lead pellet," and he put the small ball of lead on Granny's Formica table.

The pellet rolled off onto a tall stack of newspapers sitting on the chair next to Bob. When Bob picked up it up, he noticed the manila envelope it fell on. The envelope had "The Will" handwritten on the top two corners, which was underlined twice.

"Oh my goodness!" Bob said.

Tracy looked at him, and Bob picked up the important looking envelope.

"Shouldn't this be somewhere else?" Bob asked.

"That's just recyclin' I been savin'," Granny said.

"Granny?" Tracy asked. "What's going on?"

"There's nothin' goin' on," Granny said, "because there's nothin' in there."

Bob looked, and there wasn't. Granny looked at Tracy squarely.

"Now you know," Granny said, "Moody always wanted you to have the farm."

"I thought so too Granny," Tracy said, "although, he never said it outright."

"But when it all came down to it," and Granny was vague, which even Bob picked up on, because Granny was never vague. "There wasn't anything to it," and for the moment, that was that.

By the end of the month, Bob and Tracy were back in Rand for Memorial Day. The pair went with the family to decorate graves at various cemeteries, and Granny showed Bob where she was going into the ground. Recently, Granny had a cataract removed so she had to wear large sunglasses. Bob dubbed them her 'rock star glasses'. Granny immediately adopted the nomenclature because by this time, Bob liked Granny as much as Granny liked Bob. They made each other laugh constantly, because of the way they each turned a phrase.

Then, Bob decided Granny needed something pretty to look at when she was done with her sunglasses. So, when Tracy took Granny for her check-up, Bob started digging next to her sidewalk. Granny's hostas were choked with grass, and Bob moved them under the oaks on the side of her yard. Then Bob began in earnest, preparing the rocky ground for a rose bed to line Granny's walk.

The first gun-related incident happened when Miss Mary pulled into her drive. Miss Mary lived two houses down, and was a seemingly sweet, plump-faced white woman. As Bob found out later, Granny said she had a good side and a bad side.

"You gotta watch Miss Mary," Granny said. "The bad side is klepto, an' the good side is paralyzed," and both things were true.

As Bob was about to experience, Miss Mary had obviously had a stroke, which was why she was running around town in her minivan. Later, Tracy corroborated about the kleptomania.

"She seems innocent enough," Tracy said. "Then I gave her a ride back from church one day. She thanked me for the ride, and positioned herself to get out on the passenger's side. Then she swiped every pen an' piece of change I had in the middle console before she left out an' slammed the door."

At the moment, Miss Mary pulled into her driveway, which was on Granny's side of her house. She pulled into the hill to her basement garage, and was eye-level with the ground. Then she rolled down her car window, and took a closer look at the white man digging up Granny's yard. It was a hot day without any wind, and Bob had been at it for a while. By this time, Bob had also hung out with Tracy and his 'sister-cousins' enough to pick up some syntax. Unfortunately, Bob had never even heard of Miss Mary.

"Where's Jackie?" Miss Mary asked roughly.

Bob looked over, and eventually found the eyes that peered up from the ground two yards over. The only problem was that Bob didn't know where 'Jackie' was. Bob only knew Granny, and had never heard anyone call Granny by her first name. So, Bob assumed the woman was addressing someone else and didn't answer. Miss Mary became concerned.

"Where the hell is Jackie!?!" Miss Mary demanded. When Bob realized he was the one being yelled at, he decided to 'go Granny Moody on her ass'.

"Who wants to know?" Bob yelled back, which was all Miss Mary needed to hear.

Miss Mary slammed her minivan in reverse, and 'squealed tires' out of her driveway. She continued backwards up the road past the entrance to Granny's driveway, and then 'squealed tires' until she was even with Bob and slammed on the brakes. Then, Miss Mary narrowed her eyes at Bob, who stood ten feet from her with his pickax, and she put her car in park. Miss Mary studied him again before deciding to go for her glove box, and Bob realized things were getting serious.

"I don't know where Jackie is," Bob explained. "But Granny is with Tracy at her eye doctor's appointment."

Miss Mary put her revolver back in her glove box, and turned to look at Bob with an odd smile. "So, what's you're name?" she asked.

"Bob," Bob said, and the good half of Miss Mary's face lit up.

"So you're Bob," Mary said sweetly, which was quite a switch. "Jackie didn't tell me Tracy was comin' to town."

"She didn't know," Bob explained, "because we surprised her. That's why we're moving her hostas and putting in a rose bed – to surprise her."

"Well, if that isn't just the sweetest thing!" and now Miss Mary was almost Bob's next of kin. "I've heard a lot about you, an' we're so glad Tracy finally found someone."

Bob didn't know what to say to that.

"We're all just so pleased," Miss Mary said sweetly, immensely pleased with herself. "So you just carry on. An' don't forget to drink your water. It's a warm one."

Then Miss Marry reversed gently out of Granny's driveway, and returned to her driveway without telling Bob her name. Later, Granny figured out it was 'Klepto Mary' that almost mowed Bob down on her front lawn, and they were introduced. The day after, Bob almost shot himself helping turn Granny's mattress. No one told Bob about the rusty ax and loaded pistol Granny kept under her pillow.

When Bob got there first to remove the bedding, he jumped back before the gun went off. However, Bob and Tracy put in Granny's roses without further skirmish. The pair headed back to the townhouse and then, at long last, the final series of events were set into motion.

Back in January, Tracy quit his job at DC Metro after he was almost in a knife fight with a deranged lunatic. Tracy had gone out to get coffee for everyone. When he came back, Tracy wondered why police officers and dogs had surrounded the building. No one said anything as Tracy swiped his ID card, rebalanced his macchiatos, and headed for the Accounting Department where he worked. When Tracy went to open the door, it was locked. He looked through the wire-reinforced window, and his co-workers were nowhere to be seen. When Tracy knocked, everyone's head popped out from under their desks.

"It's Tramele," they said in hushed tones. "Should we let him in?"

"Hey guys," Tracy said. "What's goin' on?"

"Shhhh," everyone said. Then a brave soul came and opened the door for him, shuttled him in, and quickly locked the door again.

As it turned out, someone was running around the building with a knife, trying to steal the payroll that was in a large safe two doors down. That was enough for Tracy. When he came home, Tracy re-enacted the incident for Bob in front of the fireplace.

"They let me in the building," Tracy said. "They let me come all the way up all those steps - all the while knowing everything was on lockdown? An' they don't offer health insurance until I work there for a year?" and Tracy had made up his mind: "Girl, bye."

So, Tracy ended his contract and quickly found another. Then, spring turned into summer. Soon, Tracy's ninety-day contract was over the day before the Fourth of July holiday, and Tracy checked in for his next move.

"Ok Lord," Tracy said. "Where am I supposed to look for the next contract?"

He answered immediately:

"Take Bob out for a bike ride for his birthday."

To Tracy, this made less sense than usual. Tracy was also surprised to hear from Him, because Tracy had been on radio silence since he met Bob back in November.

"Lord," Tracy said. "I ask You for a job, and You want me to go on a bike ride?"

"Take Bob out for a bike ride for his birthday," He repeated rapidly.

"But that makes no kind of sense," Tracy said.

Then Tracy remembered the waterbed, desk, and other things He asked of Tracy that didn't make sense, but made faith. Although, Bob had gotten a bike before the couple met, which inspired Tracy to get one. They bought a roof rack for the Subaru, and got a yearlong pass for the Maryland Parks system. Bob and Tracy enjoyed how other Subarus with bikes on their roof honked their horns at them. When they passed each other, Bob and Tracy would shout in unison:

"We got bikes!" and they pumped their fists and said, "Yeah!"

So the Lord's request wasn't totally from left field, but Tracy felt a sense of urgency. Since Tracy met Bob nine months earlier, Tracy's life events seemed to be speeding up. Tracy felt like he was going somewhere, which he was. In fact, the Lord's plan involved flinging him into an unknown farther than Tracy could imagine, and the arc of his life was about to have a landing point.

But at this moment, Tracy became pragmatic.

"When is Bob's birthday?" Tracy asked, but He was too excited to be specific.

"Go now," He said.

"Now?" Tracy asked.

"Now," He repeated, and the Tall Shiny Silver Figure's exhilaration was reminiscent of the first time Tracy met Him when he was three.

"Where should we go?" Tracy asked.

"Go to the other side," He answered quickly. Tracy understood that meant across the water, which from the townhouse meant the Eastern Shore of Maryland. So the next morning, Tracy called their lesbian friends.

Rae and Kate had met shortly before Bob and Tracy did. The two couples were almost identical, except for their opposite sexuality. Rae had sung in Bob's church choir for years, and Bob knew Rae's girls since they were tiny. Once Rae finally came out, Bob was her support system when Rae found Kate. Soon after, Kate became the other pea in the pod for Tracy.

The upshot was that Bob and Tracy's 'lesbian wives' naturally had more camping equipment than any gay man could possibly need or want. When the Tall Shiny Silver Figure told Tracy to 'go to the other side', they were Tracy's first call for help, which they answered with gusto. So by late morning, Bob and Tracy had the necessary equipment to head to the Eastern Shore. Tracy planned to use their park pass to go camping, and the culminating journey was begun.

- Kate and Rae with Tracy and Bob

Chapter 44

- the radar station

By the afternoon of July 5, 2007, Bob and Tracy were headed across the Chesapeake Bay Bridge from Annapolis. Tracy was instructed to 'go to the other side', but He wasn't more specific than that, and the Delmarva Peninsula was more than one hundred miles long in Maryland alone. Tracy's plan was to go to a state park near Crisfield. He had researched it the night before, and the park honored their pass. However, Tracy still hadn't told Bob anything about his relationship with the Tall Shiny Silver Figure, which made things vague as far as Bob was concerned.

"So," Bob asked. "Where are we going?"

"I told you," Tracy said. "We're gonna celebrate your birthday."

"Ok," Bob said.

In the past, Bob was the one who did such things for others. Now that the shoe was on the other foot, he realized how it might be more fun for the person orchestrating the surprise.

"I've been to Rehoboth Beach," Bob said, "and that's a nice place."

But Tracy drove through the intersection that turned east to the ocean, and kept heading south.

"You'll see," Tracy said, but he was flying as blind as Bob.

Eventually, the pair made their way to Janes Island State Park, and it was close to four-o'clock. They found where the campsites were, and pulled the Subaru into a sandy space under forty-foot loblolly pines. Tracy pulled out the abused box of tent parts Rae and Kate gave them, none of which made any sense. Their lesbian cohorts actually gave them two tents, which could be constructed with a living room, sleeping quarters, and possibly a gallery. But the two gay boys couldn't make heads or tails of it, and there were no instructions.

"Do you think they have cabins?" Bob asked.

It was now late afternoon, the sun was headed toward the horizon, and mosquitoes were gathering.

"Let's check," Tracy said immediately.

The couple headed to the ranger's office, and Bob noticed that the map on the wall of the building was actually a chart. Then he noticed the racks of canoes and kayaks stacked by the launch area, and the small inlet that separated them from a pristine island of pines.

"Hey Tracy," Bob said. "Look at this."

Tracy came over.

"These aren't bike trails," Bob explained. "They're kayak trails through the marsh."

"What?" Tracy asked, and was annoyed.

"See?" Bob said. "The trails are only one or two miles long, and they're blue. I like canoeing, but I haven't spent much time in a kayak."

"Aw hell no," Tracy said, who instantly heard the theme music from "Jaws" mixed with the banjos in "Deliverance", and he was losing his patience. "Let's just see if we can get a place to stay."

Bob and Tracy headed to the door of the ranger's office, but it was locked. When they looked through the window, the ranger was at her register counting the drawer. They knocked, but when the ranger saw them, she motioned that the office was closed.

"We were just wondering if you had any cabins available for tonight," Bob said through the glass.

Then, when the ranger came over to the door, a remarkable thing happened. She didn't say anything, instead, she pulled the shade down over the window - so the ranger literally kept the door shut, and fully closed the window in front of Bob and Tracy's face.

"Let's get something to eat," Tracy said testily.

The couple repacked the mangled tent parts into the Subaru, and headed back to civilization. By this time, Bob knew Tracy loved soft-shelled crabs. Crisfield, Maryland, was famous for the delicacy, and they headed to a restaurant that was supposed to be the oldest and best. What they got from the huge steamer on the slow night were tiny purplish-red rocks. They resembled crabs only by the fact they had two melted claw appendages jutting from them, and they were inedible.

"Come on," Tracy said. "Let's go," and he was more than miffed.

They hopped back in the car to steam back home. Bob knew not to say anything, and had no idea what was going on. Tracy didn't either.

'What's going on Lord?' Tracy fumed. 'You're the one who told me to 'go to the other side'. Here we are, and nothing is working.'

There was no answer, and Tracy thought he missed God. There was something he wasn't getting, and nothing made any sense. After they had been on the road an hour-and-a-half, it was close to eleven-o'clock. Bob wasn't having much fun on his 'birthday trip', and he saw a sign for St Michaels.

"My parents used to talk about St Michaels," Bob said.

"What?" Tracy asked absent-mindedly.

"After my parents married, they came to St Michaels a few times. This was long before they had us, and we moved to Maine. My Mom used to tell stories of 'the town that fooled the British', and the Cannon Ball House," and they passed a highway sign informing them St Michaels was ten miles away.

"Do you want to go there?" Tracy asked.

"It's pretty late," Bob said, "and you have been driving all day."

"Well," Tracy said. "That sounds like a good idea," because he was tired, and was at the end of his rope.

So they went to St Michaels, pulled into the motel, and Tracy collapsed. Before Bob went to sleep, he went back to the lobby for information about the area. There, a skipjack brochure caught his eye. Bob grew up in a boatyard, and his family moved to Maine because of his 'sister' - a Friendship Sloop built in 1902. The Rebecca T. Ruark was a local skipjack built in 1886, and was similar to the wooden sailboat of Bob's childhood. He thought it might be fun to sail on it with Tracy. Then, Bob went back to their room, climbed in bed and went to sleep. The next morning Tracy woke up, and asked the same thing he did every morning.

"What are we going to do today Lord?"

"Why not wait for Bob to wake up and ask him?" He said.

"Why do we have to wait for Bob to wake up?" Tracy asked indignantly. "You didn't even tell him I don't have a job."

There was no answer, so when Bob woke up Tracy asked him.

"Do you know there's an island farther down the road?" Bob asked, and Tracy waited to see what Bob would say. "Well, I saw a brochure for an old sailboat that does tours, and since today is my birthday,"

"Today is your birthday!?!" Tracy interrupted.

"Yeah, so, I thought it might be fun to go on a boat ride,"

"Wait," Tracy interjected. "Today is your birthday, not yesterday?" and Bob nodded yes. "Oh wow! So I didn't miss God!" and Tracy was ecstatic.

So Bob made the call, and they found out the skipjack was booked for the afternoon. But they could go on the sunset sail at six-thirty, although it was a long time to wait.

"Are you sure you don't want to go back home?" Bob asked. "Because I know you're tired."

"No, no, no," Tracy insisted, and his mood had changed significantly. "*Today* is your birthday."

"Ok," Bob said, "but it always has been," because Bob had no idea why this was so important. "Why don't we go down to the island and look around."

"That sound like an idea," Tracy said, who was now letting Bob lead.

Then they headed to Tilghman Island where the skipjack was docked, and ate at a restaurant on the Narrows by the drawbridge. After lunch, Bob and Tracy hopped back in the Subaru to explore the island. This didn't take long, because the island was basically a single road that dead-ended into a huge parking lot. They parked and got out to look at the Chesapeake Bay, but they still had another three hours until the sailboat cruise.

"So," and Bob looked around. "Do you want to get the bikes down and ride around?"

"Sure," Tracy said, who didn't think much of it. He was too distracted by the large fenced-in area with a three-story tower, which somehow looked connected to Area 51.

There was a radar station at the end of the huge parking lot, and there were no cars or other signs of life. After he read the sign, Bob found out it was the first erected at the end of World War II to test radar equipment. The naval radar lab was across the bay. The station communicated with the lab for radar testing, as well as monitored boat traffic going in and out of Baltimore.

However, all Tracy saw was a military installation. He was concerned about his security clearance, and Tracy's résumé was already circulating for his next contract. He didn't want to have to explain anything to his new employer, so he was wary.

"Do you have the keys?" Bob asked, and Tracy handed him his keychain to unlock the bike rack.

Then, Tracy stalled getting his bike off the car as he considered the radar station. Bob had his bike together, and was soon riding around the parking lot. Bob looked farther down the road and saw a sign for a bed and breakfast, and rode back to report his findings.

"Hey Tracy," Bob said. "There's an Inn past the radar station. Do you want to check it out?"

"That looks private," Tracy decided, "so we probably shouldn't go down there."

"How can an Inn be private, if there's a sign advertising it's down the road?" Tracy didn't answer.

Bob was weary of how arduous his 'birthday surprise' had been to this point. So Bob went down to the gate this time, and read the sign about the bird sanctuary and the Inn. Beyond the gate, the road turned to gravel. There was a sharp turn to the left, which revealed a grand expanse of water. In the distance was a tilted lighthouse in the middle of the bay, which the land had abandoned decades ago. Bob became intrigued, and he rode back again to tell Tracy.

"This Inn seems like it's beautiful, and the view is fascinating,"

"I really don't think we should go down there," Tracy said, who had suddenly returned to the mood of the previous day, and Bob decided he had had enough.

"Well, it's my birthday," Bob stated. "So I am going to go see what I can see," and he took off on his bike past the radar station, rode through the gate, and went down the gravel road until he rounded the corner out of sight.

"Lord," Tracy said, and he was furious. "Bob just took off through that gate, and he has my car keys."

His answer was immediate. *"What did I tell you to do?"* He asked.

At first, Tracy was perplexed. Then Tracy remembered His instructions.

"You told me to take Bob out for a bike ride for his birthday," Tracy recited.

"Well," He said. *"This is Bob's birthday, and this is Bob's bike ride. . ."* and Tracy felt a smile from Him that was unusual... *"I suggest you follow him."*

Tracy grudgingly mounted his bike and rode through the parking lot, but he stopped at the corner of the radar station. He dismounted in front of the government-issued barbed wire fence, took his wallet out, and held it against the crystalline blue sky reflecting off the Chesapeake Bay.

"Lord," Tracy declared, "if I lose my security clearance because of this stupid bike ride; You, me, and Moses are gonna sit down an' have a conversation."

Then, Tracy pushed his wallet back into his pocket and aggressively rode down the gravel driveway to get his keys. But the driveway was a half-mile long. It meandered along the marsh to Tracy's left, and there were open miles of water to the right. Along the length of the shore was a carefully angled bank of ton-sized granite boulders known as riprap.

To Bob, who grew up on an island that had been a granite quarry, he felt at home in a way he never had in Maryland. Because it was the end of the peninsula, the vista also looked like where Bob grew up in Penobscot Bay. The view fascinated him to the point he had to dismount his bike at the top of the lawn in front of the Inn. Bob stood there, entranced by the fact someone had put Maine smack-dab in the middle of the Chesapeake. Tracy caught up to him, but before Tracy could demand his keys back, an older man came from what looked to be the service-entrance past the front door of the old house.

"What are you two guys doing here?" he asked, and it was hard to decipher whether his manner was just gruff, or sardonic. "Do you have a reservation?"

When the man came for them, he walked with a swagger that meant he owned the place. He had carefully combed black hair, which obviously lost the battle with the wind constantly. He had a barrel chest, was energetic, and there might have been a twinkle in his eye that suggested good humor. However, at the moment, the man was Tracy's worst nightmare. He was sure all the man saw was the interracial gay boys that had invaded his private sanctuary, and Tracy was sure naval officials had already been notified to take them away to the brig.

"I'm sorry sir," Tracy said. "If we were trespassing we do apologize. We were just out on a bike ride, and we stumbled upon this place."

"Are you two looking for a room?" the Innkeeper asked.

"Well," and Tracy finally looked around. "What is this place?"

"We're a bed and breakfast," the Innkeeper said.

Bob looked at Tracy, because he didn't understand his nervousness.

"Well," Tracy said, "we have plans to go on a sunset sail this evening."

"On the skipjack?" the Innkeeper asked. "You'll have a good time with the captain. He's a trip."

"Yes," and Tracy relaxed and looked at Bob. "And I'm sure we don't want to drive all the way back home afterwards."

Bob nodded in the affirmative.

"So sure. Why not?" Tracy decided.

Then, Tracy silently unpacked a litany of how he could keep his security clearance, even though the room probably cost more than he wanted to spend. It was paramount for Tracy to keep what God had given him since his Mom died, and staying here meant he could protect his work experience, from nuclear inspection, to requesting his own teams as an independent consultant for Oracle contracts...

"I tell you what," the Innkeeper said.

"What?" Tracy asked, because his entire work-life, and what God had brought him through to this point had just passed from beginning to end in front of his mind.

"Lean your bikes up against that big holly tree over there," and the Innkeeper pointed. "Then, take a walk down to the dock. By the time you get back, I'll be finished cleaning up breakfast."

"Ok," Tracy said.

Bob was delighted but stayed clear, because his birthday surprise was finally getting somewhere.

"Then, you can meet me in the office," the Innkeeper said. "I'll have the paperwork ready, and you can rent that last cabin for the weekend."

"For the weekend?" Tracy asked.

"Well, it's Friday," the Innkeeper said, who was a consummate salesman. "By the way, my name is Tom."

They shook hands, and Tom went back into the house. Bob and Tracy leaned their bikes against the trunk of the immense holly tree by the office, and they headed for the dock.

"This is where you are supposed to live," He said, and He was beaming. But as the couple continued down the rounded driveway to the back cove, Tracy began to wrestle with God.

'Newsflash Lord,' Tracy thought. 'I don't have a job to afford all this,' and then Tracy thought that was a little harsh. 'But, if this is you Lord, confirm it,' although Tracy still couldn't believe it. 'But if this is you Satan, I bind you according to Matthew 18:18, and I loose you from your assignment against me this day,' and Tracy bowed his head and said aloud, "in Jesus' name."

"What?" Bob asked, but Tracy didn't reply.

As they reached the dock, both were affected as the events of two lifetimes unfolded. In a one-dimensional way, Bob was like a fish to water. As he walked down the dock, Bob heard the waves washing up into the crevices of granite boulders - a sound he hadn't heard since he was a boy on the island. For Tracy, reaching the dock was the culmination of two worlds, and, unbeknownst to Tracy, a bridge was about to be crossed at the all-important page of his picture book, and Bob would confirm this.

Chapter 45

- the back dock

Bob and Tracy walked down the long dock. Bob looked over the broad expanse where the Choptank River met the Chesapeake Bay. Tracy peered over the end to see how deep it was, and did a necessary scan for shark fins. Tracy also pondered His last statement, which was, 'This is where you are supposed to live.' As Tracy thought it, Bob was in hysterics.

"I just heard from God!" Bob shouted, "and He said this is where we are supposed to live!" Immediately, Tracy thought he should test that spirit and faced Bob squarely.

"Oh, you mean rent that cabin for the weekend?" Tracy asked quickly. "Because that's exactly what we're going to do. We're going to go back up to the office, give Tom my credit card, and rent that cabin for the weekend," and Tracy turned to look across the river.

'This isn't fair Lord,' Tracy said to himself. 'I've only known Bob for nine months.'

"*You said it yourself Tracy,*" He said. "*Remember? Back in Ohio?*" and He quoted Tracy: "*If a woman can birth something in the natural in nine months, surely You can birth something in the supernatural.*"

Tracy pondered that statement for a split second, before Bob became dogmatic. Bob stomped his feet and pumped his arms for emphasis like a child.

"No Tracy," Bob decreed. "I did just hear from God, and He also told me to tell you to look!" and Bob's arm went up of its own volition.

Unknown to Bob, he pointed to the most southern end of the island. From the end of the dock, a very large cross was clearly visible. This was also the vantage point from which Tracy 'painted the vision and made it plain' in the sixth grade. This moment was also the first time Tracy saw the cross since being on the property. Upon seeing it, Tracy was pulled out of his body.

Immediately, Tracy was in what he recognized as the realm of his own three-year-old existence. He was in the hospital room, and watched his three-year-old self about to be put into the ice water. However, now, adult Tracy hovered in the air much like Scrooge, except there wasn't a spirit beside him as a guide. Instead, Tracy received a revelation that time was a series of frames, which he didn't yet fully understand. What was brought to Tracy's remembrance was from Hebrews 11:3:

"3 Through faith we understand that the worlds were framed by the word of God, so that things which are seen were not made of things which do appear."

This understanding unfolded as Tracy hovered in the hospital room. He watched his three-year-old self fight the doctor, so he wouldn't be put into the ice water. He watched Moody reach for 'his boy' with tears in his eyes. The Tall Shiny Silver Figure stood behind Moody with His hand outstretched. But looking at the scene as an adult, Tracy's emotions got the better of him. Because Moody had become Tracy's best friend in this world, he wanted his three-year-old self to go to Moody instead of the Tall Shiny Silver Figure.

"Don't talk to strangers," Tracy cried to the three-year-old.

To his surprise, three-year-old Tracy paused time and yelled, "Stop!" Then little Tracy looked up at adult Tracy and said, "You cannot change the decisions we have made."

The scene was now framed: the doctor held Tracy as a toddler above the white basin, and Moody and the Tall Shiny Silver Figure stood on the other side.

"You are only here to understand why we made these decisions," the toddler Tracy explained, "and remember what we are supposed to do going forward. So ask questions, so you can understand what we are supposed to do next," and then the three-year-old spoke to Tracy in an excited whisper.

"Because we're about to see the book, and we haven't seen the book since I was in the hospital," and Tracy's toddler self smiled broadly at adult Tracy. "It has wonderful pictures in it, and He's about to let us see it again." Then three-year-old Tracy instructed adult Tracy, and addressed by his name in the realm they were in. "Now ask questions Forty-one, so we can see every detail in the book," little Tracy said.

Tracy now knew the toddler's name was Three, which made everything so much easier. It was also revealed to Forty-one that Three was instructing him how to operate in this realm of existence, because Three was the closest in age to when they first saw the picture book.

"But don't get distracted," Three said. "We have a very unique opportunity to go back and see the picture book, which not everybody gets. Most get distracted by the beauty of heaven, and they get so distracted, they don't want to leave."

That statement made Forty-one think of Lucille, Harry's mother. She was so tired, she didn't want to leave heaven to say goodbye to Harry, the son who carried the blessing that had gotten them this far.

"Don't waste this moment smelling the flowers," Three said again. "They will always be there. They are part of creation. So don't marvel at creation – seek the Creator."

As Three spoke, Forty-one realized Three was just one of more Selves he could meet, who could help guide all of them to their purpose.

"That's why we are here," Three confirmed. "To learn more," and Three turned back into his frame of time. "Ask questions," Three reminded. Then, the toddler looked back at Moody and the Tall Shiny Silver Figure to choose, and a manner of time resumed between Forty-one's questions...

"Why do we go to the Tall Shiny Silver Figure?" adult Tracy asked.

"Because He looks like what our imaginary friend sounds like," Three answered.

"Oh," and Forty-one remembered thinking that.

"Pay attention Tracy," Three reminded again. "And you are going to have to ask better questions if we're going to get any further," which made Tracy think of Peter at the transfiguration, blurting out how he wanted to build Moses, Elijah and the Christ booths. God had to tell Peter to shut up and listen to His Son. But then, Three became so excited he had to whisper again.

"We're getting ready to go," and Three reached his hand out to Him, and He took the child's hand! Then they were instantly warm and well...

But unlike what Tracy experienced when he was a toddler, Three sat on the Tall Shiny Silver Figure's lap, and Forty-one stood behind the Tall Shiny Silver Figure's chair. Forty-one looked over His shoulder, and He showed both of them the wonder...

"I want to show you some things," the Tall Shiny Silver Figure said, and he spoke very fast. Then their book was open to them and Three was delighted, exactly as he was when he first saw the book.

When they saw the page of Vera grabbing Three under her arm, and racing to Freddie's grandparent's house in a panic about 'the man who asked Tracy about the 'love walk', all of them laughed. Tracy also smelled his Mom from her holding him under her arm, a fragrance he hadn't experienced in decades.

Then, the Tall Shiny Silver Figure separated Himself from Himself, which He could do infinitely. As He kept showing Three the picture book, from His loins up, the Tall Shiny Silver Figure turned in His chair to look behind at Forty-one.

"Do you have any questions?" He asked.

"Why did Your voice change when I came back from sitting in Your lap?" Forty-one asked.

"Because you grew up in Me," the Tall Shiny Silver Figure answered, and they went back to look at the picture book.

Then, Forty-one-year-old Tracy realized he could go further. Tracy understood that he could study the déjà vu moments in his picture book past his present age, and that he could review them to prepare.

When the Tall Shiny Silver Figure heard that, He fully separated from Himself. He stood beside Forty-one as His other Self stayed with Three. Then, Tracy looked through his picture book past the age of Forty-one.

"Tell me about this chapter," Tracy said. "The Key, the Door, the Room, and the Table," and the Tall Shiny Silver Figure looked at Tracy with the most joy Tracy had ever seen Him have.

"It is interesting you would catch that." He said. *"Are you going to ask about the chair?"*

"The chair?" Tracy asked.

"Oh yes," He said. *"The chair activates everything."*

"What do you mean?"

"You can not get there unless you are seated and resting," He stated. *"The chair is actually the key, and the key is the access,"* and He paused for Tracy to absorb that information.

"So, now that you have access," and He smiled, *"which was because you asked..."* and He winked, *"because asking is the access..."* and Tracy understood that all of those words were synonymous.

Then He took Tracy up two steps, because the Kingdom of God wasn't far away. Tracy was expecting a giant escalator, or an endless ladder from the Old Covenant. But the journey to heaven was nowhere near as dramatic. Tracy simply turned to his left, took two comfortable steps up, and Tracy stood in front of what he knew was his door. The endless hallway was white, and all of the numerous doors seemed the same.

"Oh," Tracy said, "this looks like what Mom went through."

The door looked exactly like the one Tracy saw in the vision of the hospital with the partying imps, when Vera stood before her door at the top of the staircase, before she was taken up by His hands.

"The doors are identical," He confirmed. *"Beyond each door is unique to each individual. Your mother went to her room. But you have to ask permission to go into another's room, because you only have access to your own,"* so Tracy stopped wondering where his mother's door was. *"But I am here to show you your room, because you have to walk in this dual citizenship."*

Tracy stood on the threshold, and checked to see if Three was ok. Of course he was more than fine, sitting on His lap, enjoying the wonders of the picture book.

"I am with you always," the Tall Shiny Silver Figure explained, which Tracy understood more deeply.

The Lord was not only with Tracy in the present, He was with him in the past, and would be with him in the future simultaneously. Then Tracy took a step toward his door, and it opened like the pneumatic doors on the "Starship Enterprise", just as he hoped. Tracy also knew the door opened because it knew him.

When Tracy stepped into his room it was all white – the walls, the single chair, and the long table that stretched the length of the narrow space. There were no windows, only a single doorframe at the far end to the left. His room wasn't what Tracy expected, but with great aplomb, the Tall Shiny Silver Figure spread His arms in a grand gesture.

"Ta-da," He said, and was immensely pleased.

Tracy heard Granny say, 'Fix your face Tracy,' which he did, because Tracy expected many rooms, marvelous furnishings, and exquisite music akin to the images in the picture book. Instead, Tracy 'heard crickets' in the incredibly austere, long white empty room. Then Tracy was honest.

"What's so fabulous about this?" Tracy asked. "I was expecting a mansion."

Immediately, He was in Tracy's face: *"Many people do, but they are the ones who have to decorate their room,"* and Tracy understood the term 'decorate' was unlimited. *"One could have many mansions, or this one simple room,"* He explained. *"It depends on what you ask for. . ."*

"You have not, because you ask not," Tracy recited.

"Exactly," the Tall Shiny Silver Figure said.

They stood just inside the door. The chair was in front of them before the long narrow table, and the lesson Tracy was about to learn was important for both worlds.

"Just as you have to be seated and at rest in order to get to your room," He revealed, *"once you get here, you have to be seated at your table in order to activate it. Otherwise, it is just a blank room. Nothing will respond to you. What you see here right now is what a lot of people have on earth. They must get beyond that and start asking Me for what they want, because My Blood paid for them to do that. Once they are in their room, they have to keep asking,"* and He looked at Tracy and smiled. *"You have been decorating your room for a while."*

"How come it looks blank?" Tracy asked, and He was more pleased.

"It is blank because you did not sit in your chair to activate it." He answered. *"It is no different than putting your key into the lock of the door to your house on earth. Then you go inside, take off your coat, sit down on the couch, and grab the remote that activates 'your room'. From that point, you can put the remote down anytime you want, or get up for a snack, but your room will be activated until you leave."*

Tracy understood the remote as the way to activate the lights, TV, and stereo system in his living room at the townhouse. But he was unclear how his pristine, white heavenly room correlated, so the Tall Shiny Silver Figure answered.

"Have a seat," He said.

As soon as Tracy went to sit, his chair pulled out, and then pushed itself underneath him as he sat. Then, a smorgasbord of food came alive on the table like at Thanksgiving. Simultaneously, lights and colors of all description decked the walls with fixtures, shelves, draperies and ornaments. Exquisite music played, and doors appeared that joined to Tracy's other rooms, which Tracy knew could be infinite – room after room.

But in this moment, the large picture frames were most fascinating. They were rainbow colored, and danced as a multifaceted prism. Within each frame were what looked like tall thin strips of beveled glass, except they were slices of time captured in light. Similar to an accordion bellows, as Tracy approached, scenes from when he was eighteen expanded in order from his birthday on April 10th until April 9th the following year. Each frame was a different year of his life, and each bevel showed his life events in chronological order. As Tracy passed by a frame, that particular year of his life fanned out before him between the bevels. Then, it was revealed that Tracy could go into each bevel, and he could experience that moment of twelve, or twenty-five, or thirty-three again - the same way Tracy experienced Three before he was shone the picture book. Then, Tracy knew that he needed to understand more.

"You mentioned a remote," Tracy said.

"Go back and sit down," He said, *"or it will not work."*

Tracy immediately went back to his chair and sat down. He looked for his remote on the table, but there was only the plethora of food. Tracy noticed the food was just past his reach, and smiled in the knowledge he wasn't to reach for it. That would be considered work, which wasn't allowed in such a place of rest. In heaven, 'work' was speaking, which Tracy had learned from his lessons about speaking in tongues. But on earth, Tracy used his tongue to defeat demons. Now that Tracy was in heaven, his speech was something he wasn't sure how to operate.

"So where's my remote?" Tracy asked.

"What do you want?" He asked.

"I don't understand."

"The remote is in your mouth Tracy. Here, you really do speak and call things that be not as though they were, and then, they will be as soon as you speak them."

Tracy still didn't understand, so the Tall Shiny Silver Figure prompted Tracy to the next revelation.

"Now," He said, *"as apposed to yesterday or tomorrow,"* which He said as a joke. *"Now it will work,"* and He looked at Tracy with anticipation. *"Right now,"* and He smiled. *"Now what do you want?"*

So Tracy focused on 'now faith', and Tracy wanted his remote, because he understood his remote operated everything.

"I want my remote," Tracy said, in order to make it appear.

Immediately, the doorframe in the far left corner opened a door, and a tuxedoed butler came through the opening and stopped. He stood with His feet together at the end of the long narrow table, and held a small tray. On it was a goblet and small plate.

Then the butler walked around the end of the table and up the length, but He didn't say anything. The butler acknowledged the Tall Shiny Silver Figure with a wink as He passed, and placed what Tracy recognized as communion elements within his reach, and instantly, Tracy understood:

Tracy knew his request had to go through the New Covenant to be approved, which the Tall Shiny Silver Figure had paid for. Tracy also knew that the butler was the Holy Spirit, and that He was here to take Tracy's order after he took communion. Further, as Tracy looked at the plate and the goblet, he understood the communion elements in heaven were God's Word and the Joy of the Covenant.

So, Tracy took communion as the Tall Shiny Silver Figure and Holy Spirit looked on. Then, Tracy knew to make his request, and he asked for what he figured was the wisest thing.

"I want continual visits," Tracy stated, which made Both smile as parents would.

"That is a given," the Tall Shiny Silver Figure said. *"Because once you have received this revelation about communion, you can visit anytime you want - as often as you do this..."* and Tracy understood. *"So ask for something else,"* He said, and it seemed He wanted to give Tracy another level of Grace, but Tracy could only think of one thing.

"Just keep talking to me?" Tracy asked, as if searching for the correct answer, and He smiled radiantly.

"Not only will I keep talking to you, I will talk to everyone who catches this revelation," the Tall Shiny Silver Figure answered.

Then the Holy Spirit took the tray. Tracy remained seated as He went down the length of the room, around the end of the table, and left through the door. Tracy knew that from that point on, he could come back to his table at anytime. Tracy was also made to understand the Lord showed him his room for two reasons. First, communion in his room was necessary for him to go forward, and second, Tracy had to sit at his table in heaven and say yes, because he was about to say yes on earth.

Chapter 46

- the cross

After communion, Tracy and the Tall Shiny Silver Figure left his room. Then, Forty-one went back to look over His shoulder, and He and Three looked at the all-important page in the picture book.

"Remember this!" He exclaimed emphatically, and He laughed and bounced little Tracy on His knee. The music from the page was exquisite as He held the book up with amazement. Then He said it again with ultimate exuberance.

"Remember this Tracy. Just get here!" and He was practically dancing. *"Whatever you do, just get here,"* and His breath was caught with relief.

"Just get here, and I will come and see you again!" He said. *"When you see this again in real life, I will come back and visit you. If you say yes, I will take over your life, and we will have a really good time. Just make it to this Tracy... Just make it to this Tracy..."* and He turned to Forty-one and said: *"This is that..."* and Tracy was gently placed back into his forty-one year old body with a quiet whisper... *"this is that..."*

"No Tracy," Bob decreed. "I did just hear from God, and He told me to tell you to look!" and Bob's arm went up of its own volition.

Then, it was revealed to Tracy that he was trained to deal with this transfer between worlds. Tracy remembered the time he was driving his team in the rental car. He stopped at the red light, and the angel grabbed him to show him the zoetrope of images he was about to visit in Europe.

When Tracy was returned to his body, he was literally jolted. As he sat with his foot on the break in this world, Tracy's entire body was tensed as with an electric shock, and the last thing he wanted to be doing was driving a car. However, because Tracy sat behind the wheel, he was forced to navigate the physical world, immediately after being in the supernatural. When he was returned, even though Tracy's body was foreign to him, he had to concentrate to operate his limbs, calm his grip on the steering wheel, and feel the brake before the light turned green.

"Yes Tracy," He confirmed. *"You are a dual citizen, designed to operate equally in both worlds at will."*

"Are you ok?" Bob asked. Tracy looked beyond Bob as if he saw through him, and then Bob noticed. "You smell funny," and Tracy came back to this to world fully.

"You smell that too?" Tracy asked. Tracy picked up his collar with both hands to smell his shirt. He inhaled deeply to get as much of it as he could, and his eyes welled with tears from the essence he hadn't experienced in eighteen years.

"Yeah," Bob said, and smelled the same thing as strongly. "What is that?"

"That's Bootsie," Tracy said, "my Mom," and Tracy saw into the frame, and the moment in time recorded by the beveled glass as clear as he was standing on the dock.

"She just picked me up out of the doorway," Tracy said, "and ran across the street with me under her arm when I was three."

Bob looked at Tracy with wonder in his eyes.

"I can't explain it," Tracy said, because he couldn't begin to explain anything he had just experienced.

Instead, Tracy turned away from Bob, and he threw it right back on Him. 'Lord,' Tracy thought. 'I don't understand what just happened. I smell Mom all over me.'

That wasn't answered. Instead, Tracy kept smelling his collar to hold onto the scent of Vera as long as possible. Then, he looked over the broad expanse of the river to the south. When Tracy saw the cross again, he remembered:

"When you see this again in real life, I will come back and visit you."

As Tracy saw the cross that he drew in the sixth grade for the first time in 'real life', which was now at the end of the point, Tracy knew he had arrived at a set time. He was at an orchestrated crossroads, and this was the moment of impact. This was the predetermined point in time when the natural collides with the supernatural – this was that. Tracy also understood from recently sitting at his table, that if he recognized the impact prior to it happening he could take advantage of it, which was why Tracy was shown his room.

But Bob knew none of this, and was ecstatic as they left the dock. He literally ran circles around Tracy, bouncing up and down like a cartoon character.

"I just heard from God! I just heard from God! I just heard from God!" Bob yelled, because he had never experienced Him so directly, and the presence of His voice alone was more than he could handle.

To Tracy, Bob was more annoying than Freddie ever was, and he knew he had to stay focused. Tracy knew his emotions could sidetrack him, just like Three said. Tracy didn't want to get stuck in the mud anymore, and wanted to see the supernatural done in the natural. Tracy also understood that what was about to happen was a make or break moment. Although, if the Tall Shiny Silver Figure orchestrated it, Tracy knew He would carry him through it. So, the couple walked back up the curved drive to the office, Bob skipping and laughing, and Tracy in a deep well of preparation.

'Lord,' Tracy thought. 'I don't understand all of what just happened, but I am taking my 'butt' out of the way so you can bless me.' Then Tracy looked around, and turned in a circle pointing both his index fingers in every direction as he turned.

"This is where we're supposed to live!" Bob sang, and did another circle around Tracy. Tracy kept turning and pointing, and Tracy recognized the two of them as a wheel in the middle of a wheel.

'But if You want to love me this much,' Tracy added, 'don't let me stop You, just help me receive it.'

"*Alright,*" He said. "*Because you asked like that, I will confirm it for you one more time. But this time, when I do, write it down.*"

"What do you want me to write down Lord?" Tracy asked.

"*I will tell you what to write down, and when to write it,*" He said.

'Fine by me,' Tracy thought with the sarcasm of this world. 'Remember, I don't have a job no way. I've got nothing to lose. I'm just on a bike ride. Besides…' and Tracy became bewildered…

As he went, Tracy realized his entire body felt like when he painted the vision in the sixth grade. Tracy had experienced the same tingle when He took possession of his arm to draw the flowing wheat grass, except now, Tracy's entire being was quivering. He experienced an alert sense of awareness that was not his own, as if he was inside a bubble looking out. Anything that wanted to come into his bubble had to come through a force field of angels who were continually vigilant. As Tracy felt their alert presence, he visualized a peace he had not known before, and it was easier for Tracy to connect his déjà vu moments.

'This is the time You spoke about,' Tracy thought, 'when You told me that one day You would take over my life, and that we would have a really good time.'

"Yes Tracy," He said warmly. *"You are almost there."*

As Tracy pondered that, he had another revelation. 'You've been talking to me an awful lot lately,' Tracy noticed, and He smiled.

"I need you to tell My people that their parents were not the first ones to invent the 'Hot/Cold' game," He said. *"As My people get closer to their Promised Land, I will direct them the same way,"* and the Tall Shiny Silver Figure could hardly contain Himself. *"You are almost there,"* He whispered, and Tracy opened the door to the office.

"Welcome gentlemen," the Innkeeper said, and peered over his wire reading glasses. Tom sat in a large black office chair, behind a tall white counter and long homemade desk. His chair could face the computer cabinet to his right, or swivel to face guests entering the office, so Tom remained seated when Bob and Tracy walked in.

"I see you didn't let the cross scare you," Tom said.

"Yeah," Bob said. "What is that for?"

"We have cross burnings every Thursday night," Tom said with a straight face.

Immediately, Tracy recognized the offense before the blessing, and decided to neutralize it.

"And a barbeque on Saturdays, I hope," Tracy quipped, "because if so, count me in as grill master," which made Tom look over his glasses again.

"That was pretty good," Tom noted, "and you were quick with that. I think you're going to have a good time while you're here," and he handed Tracy the paperwork to rent the last cabin, and Tracy gave him his card.

"After this is over with," Tom continued, "let's sit down and have a drink on the back porch."

The boys thought it was a little early, but liked the idea. Tom handed Tracy the receipt on the counter. As soon as he signed, Tom swapped the receipt for the keys in a simultaneous action from his chair. Then he launched into his check-in speech.

"Now gentlemen," Tom said. "The big key goes to the padlock on the gate, and the small key goes to your cabin. Parking is on the left side past the office, and the driveway is one way. Remember that, because it pisses me off when people can't figure out how to read the giant 'One Way' sign posted in front of the house. And mind your speed, because it's a driveway, not a highway. Breakfast is eight to ten in the main house, and we lock the gate at five-o'clock," and Tom looked over the top rim of his glasses. "And make sure no one piggybacks behind you when you open and relock the gate, because I'm tired of chasing people out of here," and Tom paused.

Tracy noticed that Tom was interrupted, and had a bewildered look on his face. Then, Tom tilted his head to the side, and Tom looked off in the distance before he leaned forward and said,

"Do you guys want to buy this place?"

Instantly Time Stopped

A doorframe of light appeared behind Tom. At first, Tracy thought it was the door to the backroom, except it was much taller. But, rather than opening as a single door, the way it had behind Moody before Tracy was about to be put into the ice water, this door kept opening. At first, it opened like French doors. Then, the doorway opened as a curtain to an immense stage, and Tracy was at the center.

From Tracy's perspective, what was revealed was row after row of clouded balconies with people peering over them. Similar to a stadium, except it was in the dimensions of heaven, thousands upon thousands of witnesses appeared decked in special attire. Their rows made a grand coliseum, only this time Tracy noticed the hats the witnesses wore were unique to each individual. Each hat had a feather that shimmered with iridescent rainbow colors intermittently, which was how they communicated.

Then, it was revealed to Tracy to understand each person's feather as a flame, and was reminded of the feathers that had appeared above the Holy Spirit as a Phoenix. Then, Tracy understood the flames were how each witness was 'made to know, even as also they were known'.

This wasn't to say the stacked clouds of witnesses were quiet - far from it. The roaring cheers of the vast assembly engulfed Tracy. They were wild as they toasted each other, before joy was refilled from the bottom of their goblets. They slurred and stammered, completely drunk in the Spirit. Front and center were Tracy's familiar cheering section. He recognized Moody, Freddie, Vera, and Granny Berger, even though their heavenly bodies were at the sum peaks of their lives, and they were as care free as butterflies.

"You made it brother!" Freddie hollered.

"Hallelujah!" Granny Berger shouted. "I've been prayin' for this day."

"I love you honey!" Vera screamed, and when she waved, a unified cheer erupted from the crowd. Moody beamed, and then Freddie spilled joy all over him. Moody laughed when he went to brush it off his new clothes, except it disappeared before he had a chance.

All of this was overwhelming for Tracy, who knew not to let his emotions get the better of him. Without an outlet, all Tracy could do was run back and forth in front of the long white counter of the office. Tracy looked for an exit on stage left, and ran to the other end to escape stage right, but he was trapped in the moment of his appointed time. His stage was set, and Tracy felt like the grand prizewinner as more and more rows of clouds billowed behind another, higher and higher. More witnesses appeared in astonishingly brilliant multicolored attire, and were even more absurdly drunk in the Spirit. Then, out from behind Tom's chair, the Tall Shiny Silver Figure popped out to Tracy's right. He stood and spread His arms with an excited shout, and He sounded like a game show host.

"Tracy! I have been waiting for you to get here since…" and He pulled up His left sleeve to reveal what looked like a wristwatch…

…and Tracy marveled at the time piece, because a holographic image shown above it. The universe spun backwards above the watch, which narrowed to the solar system, and then down to earth, and zoomed in on the United States to West Virginia. Then, Tracy saw scenes of his life flip backwards to when he was three years old and in the hospital room, which was when He yelled…

"…*you were three years old! Wow!*" He exclaimed, as if completely amazed.

But everything Tracy was experiencing made his flesh want to run for the hills, so He added, "*Oh yes, peace.*"

Tracy instantly calmed down, and all manner of disbelief and unease left him.

"*I should have said that first,*" He said apologetically.

Tracy stood in His presence, as Tracy had so many times before in his life, but this wasn't a vision, this was on earth. In addition, the multitude of witnesses not only sparkled - they made a sound like a drone buzzing with excitement as the Tall Shiny Silver Figure spoke. Not only that, with so many people watching so excellently dressed, Tracy felt naked. Before Tracy could say they were a distraction, the Tall Shiny Silver Figure turned and faced the multitude.

"*Ok, ok,*" the Tall Shiny Silver Figure said, and He raised His arms as a fifth-grade teacher would in front of an excited class on a field trip. "*You are only here to be a witness,*" He announced with love.

With those words there was a hush - although it was interrupted by drunken giggles, and intermittent shouts of 'Tracy!' and, 'He's finally here!' across the breadth of the arena. The humongous crowd settled down, and only sipped their goblets of joy. Then, Tracy finally had the wherewithal to turn to Bob.

"Bob," Tracy said. "Bob, do you see this?" and Tracy waved his hand in front of his face. But there wasn't a blink. Bob and Tom were frozen in mid-breath, and He turned from the crowds to face Tracy.

"*Tracy,*" He said. "*I stopped time so we could have this conversation. No one can see or hear us but you.*"

Tracy realized the word 'us' included the throng of witnesses, which seemed ironic by an earthly standard, but appropriate for the immense, opulent grandeur of His Grace.

"*All you have to do is say yes Tracy,*" as He stated before, "*and I will take over your life from here,*" and He smiled, "*and we will have a really good time.*"

Then, He looked at Tracy the way He did when they discussed 'now faith', when Tracy had sat at his table in his room before Tracy took communion with the Holy Spirit.

"This is that," He repeated with expectancy.

The many clouds of witnesses paused. Suddenly, you could hear a pin drop except for the collective understanding of the theme from "Jeopardy" that played in everyone's mind before time would be up, and it was Tracy's choice if he didn't have enough faith to take on what the Lord had for him…

"Yes," Tracy stated.

The clouds and clouds went wild with cheers. Yet above the frenzy, Tracy could hear Vera, Freddie, and Moody scream with abandon. But Granny Berger couldn't contain herself, because she not only loved "Jeopardy", her great grandson answered correctly!

"You go boy!" Granny Berger yelled at the top of her new lungs.

Then, the Tall Shiny Silver Figure hunkered down like a football linebacker and Tracy was the quarterback, and Tracy got scared.

'I ain't never played football,' Tracy thought. 'That was Freddie, who only did it to meet girls…'

"I did not ask you all that," He said quickly, and did not change His stance.

So, Tracy thought he was about to be squashed by an overabundance of love. Instead, His right arm extended from His body, which was followed by His hand and index finger that stretched until it hovered above the guest book on the counter in front of Tracy.

"Write this down," He instructed. Then He looked into Tracy's eyes, and He quoted without the use of speech: *"…and to whom is the arm of the Lord revealed?"* as His finger touched the guest book. He continued to communicate with His eyes, and the Tall Shiny Silver Figure downloaded future events into Tracy, as He moved from His stance to catch up with His finger.

As He got closer, the pupils in the Lord's eyes turned to a flame, which Tracy recognized as his own reflection, but was actually the image of the Holy Spirit within himself.

"Is that how You see me?" Tracy marveled.

The Tall Shiny Silver Figure was immensely pleased, and Tracy realized how he was transforming Grace upon Grace. Then, He walked through Tom, through the desk and counter, and toward the door behind Tracy. Yet His index finger never left the guest book, and His eyes never left Tracy's gaze.

But everything else of the office became translucent as He walked out the door, and His elongated arm kept His finger on the guest book. Then, He began to float upward, and a cloud enveloped the Tall Shiny Silver Figure. As He rose, the cloud descended the length of His arm to His hand, and when the sleeve of the cloud reached His fingertip, it was retracted from the page and time instantly resumed.

"Do you guys want to buy this place?" Tom asked, and Bob gasped.

Tracy stared behind Tom, because the entire host of witnesses had disappeared, which left an amazing void. Tracy did have the presence of mind to remember His last instruction, which was 'write this down'. Tracy wrote his name, Bob's name, and then wrote the address to the townhouse, his email address…

'You're not saying anything Lord,' Tracy thought. 'I have seen and experienced too much today not to believe what I saw. I experienced time repeating itself, flipping through the pages of my book backwards, and a gazillion people goading me on. Not to mention Mom, who I smelled here in this realm,' and Tracy was determined. 'So, I will doodle all over this page for a year…'

As soon as Tracy committed himself, and purposed his flesh to stand in that moment without saying another word until the Tall Shiny Silver Figure answered, instantly, Tracy heard Him, and he wrote it down:

"B.T.W. Owners Don't Sign The Guess Book. Happy Birthday Bob."

'Oh,' Tracy realized. 'I misspelled the word guest. Should I cross it out?'

"No Tracy," He said. "Guess what I am about to do next."

1-6-07 TRAMELL STAPLES 7016 COMMANDER HAVE TRAMELL@HOTMAIL.
BOB ZUBOR BRANDYWINE, MD 20613 COM
B.T.W. OWNERS DON'T SIGN THE GUESS BOOK
HAPPY BIRTHDAY BOB!!!

Afterwards

Cue Music: To be read hearing "Walking on Sunshine" by Katrina & The Waves…

Bob read over Tracy's shoulder and told Tom that 'owners don't sign the guest book', so they were going to buy the Inn. Bob and Tracy's first morning on the point was July 7th of 2007, or 07-07-07.

However, that took three years. Every morning by His instruction, Bob and Tracy sat on the front steps of the townhouse, pointed east and said, 'Black Walnut Point Inn, come to us now'. In the meantime, He prepared them. Bob learned what Tracy had experienced with Him, was born again, and on June 6, 2010, the 'Secret Place of Peace' was moved from Lot 91 to the end point of Tilghman Island.

The following summer, Granny came to visit the Inn she had heard about for three years. Being from the mountains she wondered, 'How high does that water get?' However, she was delighted, and saw all that the Lord had done for Tracy before she went to be with Him the following year.

Then Bob and Tracy set about transforming the Inn. They offered a Sanctuary Discount, and began planting gardens according to what seed He showed them to put in the ground. As with all things with Him, everything increased, and over the years Black Walnut Point Inn became a haven where the most usual statement from guests was, 'Heaven on earth'.

Then Maryland voted for gay marriage. Bob and Tracy were the first on Black Walnut Point to marry. Six other couples joined them, which got the attention of the Washington Post, television and international media outlets, which put them on the forefront of the revelation Tracy had received.

To celebrate their marriage, Tracy's father and family came to the Inn, and Tracy was pushed into his ministry. Now, Tracy marries many of the couples that come to Black Walnut Point to celebrate love.

"Whatever you do, just get here," He said, which Tracy did, and he said yes. Then Tracy realized the revelation of Peter, and that He is the Christ, the Son of the Living God. Now, Tracy continues demonstrating the 'love walk' to everyone who asks how he arrived. There, Tracy lives in his dreams, sees rainbows often - prisms of light through water - and he walks on those promises, walking on sunshine.

Selah

John 3:

² *Beloved, I wish above all things*
    that thou mayest prosper and be in health,
    even as thy soul prospereth.
³ *For I rejoiced greatly,*
    when the brethren came
    and testified of the truth that is in thee,
    even as thou walkest in the truth.
⁴ *I have no greater joy*
    than to hear that my children walk in truth.